UP THE SPINE AND DOWN THE CREEK

A PICTORIAL HISTORY

FROM QUEEN CHRISTINA TO WILLIAM PENN

by

Nancy C. Sawin

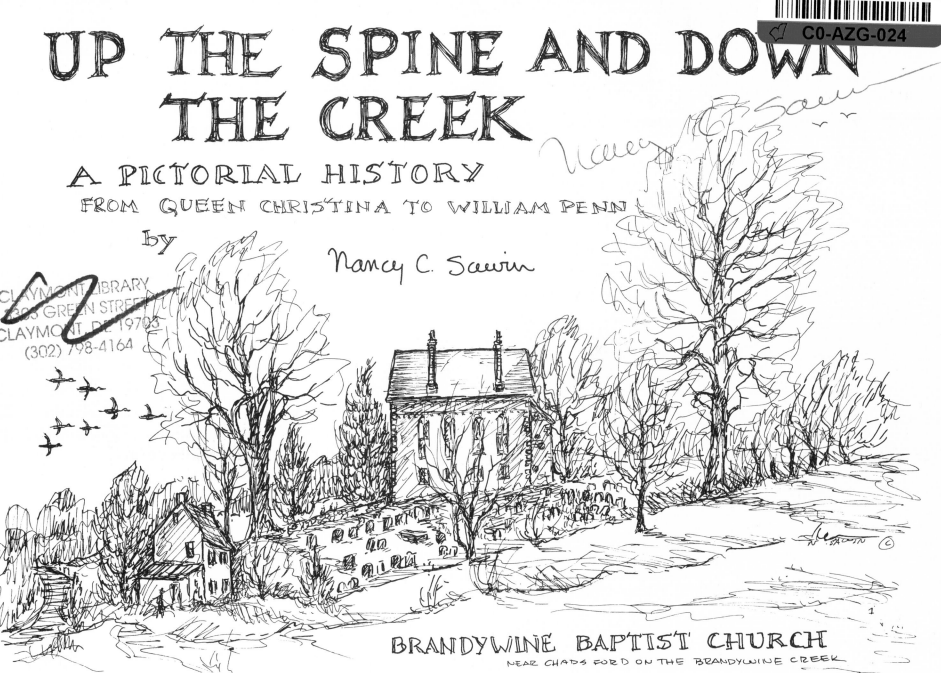

BRANDYWINE BAPTIST CHURCH

NEAR CHADS FORD ON THE BRANDYWINE CREEK

FIRST EDITION - PUBLISHED BY NORTH LIGHT STUDIO, HOCKESSIN, DELAWARE; PRINTED BY DOVER GRAPHIC ASSOCIATES. DOVER. DE.
LIBRARY OF CONGRESS # 8261838 COPYRIGHT 1982 SAWIN© PAPER MANUFACTURED BY CURTIS PAPER CO. NEWARK. DE.

INTRODUCTION

MERMAID TAVERN
CIRCA 1735
ABOVE MILL CREEK

Once upon a time and not so long ago, the Stedhams, the Darlingtons, the Brackins, the Pierces, the Sharplesses and the like made their way up spines and along creeks and caught glimpses of the rising sun. Then and there began an era, the age of 18th and 19th century Northern Delaware and South Eastern Pennsylvania, the age of tallow candles with needed trimmings and darkening snuffers. So come along, follow Nancy Sawin as she sketches her way along spines and creeks and see what she has spirited.

No, Nancy is not really recalling an age with its old order of things. She has made this portion of her native land into her ouija board. With artist's trappings under her hands she has done wishful sketchings, but not wishful thinking. The result is clearly her own history telling spinning jennys. Accordingly, she sketches numerous yarns simultaneously. Yes, hers is an outline of features and designs and occurrences dramatically profiled through her mind's eye.

It is love of the past that inspired these sketches and made a mark. In a sense, Nancy has identified her own *watermark* on paper, much as did Benjamin Franklin and George Washington in American Colonial days. In 1690 William Rittenhouse, living near Germantown, Pennsylvania, started his paper making business using much the same method as had a Chinese court official, Ts'ai Lun in 105 A.D. Fermentation, not for wine but for paper, produced a chemical transformation of cotton and linen rags. The resulting stock was caught up in a molding frame. It was the wirestrung molds in the frame that left markings in the finished paper. These were called *watermarks*. With time, a variety of

watermarks were developed and some were personalized. The difference is that in **UP THE SPINES AND DOWN THE CREEKS** Nancy Sawin produced her own watermarks, so to speak, and high watermarks at that.

Every artist, it seems, must dramatize him/herself and play a part. So Nancy has found a pose and has brought her pose to the public in her sketch books. Hers is not a bad pose at all, certainly more than a mere confectioners. So every turn of a page, or turn of a spine or creek if you wish, brings its opportunities, its unveiling graphics, its leftover realities of yesteryear, its *amor patrise*.

It is said that people who write prefaces are charlatans. If this is true, than this one could be acclaimed and parodists might say — a motely view. Ah, but isn't this always so, more or less. Therefore, let's be on, and follow further gadabout Nancy, to expose the numerous lines of hers.

Now don't get the feeling you are being instructed. There is so much entertainment mingled in her sketches and accountings that one gets a sense of drama. On the other hand, don't leave your brains on the bookshelf, because there is much room for intelligent appreciation. And there you are — the operative word for **UP THE SPINES AND DOWN THE CREEKS** is appreciation.

A book of sketches, perhaps more than any other book, invites random flipping about. Most likely you did what I did — "flipped", but with respectful levity. Instinctively I came first to the map. There were the spines, the high lands, and there in the valleys were: the creeks — White Clay, Red Clay, Pike Creek, Naaman's Creek; the runs — Buck Run, Valley Run, Turkey Run, Doe Run, Beaver Run; and the big creeks, rivers really, — The Brandywine and the Christiana. Like a huge fan they funneled into the vast Delaware. There in the upper reaches of the Brandywine I counted ten fords. In those early days when clearing the land took precedence over building bridges, settlers sought out crossings shallow enough to allow fording. There was the now famous Chadds Ford; but also to name a few others: Jones Ford, Jeffires Ford, Wistar Ford and so on. Caught up on this one "flip" I saw in my mind's eye old man Wistar, robust, gaunt and steady, riding across his ford at dusk to Wistar cabin, the Wistar family and a generous fire on the hearth.

Another random pause and there in Chesterville, Chester County, was a Crossan family homestead. A sturdy looking place and a sturdy family, as a backward look from the Crossans of 20th century Delaware so clearly testifies.

Up came the Blue Pig Inn. Some name for an inn I thought, only to learn that inns took names that could be illustrated and that blue and red were favorite local ocher adaptations. So there was the Red Rose, the Eel's Foot, the Black Angus, the Hammer and Trowel, and the Anvil. The various wayside inns conjured images of the weary travelers, the warming fire, the savory smell of spitted deer meat.

Flip again and a look of disbelief. There across an entire page was a three tiered trestle bridge. Yes, this was a 19th century Wilmington and Western Railroad bridge, and authentic. Some old timers here about may recall defying strict parent admonishes and with heart in throat and a racing pulse walking the treacherous trestle. Woe-be-gone should a train come along.

Never one to overlook the unusual or its likely humor, Nancy caught a rare spectacle — an eight door privy. Big enough for a Privy Council? Who knows? Chick Sale, if you remember his devotion, would have cheered this one. The age of spectacles, you see is any age. While houses were located near to, or even over, springs, privys were always some distance away. At the Crossan place the privy was out by the barn. Fussy? No, sanitary.

Another interrogative page turn and there was New London Academy, a building of some size, apparently to provide for many, even then. All forward looking people educate their young and for varying urgencies. Education to those early area peoples was not a dispensable luxury, but a social-cultural-economic necessity. There, too, was a "Washington-Slept-Here" building, adding another, perhaps a political dimension to this early New

HOFFMAN'S MILL
1864 - NOW
BRANDYWINE
MUSEUM.

DEDICATED TO ELLEN AND SANFORD SAWIN AND THEIR PARENTS, AND THEIR PARENTS..... TO THE FIRST WHO CROSSED THE ATLANTIC TO AMERICA. I THANK THEM ALL; FOR THAT'S WHY I'M HERE.

London crossroads. Hotels are seemingly an inescapable. The New London Hotel, like others in the area, was a provision, one can conclude, for the wayfarer. This one, though, was on the site of an earlier tavern licensed in 1729 by Lazarus Finney. Was this Lazarus an epicurean?

An inquisitive turn to another page, and like the many others, it's filled with attention getters. In the upper left hand corner, the Harlan House at Embreyville, wherever that is, where Mason and Dixon stayed in 1764. In the lower right hand corner a

SPRING HOUSE - AT CHARIS HOUSE - KENNETT PIKE.

Mason and Dixon stone with the coat of arms of William Penn on it. Charles Mason and Jeremiah Dixon arrived in Philadelphia on November 15, 1763 and apparently took little time getting to work and in turn, to the Harlan House. Before coming to America both had been engaged to observe the transit of Venus across the sun as seen at the Cape of Good Hope (1761). That was quite a good bit of gadabouting for those days, perhaps comparable with Ben Franklin's frequent crossings of the Atlantic. Mason and Dixon, two eminent "mathematicians or surveyors" established the "tangent from the middle point of the peninsula line to 'the tangent point'" and in so doing gained much respect for their predecessors who had used crude chain-measurements. Mason and Dixon, however, did not mark the exact middle of New Castle, the point for drawing the twelve-mile radius, and neither does Nancy. Although on that same page she depicts the stone marking the grave of Indian Hannah who died March 20, 1802 and was the last member of the friendly Lenni-Lenape Indians living in Chester County. Of course, Nancy didn't mention either that among the other Algonquins the Lenni-Lenapes were known as the "Grandfathers". So it is understandable that the marvelous Swedes, peace loving and productive as they were, readily made friends of the "Grandfathers".

The Swedes also introduced the log cabin into the New World and on that same rich page there is a sketch of the Schoff Cabin at West Bradford. I wonder, did any of the Lenni-Lenapes call on the Schoffs to enjoy their baking or watch them weave?

And there, too, on this same page is the Star Gazers Stone, also placed by Charles and Jeremiah. Why did they call it Star Gazers? Was this representative of the "romance" of their labors.

But, alas, Nancy did not sketch even a faked vista of what was once a Mason-Dixon created "corridor". These two men did not erect a Chinese Wall to form a parallel of latitude, or a Weeping Wall, or a Berlin Wall. They chose a peaceful way and cut an eight-foot swath through the forests by clearing away the trees to form "a visto" for the posts used to mark the line of parallel. It is said that from ". . . any point of eminence in the line, fifteen or twenty miles of the visto can be seen . . ." How did the Shawnees or the Delawares take to this treatment of their forests? But, as anyone who has read this far knows, time and souvenir hunters have taken their toll. The pole markers are gone as are most of the stone markers. That's why I prefer Nancy's way of being caught up in the "creeks and spines" of this proud area. So on with our tale.

It is said that "What you look hard at seems to look hard at you", and this sketch book shows such fidelity. It has also been said, and attributed to John Ruskin who had trained himself to draw as well as write, that "the greatest thing a human soul ever does . . . is to see something, and tell what was seen in a plain way". This is what came to mind as I came upon the wide vista of the Mundy and the Clark farms on Delaware route 48 as it approaches route 41. This is the way into and out from Wilmington for Hockessenites, North Star folks, Avondale neighbors. So now when we pass these farms I will look hard at them and I hope they will look hard at me. Now more than ever I became more deeply aware that to see, to feel, to sense, to grasp are verbs, action verbs, that speak of one's way of dealing with the world. Yes, John Ruskin, you were right, "To see clearly (or perhaps just more clearly) is poetry, prophecy and religion — all in one". And so in the future my drives in and out of Wilmington have been seered and embossed by a good quantity of Nancy's mental and imaginative energy, manifesting itself often by what she has sketched in and perhaps, often, too, by what has been left out. She is not a professional historian and makes no such claim, but she has ordered some of our spines and creeks area within a coherent frame of reference. And so what is our Manifest Destiny?

We members of the T.V. generation, with our 15 second commercial clips (cut to this time to avoid taxing our memory span) are being constantly induced to believe that there are simple

C. 1850 CITY OF WILMINGTON FROM S.E.

and readily available solutions to all problems. The Green Giant, Mr. Clean, Mermaids in our dish water, are just some of our current myths. Embarrassed by these dejections, I flipped pages again and, lo and behold, as if by omen came to page 30 and Manufacturer's Sunday School, St. Joseph on the Brandywine, Mt. Salem Union Methodist, Christ Church, Episcopal, Greenhill Presbyterian and on other pages the many Friend's Meeting Houses. The towering steeples raised "admonishing fingers" and suggested a meaningful search for explanation of our present day atomic stress phenomena. Does it take a surfacing of the past, perhaps a search for roots, to find, defend and advance values?

That ended my random flipping about in **UP THE SPINES AND DOWN THE CREEKS.** This book must have a plan, a unity, an organization. And it does. But there must be some sanctification for my interrogative looking here and there. Then I remembered as Henry Adams had said in his autobiography, "All experience is an arch to build upon".

Caught up as she was in geography and people, Nancy chose what appeared to be the only organizational avenue suitable. Without being too discriminate, she plotted a four phased

SPRING HOUSE AT GUYNECOURT

3

LEWDEN HOUSE 1770
CHRISTIANA
(QUAKER-GEORGIANS)

manifold to embrace the varied features of the land and the manifest doings of the settlers. The first unit starts with Wilmington and moves north and east. Next, she moves southwest of Wilmington and north into the Clay Creek drainage areas. Then north to the Honey Brook highlands, towering 740 feet above Wilmington and providing source for the west branch of the Brandywine. Finally east across the Horsehoe Pike ridge separating the Brandywine West from Brandywine East to Ludwigs Corner and the better known West Chester area. So the landward expansion of **UP THE SPINES AND DOWN THE CREEKS** and the social-cultural expansion of commerce and church and state is moved by geographical conditions. The endless meanderings of the Brandywine and the Clays and the numerous Runs lured the venturing colonials in much the same way that Nancy's meanderings were lured.

Geographical influences on history are numerous — the Nile, the Euphrates, the Valley of the Oxus, the Aegean Sea. The story of the English, the Dutch, the Swedes meeting geographical conditions here abouts that strengthened them in their purpose parallels the ancient patterns. Here the inclosed waterways were just far enough inland to provide fertile soil and trade with the interior as well as ready contact with the sea and the homelands.

Subdivision One of **UP THE SPINES AND DOWN THE CREEKS** starts where the Brandywine and Christina join currents and flow into the sea-going Delaware. From Second and Walnut Streets in Wilmington, north and east to Stoney Run and Naaman's Creek is the setting for numerous sketches. There is Dr. Tilton's Carriage House, Quigley & Mullin's Grocery (Nancy's mother was a Quigley), Old Bailey Mill on Rattle Snake Kill, the Samuel Bush Home, Winklers, the Alms House, The Grubb Road Grist Mill, The Weldin Homestead, The Talley Farms out Naaman's Road; and so on and on.

Then east and north along the Christiana, the large White Clay drainage and the rather extensive Red Clay emanations. And here one marvels at how a queen served to compromise the White Clay-Red Clay name debate after their juncture by providing her more peremptory name — The Christiana River, and then gra-

ciously asserts her royal rights from the Brandywine for the short flow to the Delaware. From atop a Widow Watch Nancy has a panoramic river sketching. See Tatnall's Warehouse and Wharf at Newport, the High Tide sketching north of Churchman's Road. On to Lover's Retreat on White Clay to the top of Possum Park. Then meander to Polly Drummond's famous tavern, or to Pencader Presbyterian Church founded in 1707. Over to Cooch's Bridge and a Delaware Revolutionary War setting. Then around to the Old Inn and Tavern at Corner Ketch, or the Mill Creek Friend's Meeting. Then, of course, there is the Hockessin Friend's Meeting or the Kaolin Clay Quarry. And so on across the Wood dale Bridge over the Red Clay Creek. But don't overlook the Mendenhall Farm and the Brackin Farm before you go on and on.

FARM HOUSE - HEAD OF
CHRISTINA. CECIL CO.

Pause, if you wish, at Lafayette's Headquarters, Washington's Headquarters and the home of John Chadd. Don't overlook the Wyeth Studio at Brinton Mill. Up to West Chester and Recitation Hall at West Chester State Normal built of serpentine stone. If you are still with me, let's pause at Eel's Foot Tavern. Then there is the Stone Quarry at Downington and the Uwchland meeting place. See Dilworthtown's Country Store and the Eagle Tavern. Pause and reflect over all you have seen and looked at hard, and dreamed. Perhaps you found the "watermarks" of another era which although depict the fabric of a life of the past, are a part of the framework of today and tomorrow. So, leisurely return to your television, your computer, your antiseptic world, but don't substitute numbers for adjectives and adverbs.

Russ Stauffer

UP THE SPINE AND DOWN THE CREEK
A Pictorial History from Queen Christina to William Penn

All of my three score years and five have been lived between the watersheds of the Brandywine and Christina Creeks. Born in Wilmington, I spent my earliest childhood along the "Old Capital Trail" and a few more years just off the Kennett Pike. I used to visit my grandfather and grandmother Sawin in Claymont on the Philadelphia Pike. Since I was twelve I have lived in Mill Creek Hundred on the spine of the land between the Red Clay and Mill Creeks where the Lancaster and Newport-gap Pikes meet.

For the past three years I have gone forward and back across the creeks, hills and valleys of this small part of our country — the area between the Brandywine, Christina, and Delaware watersheds. I have put on paper with pen and ink what I saw and felt. It is I think a kind of record keeping or research, but with very little of it done within the walls of a library, museum or historical society.

I did use materials provided by our centers of learning, public and private: Winterthur Museum, the University of Delaware Library, public and private libraries, and Delaware and West Chester Historical Societies. Hagley Museum afforded me invaluable materials and assistance. I was able to secure photographs of buildings no longer standing, maps with historical and geographical data, and appropriate books. Every place I went, help was willingly given.

ON THE
CHRISTINA
SLOOP
"MARY ANN"
PACKET
1820

4

MUSHROOM HOUSES - CREEK ROAD - "ORSINI" WAS "MCVAUGH" HOCKESSIN

But I can only report or sketch from what Loren Eiseley, the renowned anthropologist, calls "my own wilderness". Each person will see a mill, home, church, school, creek, tavern, bridge, or farm differently. I have recorded them as I saw them. Sometimes it was in the humid heat of a summer,day, flies buzzing around my head and perspiration blotting my ink lines. Other times snow and wind made my muscles tighten and hands shake. Once at the end of a brilliant fall day I just stood in "my own wilderness" and watched the sun set across the hills at Jefferis Bridge and did nothing. It was too beautiful to draw.

On many occasions I had the good fortune of meeting and talking with the people whose families had lived in these early homes, preached in the churches, taught in the schools, plowed the land, shod the oxen and horses, milled the grain or gunpowder, built the railroad lines or quarried the stones.

Each building sketched was built by hands calloused from the stone cutter's chisel, the smithy's hammer, the carpenters adze or the mason's trowel. The plans were drawn sometimes in the mind's eye, sometimes on paper. Architects designed many homes and public buildings, but there were also master builders who could not read or write and yet designed homes, mills, and simple churches which had both grace and dignity.

There were two distinct and accepted plans for the early construction of homes in the area: the Swedish log structure and the "Quaker Plan". The log cabin had little permanent effect on local architecture. However, more and more outside wood and plaster walls are being removed to discover beneath, Swedish built log houses. The original fireplaces in their homes often went across the corners.

In 1684 William Penn wrote a brochure which was designed to promote colonization in America. He extolled the attractions and advantages of life in colonial Pennsylvania which under his original grant encompassed part of the state of Delaware. He further advised: ". . . build then a House of thirty foot long and eighteen broad, with a partition near the middle, and another to divide one end of the house into two small rooms . . ."

There were other architectural influences including the "Resurrection Manor Plan" with variations. (See page 22). New Castle has strong evidence of Queen Anne and early Georgian styles. The Regency design is evident in Swanwyck.

An architectural design unique to this area is the pent-eve or pent roof. It was used on many of the homes constructed

(See page 22).

NOTE: CHRISTINA AND CHRISTIANA USED INTERCHANGEABLY AS DO THE PEOPLE LIVING HERE. ORIGINALLY CHRISTINA FOR SWEDEN'S QUEEN.

CIRCA 1830 FARM HOUSE - CECIL COUNTY, MD.

prior to 1750. It had been popular in England and Germany, and it was used so extensively in Germantown that it has also been called the "Germantown Hood". In my drawings I have taken the liberty of removing a Victorian porch and restoring the pent-eve where I was quite sure it existed. So also with artist license I have occasionally moved a tree and always removed a telephone pole or fireplug.

The bull nose window is almost unique to Chester County. The thick stone walls were rounded on the inside to let in more light. Three of the eighteenth century homes I sketched had a paymaster's drawer under the windowsill.

As you travel up the spines of the land from the Christina Creek at Glasgow, and the Delaware River at New Castle or Wilmington to the Welsh Hills, Ludwigs Corner, or Honeybrook you will see some changes in the structure of both private and public buildings. In the southern area, brick is the predominant building block. This includes New Castle, the Wilmington waterfront, Dayett and Curtis Mills, Old College at the University of Delaware, Stanton Meeting House and Pencader Church.

As you climb the hills into Chester County or paddle and portage a canoe up the Brandywine, brick changes to stone. There is the dark stark grey of the lower Brandywine stones as seen in Brandywine Village. The softer tones begin further up the creeks. Avondale quarries produced a rust colored stone. Hornblende quarries produced stone with some browns blended with the grey and the Downingtown quarries have rock of softer and lighter tones. Used sparingly and with a Victorian flare was the green

serpentine stone found in the West Chester area.

Wood was used in all areas. Clapboard siding and even vertical boards were common. However, wood does not survive the elements as do stone and brick, so few buildings remain. There are still some early farm houses standing, built with stones the farmer picked up in his own fields and woods and beams and boards hand cut with a broad axe and adze.

Chester County barns and a few in New Castle County have a unique characteristic which has given them the name, "Bank Barns". They have an overhang on the south side so that the cattle not only have shelter from the elements in bad weather but sun in the cold weather. The entire basement floor is of earth and the main floor above, large oak boards; the center part used for threshing the grain and the two sides to store their hay and straw. The barns were built on the side of a hill, and hills are abundant in Chester County and Northern New Castle County. This allowed access at ground level to the stables and the hay mows. The lower barn supports were generally conical in shape and built of stone. The oak beams were fastened by mortise and tenon and secured with wooden pegs.

As I traveled with pen and paper I often tried to visualize the first land owners, their few belongings on the backs of oxen or horses or in a Conestoga wagon fording the streams and following Indian trails to settle on their newly acquired land. These were the virgin forests of America. Trees must be felled, the land cleared of rocks and stumps. Crops must be planted if men and animals were to survive.

ABOUT THE BRANDYWINE AT ROCKLAND

MT LEBANON CHURCH (UNITED METHODIST)

5

CLOVER HILL
A STONE IN THE WALL
HAS INITALS - E.G. -
G.G. AND THE DATE
1792 (NR. MONTCHANIN)
MONTCHANIN
STONES MARK THE GRAVE
SITE OF THE GREGG FAMILY

William Penn tried to encourage workmen to come to America. These included "carpenters, gardeners, fishermen, blacksmiths, masons, and diggers up of tree roots". Such men did come to work, but the early settler put a roof over his own family's head. This was first a log cabin and sometimes in his own generation a wood, brick or stone house, but generally it was his sons or grandsons who built such a home. It was not just the man who did the heavy work. The entire family cut down the trees, hewed the logs, laid the stone, shingled the roofs, dug the wells and dammed the springs for water.

I did my wandering in a station wagon, crossing bridges, not fords; travelling on paved highways, not Indian trails or muddy roads, and I could find ready food and shelter at almost every turn.

How our fore fathers must have valued their new found freedom and independence to brave the elements and hardships they did! How they must have loved their new land with its creeks, stately trees, wild flowers and berries, birds, animals, and a piece of this good earth they could call their own!

Each covered bridge, mill, school, springhouse, and church has a story to tell. Some were told me directly by people living nearby. Some I tried to learn from the stone, brick, and planks as I walked around them. Every farm, blacksmith shop, creek, tavern, and crossroad had a name. Often it was named for the land owner nearby. The names were changed many times from those the Indians gave them to today's P.O. box and highway route numbers.

As the names changed so did the trees, the fence lines, the homes, the highways and by-ways. There were few if any windows in the early cabins. As in Abiah Taylor's house and Primitive Hall, the windows had very small leaded panes of glass. Windows were changed to doors and doors to windows. The pent-eve was removed and porches built with columns and gingerbread added. Additions were added to additions. Dormer windows were pushed out through the roofs.

Barns burned and were rebuilt on the old foundations. Fences and fence lines changed from rough logs and stone walls to the split rail and whitewashed boards. Swamp willows sprang up along the creeks planted by the farmers so that their wood could be sold to the new DuPont powder mills down the Brandywine.

The very nature of the land dictated its use. The Brandywine falls over seven hundred feet on its way from the Welsh Hills to the Delaware River at Wilmington. The White and Red Clay Creeks fall close to four hundred. In the 18th century, water power was king. Dams and mill runs were built to provide water to the newly constructed mills. The dams caused the end of shad fishing as no longer could they come up the rivers to spawn and the Indians lost one of their major foods and fertilizers and were forced to move west.

An industrial dynasty grew up on the lower Brandywine. Eleuthere Irenee duPont deNemours built his first powder mills there early in the 19th century. Willingtown or Wilmington as it became was an important port and ship building center on the Delaware River. The Christina River was navigable for over ten miles. Sloops or shallops stopped to load and unload goods at "New Port", Stanton, and Christiana. Larger ships laden with rum, fine china, cloth, and other finished goods came up the Delaware to the port of Wilmington.

The goods were loaded onto wagons and drawn by oxen, horses, and mules up the spines of the land on the Philadelphia, Concord, Kennett, Lancaster, and Newport-Gap Pikes; Limestone and New London roads and the Old Capital Trail destined "Up Country". Some took their wares to Lancaster, Coatesville, West Chester, Downingtown and others went on across the Appalachians to the interior.

The draymen rested their teams at the top of the long hills leading up from the waterfront. Taverns located there provided them with food and spirits, and the horses and oxen with food and water. Each inn and tavern had its own sign with an emblem or picture on it to depict its name; for there were few readers in the "New World". So came their names: Buck, Glasgow Arms, Deer Park, Eagle, and Columbus.

As steam power moved into the valleys and up the hills, railroad lines were built. The mill runs began to fade back into the landscape. The small dirt roads which followed the creeks up and down their winding courses became little used. The turnpikes became the "high" ways of commerce.

Here I will stop writing and let you see the story I have tried to tell with drawings. This is how I plan to do it.

I begin in Wilmington; for it can be said what is said of London, "all roads lead to Wilmington" and so do the pikes and the creeks. I venture north up above the Delaware to Naaman's Creek and cross back and forth over the land of the lower Brandywine Valley. Then I go south following the Christina, crossing momentarily into New Castle, and then follow the Christina, Red and White Clay; Pike, Mill, and Middle Creeks to their headwaters. From there I cross over to the west and east branches of the Brandywine in Chester County and follow them to their sources. And yes, there is always some backtracking!

I hope you enjoy seeing what I saw "from my own wilderness", and perhaps you too will find the time to go slowly up the spines and float down the creeks of this remarkable bit of historical and beautiful land.

Nancy Sawin

"THE HAVEN"
FIELD STONE FARM
HOUSE - NEAR SANFORD
SCHOOL AND MILL
CREEK - CIRCA 1720

"PEACE AND
PLENTY"
TAVERN ON OLD
LANCASTER PIKE
AND BRACKEN-
VILLE ROAD

MILL CREEK?

CUSTOM'S HOUSE

WILMINGTON – SECOND AND WALNUT

OLD TOWN HALL
1798

HOME OF JONAS STIDHAM
14TH AND POPLAR

18TH CENTURY

7

WILMINGTON

1881

LOGAN HOUSE

STILL VERY
MUCH IN USE!

QUIGLEY
& MULLEN
WHOLESALE
GROCERS

BALTIMORE AND OHIO
RAILROAD STATION —
DELAWARE AVENUE

DR TILTON'S
CARRIAGE
HOUSE

ALONG
FRONT STREET
100 YEARS AGO —
(WINFIELD QUIGLEY IS THE
ARTIST'S GRANDFATHER)

8

100 YEARS AGO AT WATER AND WALNUT ON THE CHRISTINA RIVER

HARLAN AND HOLLINGSWORTH

A SHIP IN THE WAYS

FAIRBANKS STANDARD SCALES

"THE MIDDLE DEPOT" CAR BARN – CIRCA 1880

SECOND STREET MARKET

WILMINGTON

FROM PHOTOGRAPHS

RISING SUN BRIDGE
AND ROCKFORD
TOWER

OLD SWEDES
HOLY TRINITY
AS REVEREND ERISAUS
TOBIAS KNEW IT.

ASBURY METHODIST
EPISCOPAL CHURCH
DEDICATED BY BISHOP
ASBURY - 1789
WALNUT STREET AND THIRD

OLD BARLEY MILL
ON RATTLE SNAKE KILL,
BLACK KILL, KILPOT OR
THE BRANDYWINE.
(SKETCH FROM EARLY PAINTING)

WILMINGTON

MARKET STREET BRIDGE
OVER THE BRANDYWINE
(FROM A ROBERT SHAW SKETCH)

ROCK QUARRY
ON THE BRANDY-
WINE - HORNBLENDE
GRANITE

10

WILLINGTON SQUARE

WILMINGTON

WILMINGTON AND NORTHERN RAILROAD
CIRCA 1870

SAMUEL BUSH HOME
FRENCH AND WATER STREETS

OLD GREEN TREE INN
22ND AND MARKET

PHILADELPHIA, WILMINGTON
AND BALTIMORE RAILROAD

WINKLER'S - LATE 19TH CENTURY
(FROM AN EARLY POSTCARD)

THE PENNY HOUSE - CIRCA 1749

WILMINGTON

SHELLPOT PARK AND LAKE
FROM EARLY POST CARDS

WILMINGTON 100 YEARS AGO

10TH AND SHIPLEY

FRONT AND
KING STREETS

THE ALMS
HOUSE

(FROM A SKETCH
BY ROBERT
SHAW)

13

ON QUAKER HILL - CIRCA 1750
FROM A ROBERT SHAW ETCHING

FRIEND'S SCHOOL
FARM HOUSE AND
BARN

WILMINGTON

WILMINGTON SCHOOL NO. 2
FROM A GOOD ATTENDANCE
AWARD 1890

HENDRICKSON
HOUSE - CIRCA 1640
NEAR OLD SWEDES CHURCH

ALAPOCAS WOODS

CIRCA 1875

GEORGE VEALE FARM HOUSE

STONE BEHIND A
HOME ON RIDGE ROAD

23
TO P
14
TO W

THE WILLOWS
HOME OF MARY VINING 1797—1821
10TH AND MARKET
(NOT THE MARY VINING OF DOVER)

20 M
TO P

FRONT

MASON AND
DIXON
LINE

BACK

MILE STONE ON PHILADELPHIA PIKE.
IN FRONT OF THE OLD ROBINSON HOUSE

EARLY GRIST MILL
ON GRUBB ROAD IN
ARDEN - CIRCA 1830

BRANDYWINE VILLAGE

TATNALL HOUSES - BACK WING IS ORIGINAL
HOME OF EDWARD AND ELIZABETH PENNOCK TATNALL.
THEIR HOME WAS BUILT IN EARLY PART OF THE 18TH
CENTURY; THE FRONT WING IN THE LATTER PART.

In Memory of
Faithful IONE
The Ambulance Horse
Died July 12, 1909

IN FRONT OF
TALLEYVILLE
FIRE HOUSE.

CIRCA 1763

15

EARLY FARM HOUSE ON MARSH ROAD
MADE FROM BRANDYWINE GRANITE

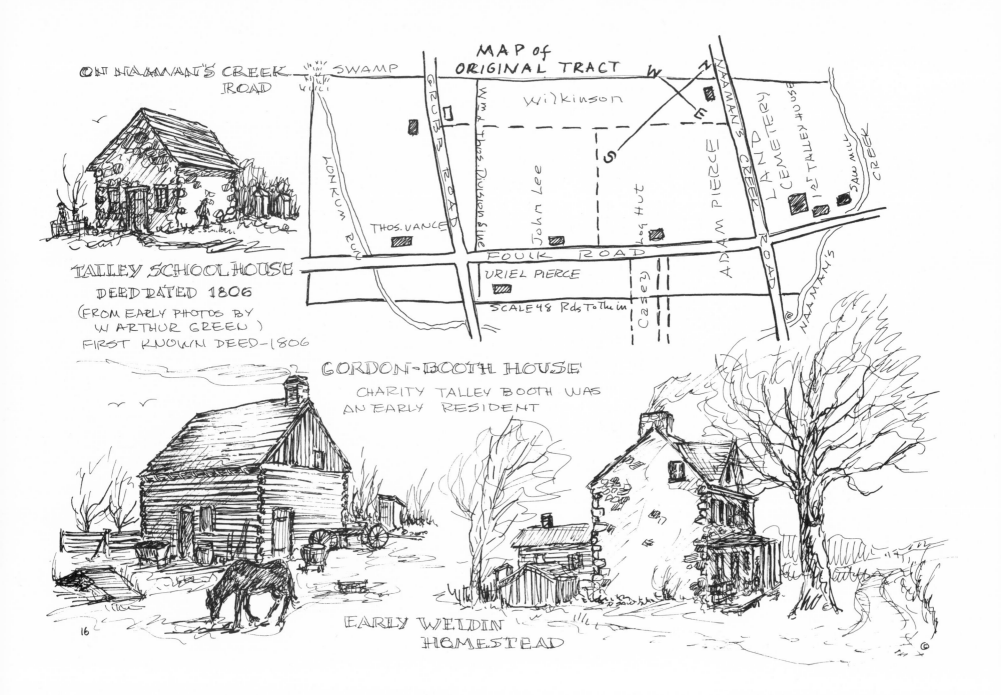

ON NAAMAN'S CREEK
ROAD

TALLEY SCHOOL HOUSE

DEED DATED 1806

(FROM EARLY PHOTOS BY
W. ARTHUR GREEN)
FIRST KNOWN DEED - 1806

MAP of
ORIGINAL TRACT

SWAMP

Wilkinson

GRUBB ROAD

LONKOM RUN

Wm & Thos. Division line

John Lee

THOS. VANCE

Log Hut

ADAM PIERCE

NAAMAN'S CREEK

LANE

CEMETERY

1st TALLEY HOUSE

SAW MILL

CREEK

NAAMAN'S

FOULK ROAD

URIEL PIERCE

Casey

SCALE 48 Rds To The in

GORDON-BOOTH HOUSE

CHARITY TALLEY BOOTH WAS
AN EARLY RESIDENT

EARLY WELDIN
HOMESTEAD

16

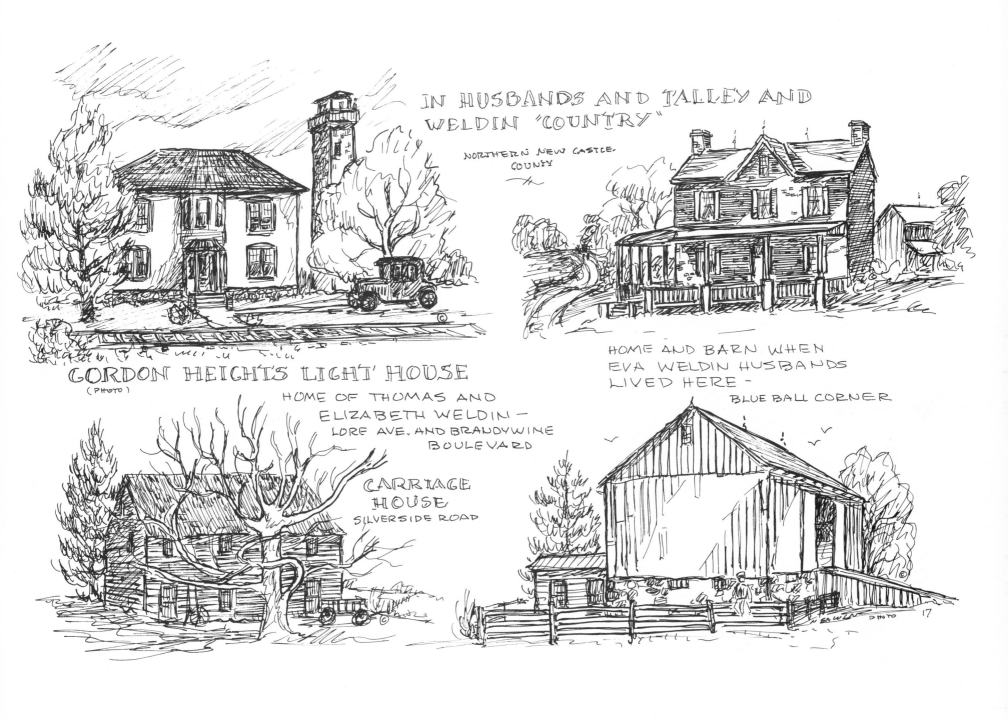

IN HUSBANDS AND TALLEY AND WELDIN "COUNTRY"

NORTHERN NEW CASTLE COUNTY

GORDON HEIGHTS LIGHT HOUSE
(PHOTO)

HOME AND BARN WHEN EVA WELDIN HUSBANDS LIVED HERE -

BLUE BALL CORNER

HOME OF THOMAS AND ELIZABETH WELDIN - LORE AVE. AND BRANDYWINE BOULEVARD

CARRIAGE HOUSE
SILVERSIDE ROAD

17

RAMSAY HOMESTEAD
RAMSAY ROAD

STILL IN THE RAMSAY FAMILY   CIRCA 1860

TALLEY FARM
TALLEYVILLE ON
NAAMAN'S ROAD
(SKETCHED IN 1976 A FEW YEARS BEFORE IT WAS DESTROYED)

18

ON THE CONCORD PIKE

TALLEY FARMS
IN NORTHERN NEW CASTLE
COUNTY

ALONG NAAMAN'S ROAD

19

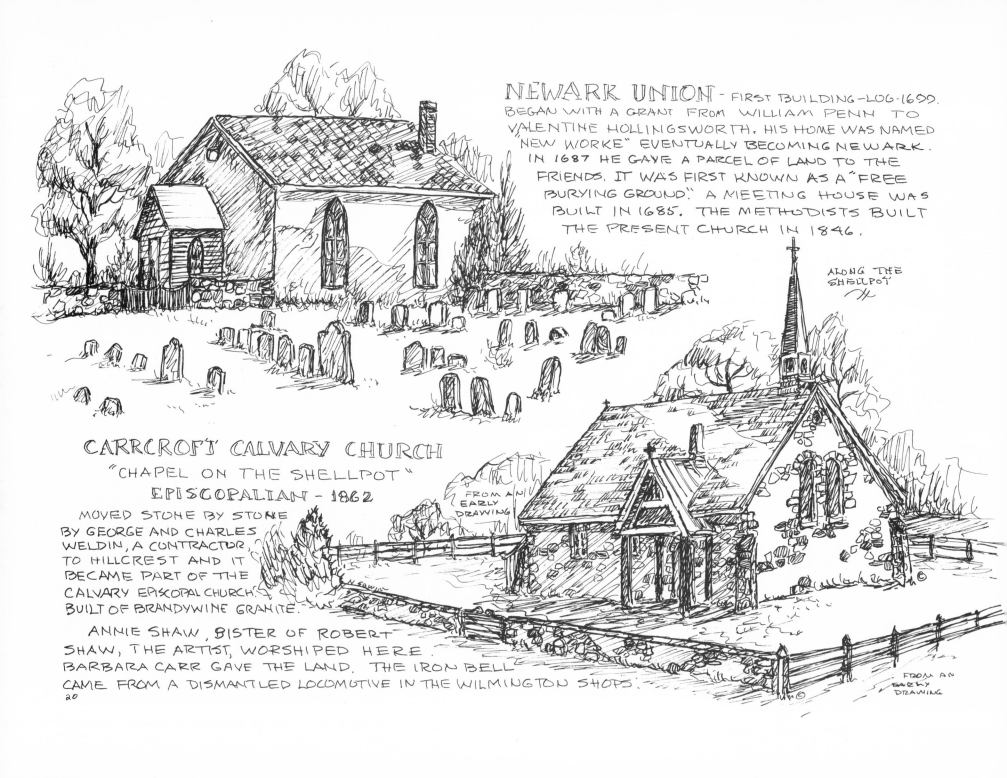

NEWARK UNION - FIRST BUILDING - LOG - 1699.
BEGAN WITH A GRANT FROM WILLIAM PENN TO
VALENTINE HOLLINGSWORTH. HIS HOME WAS NAMED
"NEW WORKE" EVENTUALLY BECOMING NEWARK.
IN 1687 HE GAVE A PARCEL OF LAND TO THE
FRIENDS. IT WAS FIRST KNOWN AS A "FREE
BURYING GROUND." A MEETING HOUSE WAS
BUILT IN 1685. THE METHODISTS BUILT
THE PRESENT CHURCH IN 1846.

ALONG THE
SHELLPOT

CARRCROFT CALVARY CHURCH
"CHAPEL ON THE SHELLPOT"
EPISCOPALIAN - 1862

MOVED STONE BY STONE
BY GEORGE AND CHARLES
WELDIN, A CONTRACTOR,
TO HILLCREST AND IT
BECAME PART OF THE
CALVARY EPISCOPAL CHURCH.
BUILT OF BRANDYWINE GRANITE.

ANNIE SHAW, SISTER OF ROBERT
SHAW, THE ARTIST, WORSHIPED HERE.
BARBARA CARR GAVE THE LAND. THE IRON BELL
CAME FROM A DISMANTLED LOCOMOTIVE IN THE WILMINGTON SHOPS.

FROM AN
EARLY
DRAWING

FROM AN
EARLY
DRAWING

20

LOMBARDY HALL
HOME OF GUNNING BEDFORD, JR.
CIRCA 1750

COOL
SPRING

(HISTORICAL RESIDENCE OF CAESAR RODNEY)

EARLY CARRIAGE HOUSE

ALONG FOULK
ROAD.

GEORGE W. TALLEY HOUSE on Shellpot Creek
MARRIED MARY BEESON

21

ABOVE
THE
DELAWARE
RIVER
NORTH
OF
WILMINGTON

N SALVIN

CLEARVIEW FARM AND PLANTATION

CIRCA 1700 - PETER BAYTON PURCHASED LAND
FROM SWEDES. OVERLOOKS DELAWARE RIVER.

PERKINS PLANTATION - 1663

18th CENT.   19th CENT.

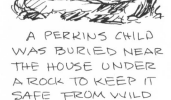

A PERKINS CHILD
WAS BURIED NEAR
THE HOUSE UNDER
A ROCK TO KEEP IT
SAFE FROM WILD
ANIMALS ABOUT 100
YEARS AGO.

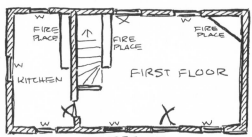

FIRE PLACE   FIRE PLACE   FIRE PLACE

KITCHEN   FIRST FLOOR

RESURRECTION MANOR PLAN

BACK OF EARLY HOME - CLAYMONT AREA

UNDER FIREPLACE

FRONT WINDOWS

18TH CENTURY QUAKER HOME - BACK AND FRONT VIEW

22

IVYSIDE

WOOD IN THE BARN HAS DATE 1876 CARVED INTO SOME OF THE BEAMS. THEY HAD BEEN USED IN BUILDINGS AT THE CENTENNIAL IN PHILADELPHIA.

FIRST FLOOR

FLOOR PLAN OF ORIGINAL PART OF HOUSE. THE LAND WAS PATENTED, JULY 8, 1753 TO ROBERT CLOUD, THE SON OF GEORGE GRUBB BY THOMAS AND RICHARD PENN.

ALONG NAAMAN'S CREEK.

STAR OF BETHEL LODGE. IOOF OF DELAWARE # 191

1858

EARLY GENERAL ST. GRUBB AND MARSH ROADS

DOUBLE FARM HOUSE · BETHEL

23

(FROM ARCHITECTS DRAWING)

ROCKWOOD — THE SHIPLEY-BRINGHURST-HARGRAVES MUSEUM

BUILT 1851-7

BUILT OF BRANDYWINE GRANITE BY JOSEPH SHIPLEY, A DIRECT DESCENDANT OF WILLIAM SHIPLEY, A WILMINGTON FOUNDER. IT IS A UNIQUE EXAMPLE OF RURAL GOTHIC ARCHITECTURE.

HA-HA WALL

COACH HOUSE AND STABLE

NEW CASTLE COUNTY

24

STRAND MILLAS - 1701

In the late 17th century, a Scotsman by birth, secured 400 acres south of the Brandywine in Christiana 100. The Greggs first home was a log cabin. In 1701 the present house was built of Brandywine "granite". As old homes were, it has been altered by its occupants. The Ronald Finches, whose home it now is, have tried to restore and to maintain its early structural features. Legend has it that it has its own ghost, perhaps shades of Glamis Castle in Scotland.

MONTCHANIN, DELAWARE

25

OLD FARM AND SPRING HOUSE × GRANOGUE

MILL HOUSE – CIRCA 1771
HAS PAYMASTER'S WINDOW

HOUSE ON SMITH'S BRIDGE ROAD

26

HAMILTON–MORRISON ON STONE × 1851

BRIDGE HOUSE × BRANDYWINE AT SMITH'S BRIDGE

WHITE FARM HOUSE - CIRCA 1750

SMOKE AND SPRING HOUSE

SKETCH FROM A
DRAWING BY
ELEUTHERE DUPONT
IN 1882.

NORTH OF THE
BRANDYWINE

SPRING HOUSE AND
SHED ON LITTLE MILL CREEK

EARLY FARM HOUSE ABOVE
LITTLE MILL CREEK

27

EARLY BUILDING

ROCKLAND

EIGHT DOOR PRIVY

WINTERTHUR STATION

TOLL HOUSE
(PHOTO)

KENNETT PIKE

HEDGE PEAR

ROCKFORD TOWER

MONTCHANIN STATION

FARM HOUSE

LOOP BACK
WINDSOR SIDE CHAIR

TRUMBLE

FROM THE
WINTERTHUR
COLLECTION

WINTERTHUR HOUSE ~ 1839-1884
SOUTH ELEVATION
OVERLOOKING CLENNY CREEK
FIRST HOME OF EVELINA DUPONT AND ANTOINE BIDERMANN

MADE AND
BRANDED BY
FRANCIS
TRUMBLE
OF PHILA. PA.
1759 - 1798

FIRST PATENT OF
THE FARM LAND WAS BY
WILLIAM PENN TO RICHARD
GREGG ~ FEBRUARY 2, 1692.

WINTERTHUR BESS ORMSBY GREAT

29

1815

MANUFACTURER'S SUNDAY SCHOOL
ALL OF THESE CHURCHES HAD THEIR
BEGINNING HERE, AND WERE BUILT
WITH THE SUPPORT OF THE DUPONT
FAMILY.   CHRIST CHURCH HAS
WINDOWS IN ITS STEEPLE AS
REQUESTED BY LAMMOT DUPONT
SO THAT HE COULD SEE THE
STEEPLES OF THE OTHER
CHURCHES.

1847

MT. SALEM CHURCH
UNION-METHODIST

AN UNKNOWN
DRUMMER BOY
WAS BURIED HERE
DURING THE
CIVIL WAR. HE
DIED OF
PNEUMONIA
WHILE ON DUTY
AT DUPONT
POWDER
WORKS ON
THE
BRANDYWINE.

CHRIST CHURCH
EPISCOPAL
THE DUPONT FAMILY
CEMETERY IS NEARBY.
1854
WILMINGTON

GREENHILL
PRESBYTERIAN
CHURCH - 1840

ST. JOSEPH'S
WAS THE FIRST
OF THE FOUR
CHURCHES TO
BE BUILT.

WHEN THE CHURCH
WAS BUILT, IT TOO
HAD A STEEPLE.

ST. JOSEPH'S
ON THE
BRANDYWINE
ROMAN CATHOLIC

1841

30

EARLY STONE HOUSE

LAMMOT DuPONT WORKSHOP

ELEUTHERIAN MILLS
FROM A PAINTING BY
BASS OTIS - CIRCA 1840

ELEUTHERIAN MILLS
1803

ELEUTHERIAN MILLS
BARN 100 YEARS
AGO.

POWER HOUSE

QUARRY

WORKMEN'S HOMES

SPRING HOUSE

32

BLACKSMITH SHOP

SODA HOUSE

HAGLEY ON THE BRANDYWINE

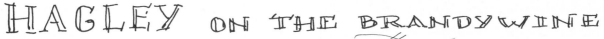

C.I.D.
"HOUSE"
Charles I. DuPont
1823

PIGEON
ROW

LONG
ROW

WALKER'S
MILL

DuPONT OFFICE

A FEW YEARS AGO!

OLIVER EVANS

DESIGN FOR A MILL WHEEL

HE WAS THE SON OF A MILLER WHO HAD A
MILL ON THE RED CLAY CREEK.

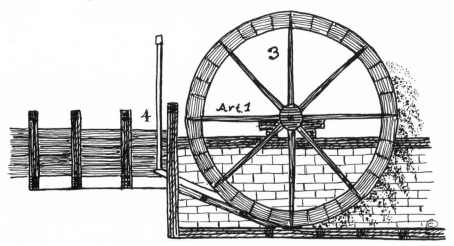

FROM A BOOK OF MILL DRAWINGS BY

ELEUTHERE I. DuPONT

DREDGE BUILT BY OLIVER EVANS IN 1804,
IT WAS THE FIRST HORSELESS CARRIAGE
PROPELLED BY STEAM IN AMERICA. NAMED
ORUKTER AMPHIBOLOS OR AMPHIBIOUS
DIGGER HE TOOK IT DOWN THE SCHUYLKILL
AND UP THE DELAWARE RIVER. ©

34

EARLY HOME NEAR BUCK TAVERN
GREENVILLE, DELAWARE

Public House

BUCK PUBLIC HOUSE OR TAVERN

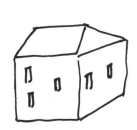

FROM AN EARLY
LAND SURVEY OF
E. I. DUPONT
LAND

BLUE BALL TAVERN
AT THE 'TOP OF' LONG HILL
(CONCORD PIKE AND ROCKLAND ROAD) 35

WOODSTOCK
18TH CENTURY

SOUTH WILMINGTON

ASHLEY HALL
18TH CENTURY

RICHARDSON PARK

1785

MILL
(PHOTO)

MILL HOUSE -
GLYNRICH
CIRCA 1723

GLYNRICH HOUSE
"QUAKER-GEORGIAN" CIRCA 1765

36

SOUTH OF WILMINGTON

THE STATE FARM AND CHRISTINA RIVER SKETCHED FROM ATOP THE MAIN BUILDING WIDOW WATCH.

FARNHURST
x

DELAWARE STATE HOSPITAL
MAIN BUILDING - 18

NEW CASTLE BUILDING
NO LONGER STANDING

FROM EARLY RECORDS:

PRODUCE RAISED ON FARM
DEC. 1, 1892 to DEC. 1, 1894

BEANS - 88 BASKETS	$28.35	
BEETS - 447 BASKETS	14.69	
CORN - 11,125 EARS	105.28	
LETTUCE - 12 BASKETS	3.00	
ONION SETTS - 3½ BUSHELS	9.75	
PARSNIPS - 121 BASKETS	30.25	
POTATOES - 406 BASKETS	141.40	
RADISHES - 3581 BUNCHES	74.57	
SQUASH - 329	8.47	
TOMATOES - 376 BASKETS	125.24	
TURNIPS - 1458 BASKETS	345.25	
TURNIP GREENS - 100 BAS.	14.70	

(PARTIAL LISTS)

ARTICLES MADE BY SEAMSTRESS
DEC. 1, 1892 to DEC. 1, 1894

APRONS	147
BOLSTERS	12
BIBS	13
BED TICKS	146
CHEMISE	326
COMFORTABLES	2
DRAWERS, WOMEN'S	340
DRAWERS, MEN'S	100
PILLOW SHAMS	31
SUSPENDERS	233
SACQUES	9

37

A TYPICAL DOOR
ON THE STRAND

NEW
CASTLE
7X

EDEN PARK ON RIVER ROAD - CIRCA 1770.
BUILT BY JUSTICE JOHN MALCOLM. IT WAS SOLD
IN 1804 TO PIERRE BAUDAY de BELLEVILLE,
SON OF A WEALTHY PLANTER IN SANTO DO-
MINGO. HE HELPED TO FINANCE THE EARLY
START OF E.I. DuPONT de NEMOURS COMPANY.
HIS ONLY SON MARRIED VICTORINE DuPONT, BUT
HE DIED WITHIN A YEAR. IT WAS FOLLOWING HIS
DEATH WITH THE ENCOURAGEMENT OF HER FA-
THER, ELEUTHÈRE I. DuPONT, THAT SHE BEGAN
TEACHING IN THE MANUFACTURER'S SUNDAY
SCHOOL. (FROM AN EARLY PAINTING)

SWANWYCK - DESIGNED BY PIERRE
BAUDUY - CIRCA 1815. A FINE EXAMPLE
OF REGENCY DOMESTIC ARCHITECTURE.

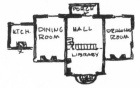

OLD COURT HOUSE -

A CENTER OF DELAWARE
HISTORY FROM THE EARLY
1700'S UNTIL 1881. IT WAS
FIRST A STATE HOUSE.

KENSEY JOHNS
VAN DYKE HOUSE.
BUILT IN 1820
BY SENATOR
NICHOLAS VAN
DYKE FOR HIS
SON, KENSEY
JOHNS VAN
DYKE. VISITED
BY LAFAYETTE
IN 1824.

38

GEORGE READ HOUSE — 1707

OLD PRESBYTERIAN CHURCH - 1707

NEW CASTLE

GUNNING BEDFORD — GRAY HOUSE AND McINTIRE HOUSE — 1730 c. 1690

NEW CASTLE TOWN HALL - BUILT CIRCA 1820.

EARLY HOME ON THE DELAWARE NEAR NEW CASTLE.

LISTON HOUSE ON THE DELAWARE. BUILT IN 1739 BY EDMUND LISTON. DUTCH-COLONIAL STYLE. BLACKBIRD 700.

THE ACADEMY CIRCA 1800

COLBY HOUSE. BUILT BY MARTIN ROSEMOUT (SP.?) IN 1675.

OLD DUTCH HOUSE CIRCA 1682

HOUSE ON THE STRAND - EARLY 19TH CENTURY.

IMMANUEL CHURCH (EPISCOPAL) CIRCA - 1705

39

OLD METHODIST CHURCH
NEWPORT

TATNALL'S WAREHOUSE
AND WHARF - NEWPORT
CHRISTINA RIVER

GALLOWAY HOUSE (DUTCH COLONIAL)

MYERS HOUSE
NEWPORT

18TH CENTURY STONE HOUSE
ON THE STANTON ROAD

DERICKSON HOUSE
ELSMERE - 18TH CENTURY

40

TWO FAMILY HOME

STANTON
HALE-BYRNES HOUSE
1750

STANTON ARM TAVERN

FRIENDS MEETING - STANTON

CHRISTINA RIVER
SKETCHED FROM A
CANOE AT HIGH TIDE
JUST NORTH OF
CHURCHMAN'S ROAD

41

"CHESTNUT HILL" AS IT WAS IN 1934. IT IS LOCATED NEAR WHITE CLAY CREEK PRESBYTERIAN CHURH. (EARLY PHOTO)

WHITE CLAY CREEK "LOVER'S RETREAT" (FROM AN EARLY POSTCARD)

A HOLLINGSWORTH HOMESTEAD UP THE HILL FROM CHESTNUT HILL.

TOP OF POSSUM PARK

EARLY FARM
JUST SOUTH OF
MILFORD
CROSSROADS

1880

1700

1790

ORIGINAL HOUSE
FROM THE FRONT

HEAD OF CHRISTIANA
UNITED PRESBYTERIAN CHURCH
1706

WHITE CLAY CREEK
PRESBYTERIAN CHURCH
1721

POLLY DRUMMOND TAVERN
POLLY DRUMMOND HILL - 1835

43

EARLY HOMESTEAD OF THE STEWART FAMILY IN NEW CASTLE COUNTY

1740 1752 1765

GLASGOW ONE ROOM SCHOOL

SALEM 1807

SALEM CHURCH - SOUTH OF NEWARK

EARLY HOMES IN GLASGOW FORMERLY AIKENTOWN

18TH CENTURY
N.E CORNER
(896 & 40)

PENCADER PRESBYTERIAN CHURCH

FOUNDED 1707
REBUILT 1852

44

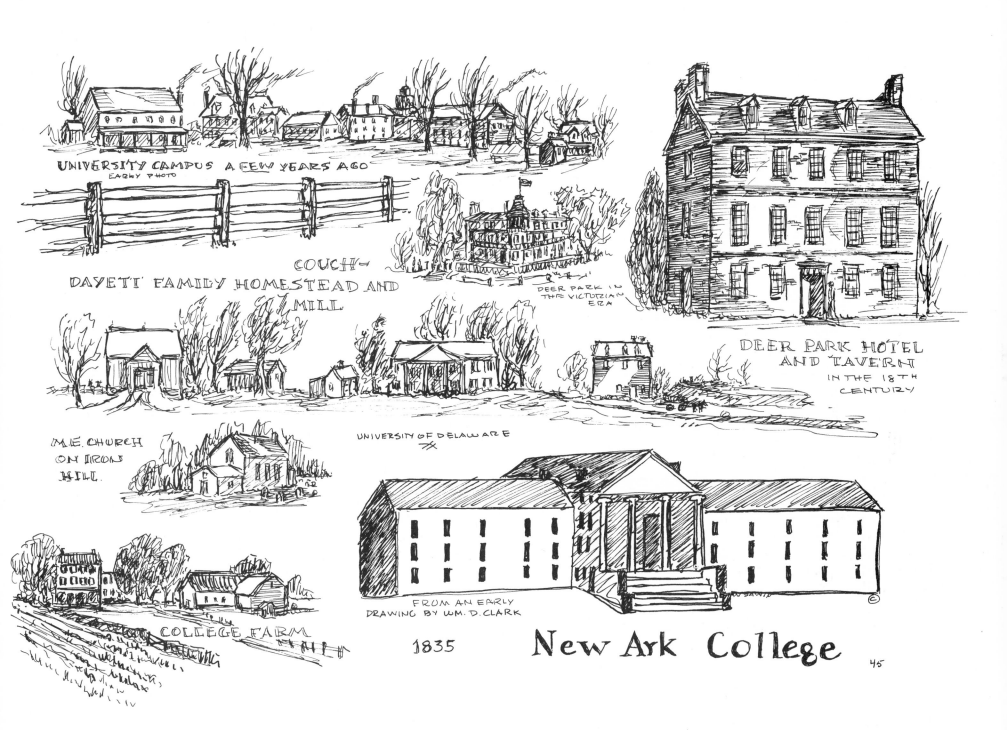

UNIVERSITY CAMPUS A FEW YEARS AGO
EARLY PHOTO

COUCH-
DAYETT FAMILY HOMESTEAD AND
MILL

DEER PARK IN
THE VICTORIAN
ERA

DEER PARK HOTEL
AND TAVERN
IN THE 18TH
CENTURY

M.E. CHURCH
ON IRON
HILL

UNIVERSITY OF DELAWARE

COLLEGE FARM

FROM AN EARLY
DRAWING BY WM. D. CLARK

1835   New Ark College

45

NEWARK ACADEMY

PENNSYLVANIA RAILROAD
PASSENGER STATION

RED MEN'S HOME
FRATERNAL ORDER

SCHOOL NEAR MILFORD CROSSROADS

c.1880

COOCH'S BRIDGE

NEWARK

METHODIST CHURCH
19TH CENTURY
(ENGLISH GOTHIC
STYLE)

PAPER MILL BRIDGE

NEWARK

46

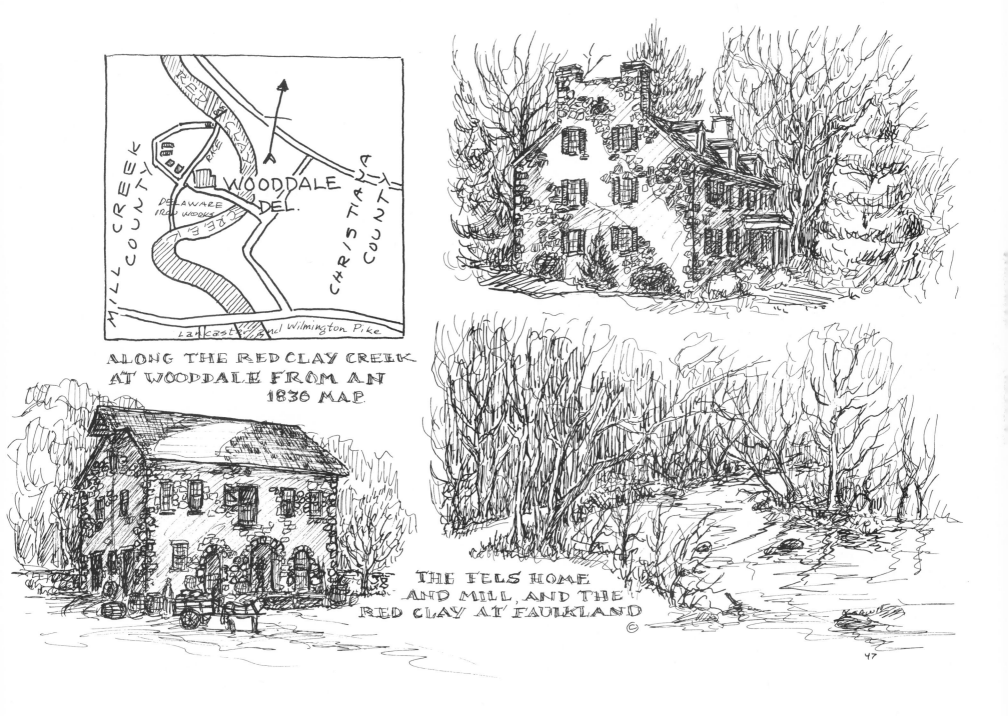

WOODDALE DEL.

MILL CREEK COUNTY

CHRISTIANA COUNTY

DELAWARE IRON WORKS

RED CLAY CREEK

PIKE

RED CLAY

Lancaster and Wilmington Pike

ALONG THE RED CLAY CREEK
AT WOODDALE FROM AN
1836 MAP.

THE FELS HOME
AND MILL, AND THE
RED CLAY AT FAULKLAND

47

WILLIAM MOORE
HOMESTEAD
ON DOE RUN

WM
1813

OLD INN AND TAVERN
AT CORNER KETCH

1804

48

EARLY FARM HOUSE
NEAR CORNER KETCH

MILL CREEK FRIEND'S MEETING

PRIVY

MILL AND POWDER HOUSE - PIKE CREEK

49

BLACKSMITH AND CARRIAGE
SHOP- MILLTOWN

ADAM GASS
CARRIAGES
& WAGONS
PAINTING, TRIMMING
AND REPAIRING
HORSE SHOEING AND
ALL KINDS OF REPAIRING
ON SHORT NOTICE

STONE BARN
POLLY DRUMMOND HILL

HOME OF THE BALL
FAMILY NEAR HYDE CREEK

MILL AT THE LINDELL'S
ON MILL CREEK

ASHLAND MILL ON RED CLAY CREEK

WOOLEN MILL - ON MILL CREEK

MADE BLUE
WOOL FOR UNION
UNIFORMS DURING
CIVIL WAR.

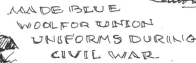

MENDENHALL MILL ON MILL CREEK

51

OLD GRIST MILL
THERE ONCE WAS A SAW MILL NEARBY.

EARLY SPRING

HOUSE - NEAR MT. CUBA

PRIVY

MILL HOUSES ON WAY ROAD
THESE OLD HOUSES ARE STILL STANDING BUT NO LONGER LIVED IN BY HUMAN KIND.

52

EARLY FARM COTTAGE
SHARPLESS ROAD

NORTH STAR SCHOOL
1847

19TH CENTURY HOME
QUAKER GREEK REVIVAL

SMOKE AND SPRING HOUSE
CREEK ROAD

MEETING HOUSE HILL

EARLY SPRING HOUSE
SANFORD SCHOOL CAMPUS

CAROUSEL FARM

LIMESTONE ROAD

CROSSING THE RED CLAY
JUST SOUTH OF ASHLAND MILL
AS I REMEMBER IT.!

ARMOUR-KLAIR
FARM HOUSE — 19TH CENTURY

53

DATE ON THE HEADSTONE
OF THE GREGG HOME
IN ASHLAND

EARLY MITCHELL FAMILY
FARMS NEAR HOCKESSIN.
DELAWARE - QUAKER HOMESTEADS

54

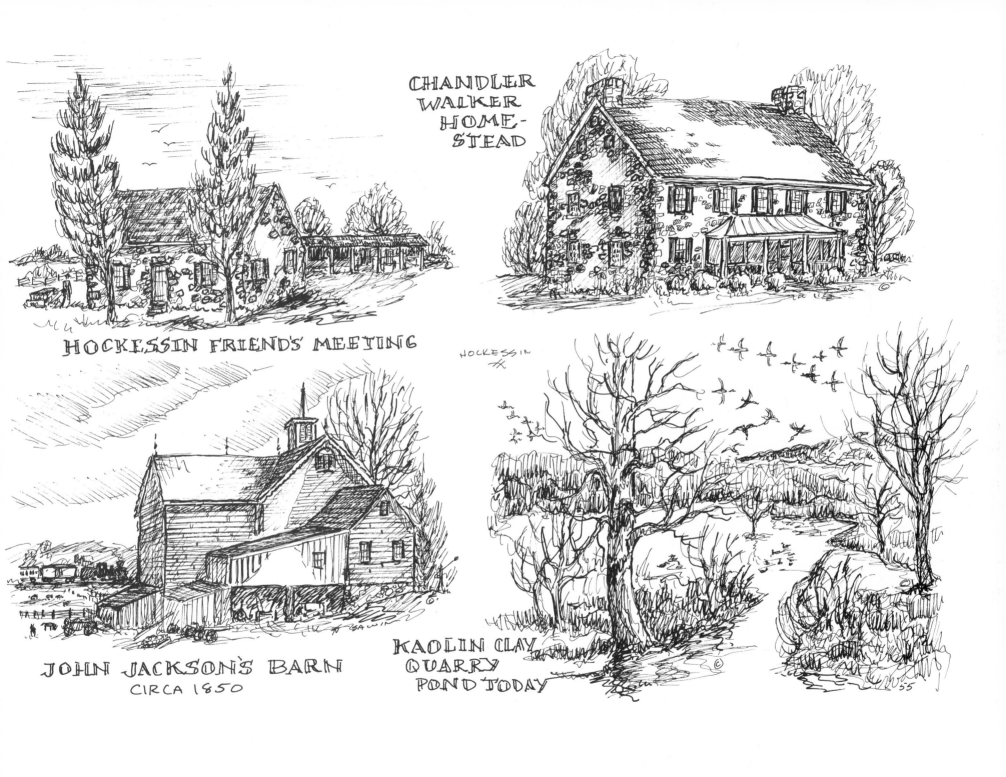

CHANDLER WALKER HOME-STEAD

HOCKESSIN FRIEND'S MEETING

JOHN JACKSON'S BARN
CIRCA 1850

HOCKESSIN

KAOLIN CLAY QUARRY POND TODAY

55

CIRCA 1726

JUSTA JUSTIS MILL AT GREENBANK
ON HYDE RUN — 1818

THE THOMAS BIRD HOUSE
AT PRICE'S CORNER, NOW
LOCATED AT THE LANDING
PLACE OF THE SWEDES
ON THE CHRISTINA RIVER

THOMAS FLINN'S HOUSE AND BARN
IN 1895 NEAR GREENBANK MILL

56

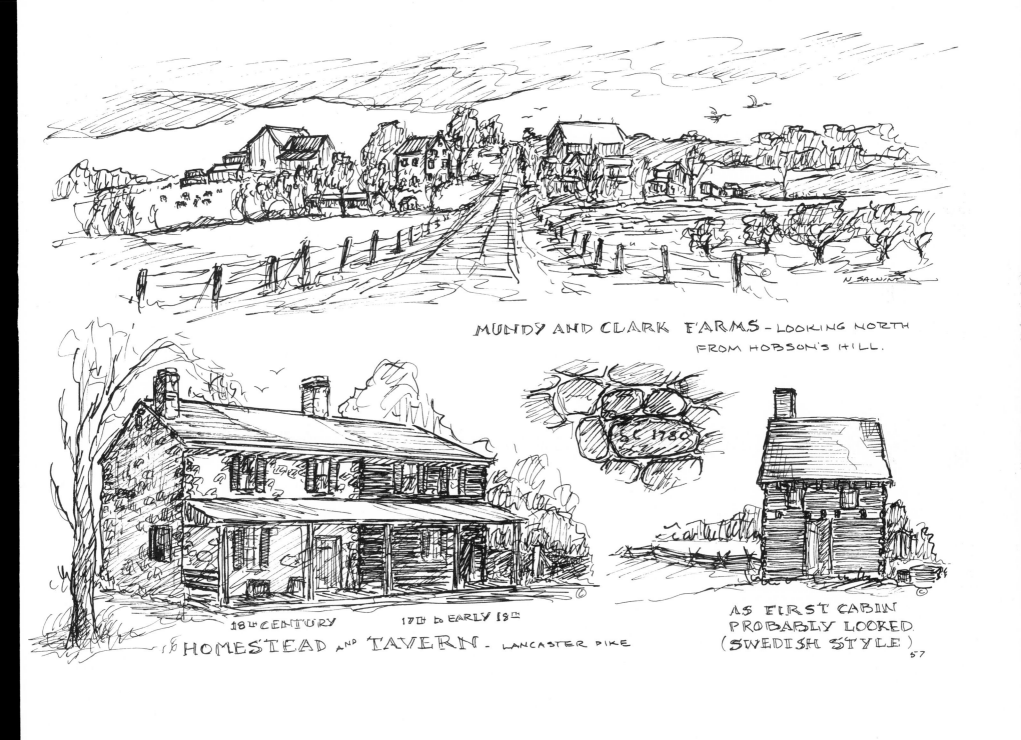

MUNDY AND CLARK FARMS - LOOKING NORTH FROM HOBSON'S HILL.

18ᵗʰ CENTURY   17ᵗʰ to EARLY 18ᵗʰ

HOMESTEAD and TAVERN - LANCASTER PIKE

AS FIRST CABIN PROBABLY LOOKED. (SWEDISH STYLE)

N. SAWIN

57

NICHOLAS SPRINGER
HOUSE - CIRCA-1762

NEAR HOCKESSIN

SIMON HADLEY FARM

ON STENNING MANOR GRANT BY LETITIA PENN
HOUSE SKETCHED FROM EARLY PAINTING.

CIRCA 1740
JOHN MONTGOMERY HOUSE
OLD WILMINGTON ROAD

DIXON PLANTATION - 1754
LAND GRANTED BY LETITIA PENN

YORKLYN

RAILROAD STATION

GARRETTS LOWER SNUFF MILL
on the Red Clay Creek

GREGG'S STORE AND
POST OFFICE - Yorklyn.

WOODDALE BRIDGE
over the Red Clay Creek

WILMINGTON & WESTERN TRAIN - 1877-1882
In 1882 the rail line became a branch of
the B&O.

59

The Brackin family came to Delaware when the Swedes were in control. Early in the 19th century they were well established in Brackinville. They had a grist and saw mill, a tavern, a black smith shop and two farms. The mill was on a small tributary of Mill Creek. As a child I explored the early mill and spent much time with Newton, Bart, and Mary Brackin, as I was their neighbor. They taught me to plow, cultivate, mow and rake hay, and milk a cow. I know this farm very well.

THE BRACKIN FARM

BRACKINVILLE

SPRING HOUSE - on James Mendenhall Farm. Each farm's outbuildings consisted of a privy, spring house, smoke house and wood shed.

60

MARSHALL
HOMESTEAD

MARSHALL'S BRIDGE
ACROSS THE RED CLAY CREEK

THOMAS S. MARSHALL
& SONS PAPER MILL

YORKLYN

in the 1880's.
(FROM PHOTOGRAPHS
IN THE MARSHALL
FAMILY ALBUMS)

The stone part of the house was built by John Marshall in 1767. In 1877 Elizabeth and Israel Marshall set up housekeeping here. The homestead is located 2 miles from Hockessin Friends Meeting by an old carriage road no longer open for travel.

61

18TH CENTURY HOME

CENTERVILLE

PRIVY

CONNOR'S COUNTRY STORE

CENTERVILLE ONE ROOM SCHOOL

FAIRVILLE

TODAY AND YESTERDAY

MILESTONE ON KENNETT PIKE

1 TO W

FAIRVILLE

LOWER BRANDYWINE PRESBYTERIAN CHURCH

62

SMOKE
HOUSE

HAMORTON
EARLY HOMES, INN, AND
CARRIAGE HOUSE

CARRIAGE HOUSE

ADMIRAL
FAHRNEY'S
GATE HOUSE

NEAR
KENNETT SQUARE - EARLY FRAME HOME
WITH PENT EVE

EARLY FARM HOUSE - NEAR STRODES MILL

63

LANDENBERG

WILMINGTON &
WESTERN
RAILROAD
STATION

BLACKSMITH SHOP
ON WHITE CLAY CREEK
BUTTONWOOD

WALNUT RUN SCHOOL (1838)

CHESTNUT GREEN
KAOLIN SCHOOL HOUSE

CROSSAN SAW MILL
LANDENBERG

BROAD RUN TRESTLE
(W. & W. R.R.)

64

CHESTERVILLE

ALONG THE WHITE CLAY CREEK

CIRCA 1794

ONE ROOM SCHOOL

CIRCA 1781

WILLIAM CROSSAN BARN

PRIVY

MILL HOUSE IN LANDENBERG

HILL FARM
(N. OF CHESTERVILLE)

MILL AND
MILL HOUSE
NEW LONDON RD.

66

MERCER ~
HOOPES
MILL

WHITE CLAY CREEK

REBUILT BY HOOPES
IN 1835

MILLER BARN
AVONDALE

FRONT

(ON THE WHITE CLAY)

CONNELL CARRIAGE SHED
AND CORN CRIB

BACK

WILLIAM
MILLER HOUSE
1731 - 2½ STOR
1771 - 3 STOR
FLEMISH BOND

AVONDALE

67

HOME AND
OUTBUILDINGS
RESTORED
AND PRESERVED
BY ELLWOOD
WILKINS.
WAS EARLY
TAVERN.

1774

SPRING AND SMOKE HOUSE

CIRCULAR STAIRWAY

KEMBLESVILLE
EARLY HOTEL AND TAVERN

STRICKERSVILLE

BETWEEN THE
HEADS OF THE WHITE
CLAY AND CHRISTINA

68

RED
ROSE
INN

JENNERSVILLE
1740

CARRIAGE SHED ~ NEW LONDON PRESBYTERIAN CHURCH ~ FOUNDED - 1726

69

EARLY WILKINSON HOMESTEAD
NORTH OF AVONDALE

NEW GARDEN MEETING

F^SO HANA WILKINSON 1786

ON THE HILL ABOVE TOUCHKENAMON

EARLY MEETING - NOW A HOME.
(NEW GARDEN)

CARRIAGE HOUSE AND HOME IN 'TOUCHKENAMON

N ERWIN

"LITTLE HOUSE"
NEW LONDON

WASHINGTON SLEPT HERE !

PRIMITIVE BAPTIST CHURCH

SITE OF MINQUANAN
INDIAN TOWN - UNAMI
GROUP OF LENNI LENAPE
PART OF 1683 WM. PENN
GRANT.

OLD NEW LONDON BUILDING

CIRCA 1741

STONE IN EARLY
EPISCOPAL CEMETERY
ST. JOHN'S CHURCH
(KELTON)

EARLY
NEW LONDON
HOTEL-ON SITE ⊙
OF EARLIER TAVERN
LICENSED IN 1729 BY
LAZARUS FINNEY

NEW LONDON ACADEMY

YEATMAN'S
MILL HOUSE - 18TH CENTURY

18TH CENTURY
BEGINNING OF
UNIVERSITY OF
DELAWARE.

71

THE BLUE PIG TAVERN AND INN
— CHATHAM

BAYARD TAYLOR'S "OLD"
CHESTNUTS OF CEDARCROFT
(KENNETT)

EATON ACADEMY = FOUNDED = 1839
KENNETT'S FIRST FEMALE SEMINARY

EARLY HOME OF
SIDNEY AND LYDIA PUSEY

KENNETT HOTEL - EAST END BUILT BEFORE 1776

BAYARD TAYLOR'S HOMESTEAD
(SOME DRAWINGS FROM EARLY POSTCARDS)

72

ANVIL INN AND TAVERN - 1884

LONGWOOD

PIERCE PARK   1730
AFTER 1906 PART OF LONGWOOD GARDENS
AND HOME OF PIERRE S. DUPONT

OLD KENNETT MEETING
1710

73

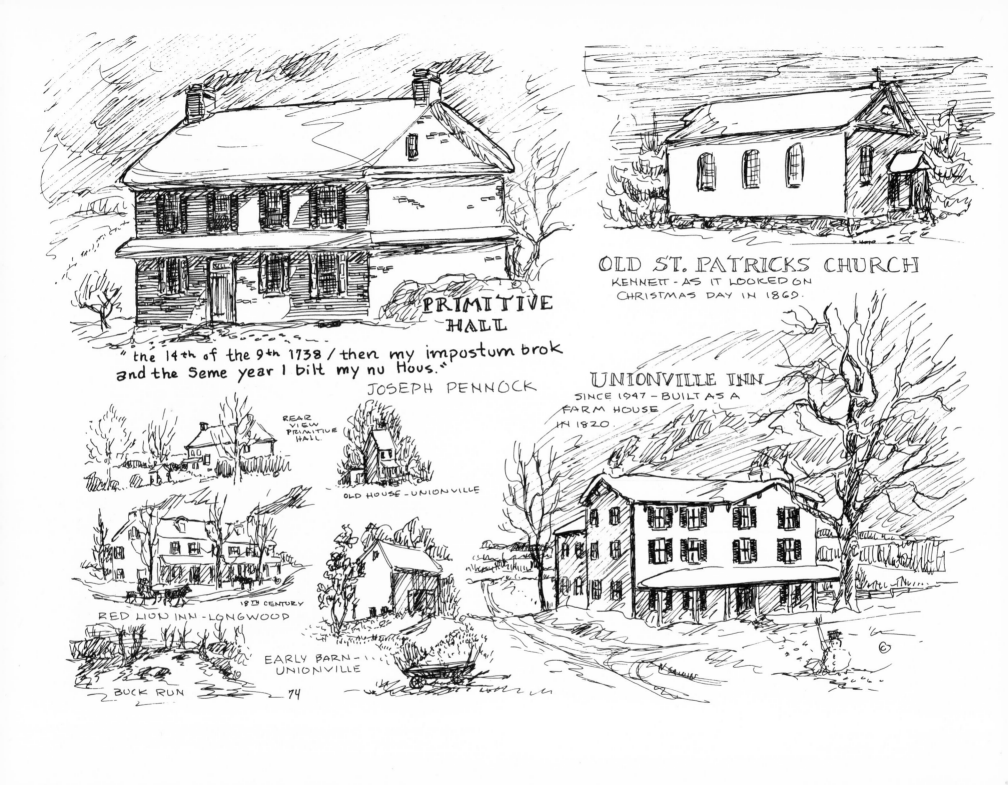

PRIMITIVE
HALL

OLD ST. PATRICKS CHURCH
KENNETT - AS IT LOOKED ON
CHRISTMAS DAY IN 1869.

"the 14th of the 9th 1738 / then my impostum brok
and the Seme year I bilt my nu Hous."

JOSEPH PENNOCK

UNIONVILLE INN
SINCE 1947 - BUILT AS A
FARM HOUSE
IN 1820.

REAR
VIEW
PRIMITIVE
HALL.

OLD HOUSE - UNIONVILLE

18TH CENTURY

RED LION INN - LONGWOOD

EARLY BARN -
UNIONVILLE

BUCK RUN   74

PIERSON & CO. WHEEL
AND SPOKE FACTORY. TOUGHKENAMON
(FROM AN EARLY ENGRAVING)

STRAHORN
BLACKSMITH SHOP
LONDON GROVE

THE WHITE CLAY
CREEK - AVONDALE

HAMMER AND TROWEL TAVERN
(INCLUDED IN BAYARD TAYLOR'S
"STORY OF KENNETT".)

FARM AND MILL ON
PUSEY TRACT
ON THE WESTERN BRANCH
OF THE WHITE CLAY.

75

LONDON GROVE MEETING
AND HORSE BLOCK

NEW GARDEN
POST OFFICE

BIRMINGHAM
OCTAGONAL
SCHOOL - 1818

BIRMINGHAM MEETING

GILBERT'S MILL NEAR CHATHAM

76

WHITESIDE FARM - HILLENDALE ROAD
18TH CENTURY BARN

SMOKE AND
SPRING HOUSE

ABOVE CHANDLER'S
MILL ROAD

CLIFTON MILLS
ON THE RED CLAY CREEK

SITE OF EARLY QUARRY
HORNBLENDE GRANITE

77

THE BARN AND FARM HOUSE
AT KENDALL

KENNETT GRANGE

TRIMBLE'S FORD
ON THE BRANDYWINE
ROUTE OF THE BRITISH AT THE
BATTLE OF THE BRANDYWINE - 1777

78

HOUSE AT HAWLEY'S MILL

POLOPSON SCHOOL - 1882

HOMESTEAD
THOMAS CARLETON
BUILT IN 1717.
USED BRANDYWINE
HORNBLENDE GRANITE

JEFFERIS BRIDGE OVER THE BRANDYWINE

STRODES MILL

1721

NEAR KENNETT

MORTONVILLE BRIDGE

79

BARN AND ONE ROOM SCHOOL
OLD LANCASTER-GAP TURNPIKE
KAOLIN

CONNELL BARN
ROSEHILL

18TH CENTURY FARM HOUSE
ROBINSON FARM IN KAOLIN

JEFFERIS BRIDGE
ON THE
BRANDYWINE

SWAMP
WILLOWS

FARM COTTAGE
NEWARK ROAD

BARN ON COMSLEY
FARM

ALONG SHARP ROAD

80

LAFAYETTE'S HEADQUARTERS

WASHINGTON'S
HEADQUARTERS
1712

SPRING
HOUSE

HOME OF
JOHN CHAD   1725

ONE AND
ONE HALF
STORY HOUSE

PRIVY

CIRCA 1712

AROUND
CHADD'S FORD

81

ISAAC GILPIN CART'
HOUSE

IG
1798

OUT BUILDINGS

HOWARD PYLE BARN FROM
A PAINTING BY N. C. WYETH

WYETH STUDIO
"BRINTON MILL"

CHADD'S FORD

82

LENAPE STATION

TROLLEY AND TRAIN NEAR LENAPE

BRINTON 1704 HOUSE

PRIVY

SMOKE & SPRING HOUSE

CARRIAGE HOUSE AND BLACKSMITH SHOP MARSHALLTON

BRINTON S. DARLINGTON HOUSE

FOUND ALONG THE BRANDY-WINE: GRANITE INDIAN AXE AND QUARTZ AND CHERT ARROW HEADS.

CIRCA 1750

83

EARLY SIGN BOARD
IN WEST CHESTER

CALEB TAYLOR'S STORE
ONE OF WEST CHESTER'S
OLDEST STORES. (PHOTO)

WEST CHESTER

13 N. HIGH ST. - PATENTED
BY WILLIAM PENN - 1702.
BECAME BANK OF CHESTER
COUNTY IN 1814.

RECITATION HALL - WEST CHESTER STATE
NORMAL SCHOOL - 1892 - BUILT OF SERPENTINE STONE
FOUNDED IN 1812 AS WEST CHESTER ACADEMY.

NEAR LENAPE

ALONG GAY STREET
FROM AN EARLY PHOTOGRAPH

BALDWIN BOOK BARN -
COLLECTORS OF CHESTER
COUNTY HISTORY. BARN
WAS BUILT IN 1822.

84

HARLAN HOUSE - EMBREVILLE
MASON AND DIXON STAYED HERE IN 1764

SCHOFF CABIN - WEST BRADFORD
(PHOTO)

31 MILES DUE
WEST OF SOUTH STREET
PHILADELPHIA
PLACED BY
MASON AND
DIXON

THE BRANDYWINE
NEAR LENAPE.

STAR GAZERS STONE
1764

GRAVE OF INDIAN HANNAH
SHE WAS THE LAST MEMBER
OF THE LENNI-LENAPE INDIANS
LIVING IN CHESTER COUNTY.
SHE DIED MARCH 20, 1802.

MASON AND DIXON
STONE WITH THE
COAT OF ARMS OF
WILLIAM PENN.

85

EEL'S FOOT SIGN

EEL'S FOOT TAVERN 18TH CENTURY
NEAR JEFFERIS BRIDGE

SPEAKMAN BRIDGE AND MILL
FROM A PHOTO CIRCA 1900 - BUCK RUN
(MILL FROM A PHOTO)

FARM WAGON
MADE IN PENNSYLVANIA

STAGE COACH

BIRTHPLACE OF ISAAC SHARPLESS
GRADUATED WESTTOWN 1867 - PRESIDENT OF
HAVERFORD COLLEGE - 1887 TO 1917.

COVENTRY - IRON WORKERS
TENANT HOUSES

86

DEBORAH'S ROCK
NEAR "ABIAH'S" HOUSE
ON THE BRANDYWINE

ALONG THE POCOPSON

ABIAH TAYLOR HOUSE ~ 1724 - CREEK ROAD
MADE FROM LOCAL BRICK - SMALL WINDOW LIGHTS - LEAD SASH AND FRETS

87

FRIEND'S MEETING

OLD LOG HOUSE - STROUD

MILL BUILDING NEAR STROUD

ALONG DOE RUN ROAD

SITE OF MILL

SPEAKMAN BRIDGE ON BUCK RUN

88

PARKE HOUSE

CALN - CIRCA 1700

LOG CABIN AT
RED FOX

HOME AT MARTIN'S CORNER

HEWN LOGS - CIRCA 1770

SPRING
HOUSE &
SMOKE
HOUSE

SWEDISH LOG
CONSTRUCTION

DENNISTOWN

RAMSAY TANNERY AND
BLACKSMITH SHOP

CIRCA 1823

89

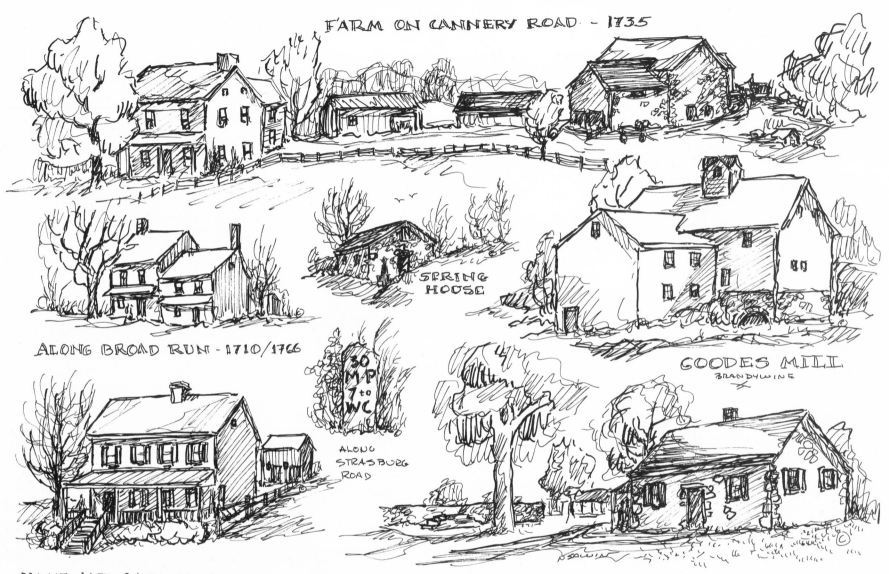

FARM ON CANNERY ROAD - 1735

ALONG BROAD RUN - 1710/1766

SPRING HOUSE

GOODES MILL
BRANDYWINE

30
M P
7 to
WC

ALONG
STRASBURG
ROAD

HOME AND CARRIAGE SHED - 1700
MARSHALLTON

WEST BRADFORD MEETING - 1776

90

STONE HOUSE - WEST
OF DOWNINGTOWN.
OWNERS SAID, "IT WAS HERE WHEN GEORGE
WASHINGTON WAS PRESIDENT."

STONE QUARRY - DOWNINGTOWN

VEHICLES AND THE BRANDYWINE
GO UNDER THE HILL SOUTH OF DOWNINGTOWN
(TRAINS GO OVER)

SMALL STONE HOUSE
ON HILLSIDE NORTH
OF DOWNINGTOWN.

SMALL CEMETERY - JOSEPH
STONE AND WIFE LYDIA ROBERTS
CAME TO "PIKELAND" IN 1745.
HE DIED IN 1793.

CARRIAGE SHED - UWCHLAND MEETING

91

GRIST MILL
IN GLENMORE,
EARLY 19TH CENTURY

WEST SIDE

SOUTH
EAST
SIDE

MILL

A SMALL FAMILY CEMETERY
"THE IRWIN CLAN"

ROBISON IRWIN DIED IN 1776

MILL

THE LEWIS MILL,
ON THE
BRANDYWINE = 1762

THE GRANARY,
(NOW A HOME)

AND

MILLERS HOME
ABOVE THE MILL.

SPRING HOUSE

TOBACCO BARN

SUPPLEE ROAD

92

"A SWAMP WILLOW"

THE BRANDYWINE AT GRUBB'S MILL

GRUBB'S MILL

GIBSON'S BRIDGE
ON THE EAST BRANCH OF THE BRANDYWINE

93

DOUBLE HOME AT
LUDWIGS CORNER

ST. ANDREWS - 1832
NEAR LUDWIG'S CORNER

RESTORED MILLHOME
HIBERNIA PARK AREA

EARLY STONE HOME
ON FAIRVIEW ROAD

EAGLE TAVERN

DILWORTHTOWN COUNTRY STORE

EAGLE TAVERN

94

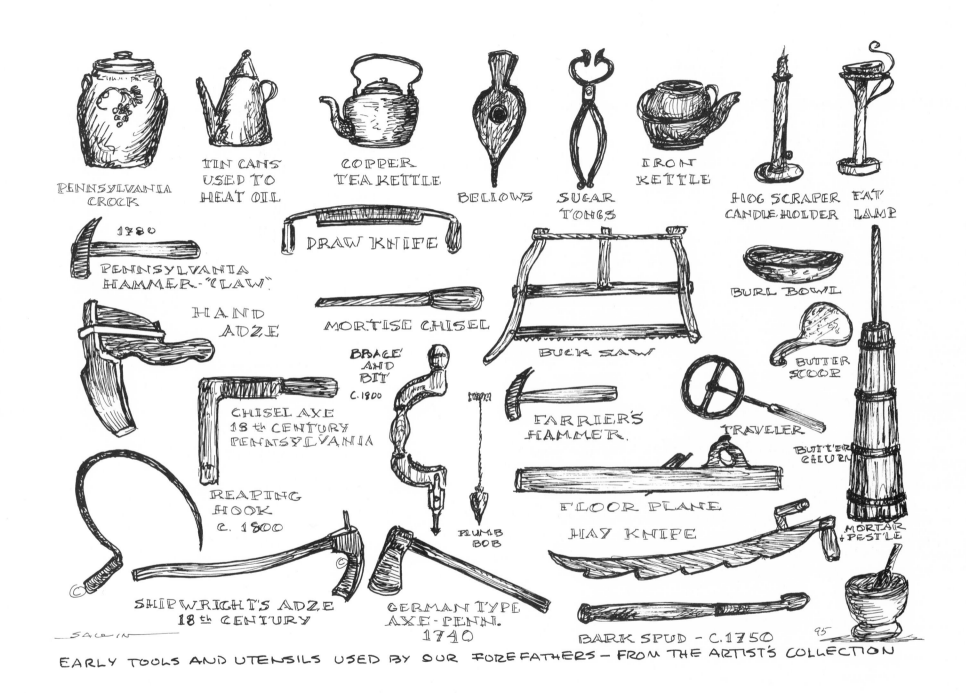

PENNSYLVANIA CROCK

TIN CANS USED TO HEAT OIL

COPPER TEA KETTLE

BELLOWS

SUGAR TONGS

IRON KETTLE

HOG SCRAPER CANDLE HOLDER

FAT LAMP

1780
PENNSYLVANIA HAMMER - "CLAW"

DRAW KNIFE

HAND ADZE

MORTISE CHISEL

BUCK SAW

BURL BOWL

BUTTER SCOOP

CHISEL AXE 18th CENTURY PENNSYLVANIA

BRACE AND BIT C.1800

NOTE

FARRIER'S HAMMER

TRAVELER

BUTTER CHURN

REAPING HOOK C. 1800

PLUMB BOB

FLOOR PLANE

HAY KNIFE

MORTAR & PESTLE

SHIPWRIGHT'S ADZE 18th CENTURY

GERMAN TYPE AXE - PENN. 1740

BARK SPUD - C.1750

95

SAWIN

EARLY TOOLS AND UTENSILS USED BY OUR FOREFATHERS - FROM THE ARTIST'S COLLECTION

INDEX

THE STRONGEST SHALL SURVIVE . . . STRENGTH TRAINING FOR FOOTBALL

Table of Contents

THE STRONGEST SHALL SURVIVE . . .
STRENGTH TRAINING FOR FOOTBALL

DEDICATION

This book is dedicated to my first coach and most trusted friend, my brother

Donald Starr of Havre de Grace, Maryland.

THE STRONGEST SHALL SURVIVE . . . STRENGTH TRAINING FOR FOOTBALL

CREDITS

Photography

Leonard Nakahashi, pages: 9, 21, 23, 59, 61, 149, 170, 185, 199, 200 & 205

Steve Dussia, All exercise photos for Big Three and Rehabilitation Chapters and 23, 40, 75, 155, 172, 173, 175, 176.

Ellen Stapleton, pages 64, 65, 78, 87, 153, 177, 179, 181, 189, 190

Richard Souther, page 195

Art Zeller, page 197

Nick Frasca, page 192

Peter Axaom, page 182

Everill Taggart, page 174, courtesy **Weightlifting Journal**

Page 25, courtesy of John Williams

Page 26, courtesy Mike Curtis

Page 37, courtesy Jaris White

All other photos by the author

Art Work

Tommy Kono, page 41

Tom Kurtz, page 54, courtesy **Weightlifting Journal**

Wes Woo, page 187, an adaptation of a cartoon by Wes Woo by Steve Dussia

Steven Dussia, page 191, cartoons of sleep and chapter head characters

Chris Train cover, section heads plus all the illustrations for the rest of the book.

I would like to make special mention of the eight athletes who came out of my strength program at the University of Hawaii who have continued on into the ranks of professional football.

★ John Woodcock, Defensive Lineman, Detroit Lions.
★ Jaris White, Defensive Back, Miami Dolphins & Tampa Bay.
★ Levi Stanley, Defensive Lineman, Hawaiians & San Francisco.
★ Arnold Morgado, Running Back, Kansas City Chiefs.
★ Charlie Aiu, Offensive Lineman, San Diego Chargers.
★ Harold Stringert, Defensive Back, San Diego Chargers.
★ Dan Audick, Offensive Lineman, St. Louis Cardinals.
★ June Jones, Quarterback, Atlanta Falcons.

Each of these players is a living testimony to the benefits of strength training. They played on a mediocre team and received very little recognition while playing some 3000 miles from the mainstream of national publicity. Each and every one of these players greatly improved his playing ability through strength training. None are super athletes, yet through hard work they were prepared when they came to tryouts.

I congratulate each of these fine young men.

THE STRONGEST SHALL SURVIVE . . .

ACKNOWLEDGEMENTS

The acknowledgement of a book is a publicly-displayed "thank you" from the author to all of those who helped to make his project a reality. Space prohibits me from mentioning all of the individuals who have played some part in the formation of **The Strongest Shall Survive . . . Strength Training for Football**, since the number would include every strength athlete whom I have talked with during the last twenty years. I will, however, mention those to whom I owe a special debt of gratitude.

I must recognize my older brother, Donald, first and foremost for the same reasons that I dedicated this book to him. He was the guiding influence in my formative years. Donald was responsible for building my early interest in sports and athletics, which has carried over to the present day.

Brother Donald was, and still is for that matter, an outstanding athlete and a natural coach. Some of my earliest memories are of Donald teaching me some particular athletic skill or explaining a rule technicality as we watched or listened to a sports event. When Donald became interested in a sport, he took great care to learn all that he could about that activity. He would devour the rule book, he would work fundamentals, then incorporate strategy into his game. He was gifted with extremely fine eye-hand coordination, physical size, and speed and payed attention to fundamentals. As a result, he became very proficient in any sport he seriously tackled.

One of the more rewarding phases of my coaching career came after I had moved to York and had the opportunity to teach my brother the basics of strength training. He responded quickly, befitting his nature, and after just one year of training, he won the Maryland State Championship in powerlifting and continues to train and compete today.

I am extremely grateful for the opportunity to thank my older brother in print for the many patient hours he spent teaching and motivating me. It was his early nurturing that brought about this book. His patience and understanding came when I needed it most. Thanks Big Brother.

Brother Donald was my first coach in a myriad of sports, but not in weightlifting. That task fell upon the willing and competent shoulders of Sid Henry of Dallas, Texas. I met Sid at the Dallas YMCA while I was a member of the Southern Methodist University football team in 1959 — the Don Meredith era in SMU history. Sid was an international caliber lifter and a fierce competitor. He promised to spend his time and energy coaching me if I would concentrate all of my physical and mental efforts into a weightlifting program. This meant giving up football for competitive weightlifting, but I was contemplating doing so anyway as my first daughter, Christi Lou, was about to arrive and the new financial pressures forced me to change my goals. So I turned myself over to Sid.

He proved to be a tremendous coach who stressed fundamentals. A very strict disciplinarian, he would not allow improper lifting form, nor a deviancy from his prescribed formula. He knew the importance of making every repetition on every set. He knew that regularity was critical for progress. When I would miss a session, Sid was on the phone wanting to know "why." He closely supervised my program, taking much time from his own, but he was most anxious to help, just so long as I was serious about becoming stronger.

His strict adherence to form and systematic training have become an intregal part of my own strength training philosophy. It could be honestly stated that without his interest and his knowledge that I would never have advanced past the mediocre level in the strength sport and certainly never would have decided to make strength training my profession.

Since I began training with Sid some fifteen years ago, I have had the opportunity to come into contact with literally hundreds of weightlifting and strength coaches from around the globe. I can sincerely say that I have never met anyone who possessed all the qualities of a Strength Coach as well as Sid. I consider myself very fortunate to have met Sid and to have him guide me through the most critical early stages of my strength training education. A great many ideas presented in this book are a direct result of my early days with my good friend Sid Henry.

I left Dallas in 1962 to attend graduate school in Chicago. Out of necessity I became my own coach, primarily utilizing the principles and programs set down for me during the three years that I trained under Sid. Competitive weightlifters have to act as coaches for each other as there are very few actual coaches available in this country. The Windy City had some outstanding weightlifters and I picked up valuable pieces of information on technique and training. I trained as often as possible at the Irving Park YMCA with Chuck Nootens, John Racklin, Fred Schutz and Clyde Emrich. Each of these athletes provided me with their views on training, and, in time, these ideas became meshed into my philosophy.

It was also at this time while I was the Youth Program Director at the Park Ridge YMCA that I became responsible for setting up and regulating strength programs for others. Tom and Rick Holbrook were two of my first pupils and I learned a great deal from teaching them the skills involved in Olympic lifting.

Following graduate school, I took a position at the Marion, Indiana YMCA and once again, became the coach of the weightlifting team. This small Hoosier town is the home of one of the most knowledgeable men on the subject of strength training in the country, although few people know of Larry Perkins. He only spends his time with a few athletes who are very intent in their goals. He loves the sport of strength and has spent a lifetime learning all that he can about his favorite subject. Larry and I spent many an evening discussing the latest theories in strength training. He did a great deal to stimulate my quest for knowledge and he added much to what I already knew.

The opportunity to move to York to work with Tommy Suggs on **Strength & Health Magazine** came in January of 1966, so my avocation became my vocation, as it has to this day. I was elated at the chance to be close to the vast storehouse of information which flowed into the center of American weightlifting. It was at this point that I really began learning, in depth, about the subject of strength training for football.

STRENGTH TRAINING FOR FOOTBALL

Tommy Suggs and I were in a position to come in contact with a vast resource of knowledge during our five years in York. We were in personal contact with the top strength athletes from around the world. We would receive research data from Bulgaria, Russia, England, Japan, Mexico, etc. Articles would cross our desk daily concerning some new theory or concept in strength training. We would travel to contests and clinics in all parts of the United States and Canada and talk to the local lifters and coaches. Each strength athlete would learn something from us and we, in turn, would add to our body of knowledge.

Part of our job responsibility at York was to serve as resource people for those who needed information on the subject of strength training. In the late sixties, football coaches became extremely interested in strength training. We would travel to football clinics, coaches conventions, and to individual schools. We would relate what we knew on the subjects of strength training and nutrition and offer suggestions. It was a tremendous learning experience. The coaches were becoming more and more aware of the aspect of strength as it related to football and they would ask us questions that would send us scurrying back to the research journals. We found that we had to do more than to merely express our opinions on the subject, we had to back up our theories with empirical data. We realized that there was a genuine need for a simplified program that would work in small and large schools with a minimum of equipment, time, and supervision . . . and still get results.

So we began experimenting. We would suggest a program to a coach and then secure feed-back later that year, or even the following year. Since York was the hub of the strength industry, literally thousands of coaches would be in contact with us during a twelve-month period. We had, in short, a huge number of subjects on which to test our theories.

After the third year, we had refined and condensed our program to where it is today. The "Big Three" and the rest of the concepts such as circuit training, the heavy, light, and medium training days, and so forth are a direct result of those years dealing with the coaches in actual strength training situations. The program got results 100% of the time. All the coach had to do was to follow the directions to the letter and the gains followed automatically.

Full credit must be given to my friend Tommy Suggs, of Lake Jackson, Texas, for his contribution to the ideas found in **The Strongest Shall Survive . . . Strength Training for Football**. It would be impossible to separate his ideas from my own as most were a result of shared knowledge. I consider Tommy to be one of the finest Strength Coaches in the world today. A former national weightlifting champion and national record holder, he became the Strength Coach for the Houston Oilers in 1973. I believe his groundwork with the team has had much to do with their later success.

I cannot close without mentioning the many, many coaches and athletes who have helped shape some part of this book. While it is impossible to pinpoint as to where a certain concept or idea originated, in all likelihood it came out of a letter or a conversation with a fellow strength athlete or coach.

I would like to record the names of a few who have had a marked influence on my thinking concerning strength training: Jack King, Larry Hanneman, George Lugrin, Ken Patera, George Pickett, Bill March, Tony Garcy, Bob Hise III, Roman Mielec, Norbert Schemansky, Russ Knipp, Peter Rawluk, Tom Hirtz, Kenny Moore, Don Reed, Tom Kurtz, Dr. John Gourgott, Louis Riecke, Bernie Simmons, Mike Hutchinson, Homer Brannum, Gerald Travis, Jim Witt, Bob Hise Sr., Hank Lujan, Joe Mills, Bob Bednarski, Dick Judd, Merle Kelly, Carlos Looper, Dave Bjoraas, Charles Herring, Joe Puleo, Dr. Gary Echternacht, Dr. Nigel DaSilva, Louie DeMarco.

Roger Yanule, Karl Buehrer, Norman Rauch, Steve Sakoulous, Bob Bartholomew, Terry Todd, Frank Gibson, Charles West, Tom LaFontaine, Mike Karchut, Frank Capsouras, Gary Glenney, Rudy Sablo, Bob Crist, Morris Weissbrot, Bill Stripling, Mike Burgener, Tim Garcia, Phil Grippaldi, Roger Quinn, Fred Lowe, Dan Cantore, Jim Schmitz, Bill St. John, Dr. John Zeigler, Tommy Kono, John Terlazzo, Steve Stanko, John Grimek, Dick Bachtell, Frank Bates, Fraysher Ferguson, John Snow, Mike Spurrier, Jack Brandenburg, Sam Fielder, Richard Krutzer, Steve Dussia, John Phillip, Larry Pacifico, Doug Young, Clay Patterson, Kevin McClaverty, Gus Rethwitch, Dave Thomas, Steve Gilardi, Bruce Buckbee, Dave Sheppard, Harvey Hanec, Bob DeVolin, Wes Woo, Aldo and Ralph Roy, Andy Hinds.

Peary Rader, George Fujio, Buster Nagao, Dave Holmes, Paul Durham, Rick Blangiardi, Steve Rosenbloom, Mike Curtis, Ray May, Bill Curry, Bill Newsome, Bubba Smith, John Williams, Jeris White, Levi Stanley, Jerry Hardy, Don Herrod, Cliff LaBoy, Arnold Morgado, Gary Spotts, Bobby Winkfield, Charlie Sutton, Charlie Aiu, George Lumpkin, Charlie Kaaihue, Ray Schoenke, Bob Grant, Doug Hepburn, Dan DeWelt, Dan Audick, Ben Weider, Ed Fisher, Bill Nelson, Larry Price, Bob Acosta, Bill Kamana, John May, Tony Ciarelli, Dean Adams, Oscar State, Ken Fujimura, Eddie Block, Ed Inouye, Randy Frish, John Woodcock, Saipele Manutai, George Kaye, Jack LaLanne, Ron Chysler, and finally, Dick Hoffman.

And a special note of gratitude to all those who helped in the actual production of the book. All are friends and everyone did a bit extra to help to make this a quality production. Cindy Wolfe, secretary; Randy Mohn, Nan Dalton and Stephanie Ciarelli, proofreading; Ellen Stapleton, layout artist and photography; Steve Gilardi, paste-up artist; Leonard Nakahashi, photography; Steve Dussia, photography and cartoons; Wayne and Annette Justice, typesetting; Chris Train, illustrations; Arnold Morgado, Nick Frasca and Steven Dussia, exercise models; Joe Gano, business manager; and Tom Straub, who financially supported the project.

Finally, to my good friend Princo, I wish to offer a special thanks, for without his belief in me, this project would have never gotten past the planning stage. His trust and support made this book possible.

Thanks everybody, I hope you enjoy the book.

End

THE STRONGEST SHALL SURVIVE ...

THE STRONGEST SHALL SURVIVE ...

THE STRONGEST SHALL SURVIVE ...

THE STRONGEST SHALL SURVIVE ...

INTRODUCTION

The need for an instructional book on strength training for football is long overdue. While most professional teams and the more progressive colleges and high schools have a Strength Coach on their staff, many smaller and less financially endowed schools are usually at a loss concerning this phase of physical conditioning.

The Strongest Shall Survive ... Strength Training for Football is a book specifically written for the junior high, senior high, and college coach who has to rely on his own resources in order to put together a strength training program for his team. It is also meant to be a useful tool for the individual football player who might wish to become involved in a sound strength program on his own. In the past, anyone who was interested in setting up a strength program would have to leaf through scores of magazines, hoping to glean one or two pertinent tidbits of information which might be helpful to his program. Regardless of the extent of his research, however, there always existed huge gaps of information. Since there has not been a single reference source published to which the coach or interested athlete could turn for the much-needed data, the trainee was often lost and confused.

The Strongest Shall Survive ... Strength Training for Football brings all of the pertinent material dealing with this facet of physical training under one cover. The two chapters dealing with anatomy, physiology, and kinesiology will serve as an introduction to this aspect of strength training in these sciences. A complete course on strength training is then presented in detail in Chapters four through seven. Within these pages, a coach or athlete will be able to learn: how to purchase the necessary equipment, how to perform the various exercises, and how to organize and supervise the program for an individual or an entire team.

The nutritional section is the most complete guide on this vital subject ever assembled for the athlete. The various nutrients are discussed at full length and their usefulness to the athlete is explained in full.

STRENGTH TRAINING FOR FOOTBALL

STRENGTH TRAINING FOR FOOTBALL

STRENGTH TRAINING FOR FOOTBALL

STRENGTH TRAINING FOR FOOTBALL

The Related Materials Section covers many aspects of strength training on which very little has previously been written. Sleep is certainly an important variable to the athlete. How much is enough and, more importantly, how can an athlete go about obtaining sound sleep? This information is presented in depth. The use of drugs by the highly-motivated athlete is a known fact, but seldom does the coach realize just how the various drugs affect the athlete's performance and his overall health. Chapter nineteen covers this rather delicate, but critical subject.

Getting the athlete back on the playing field after an injury is of prime importance to every successful coach. Resistive training can be used most effectively to rehabilitate an injured player. A complete guide as to the proper procedure to follow in rehabilitating a wide assortment of injuries is contained in Chapters sixteen and seventeen.

This book is meant to be a complete resource on the subject of strength training for football. It is a how-to-do book, and is designed to be used. The systems, ideas, and concepts of strength training as presented do work. Athletes become stronger when they follow the methods and advice prescribed in the following pages.

The Strongest Shall Survive . . . Strength Training for Football is an encyclopedia on the topic of strength training. It just may prove to be the most valuable book a football coach could ever read on how to develop a better football team. Stronger football teams do not always win as there are many more variables involved in this complicated game than physical strength, but a team which becomes stronger does become better, if all the other athletic attributes are kept constant. This book will enable any coach to build a stronger team. A stronger football team, without any question, has a distinct advantage over a weaker one in the highly physical game of football.

end

THE STRONGEST SHALL SURVIVE . . .

WEIGHT TRAINING SECTION

WEIGHT TRAINING SECTION

WEIGHT TRAINING SECTION

WEIGHT TRAINING SECTION

WEIGHT TRAINING SECTION

WEIGHT TRAINING SECTION

WEIGHT TRAINING SECTION

WEIGHT TRAINING SECTION

WEIGHT TRAINING SECTION

WEIGHT TRAINING SECTIO

WEIGHT TRAINING SECTION

WEIGHT TRAINING SECTION

WEIGHT TRAINING SECTION

WEIGHT TRAINING SECTION

STRENGTH TRAINING FOR FOOTBALL

THE STRONGEST SHALL SURVIVE...
STRENGTH TRAINING FOR FOOTBALL

More individuals are born than can possibly survive. The slightest advantage or better adaptation in one being over those with which it comes into competition, in however slight a degree, will turn the balance.

Charles Robert Darwin in *On the Origin of Species*

1

CHAPTER ONE
THE MARVELOUS MACHINE

THE STRENGTH COACH AND weight training athlete must have a basic understanding of the anatomy, physiology, and kinesiology of the human body in order to properly organize and supervise a successful strength program. Actually, this book will be most concerned with the science of kinesiology as this science combines anatomy, the science of structure of the body, with physiology, the science of the function of the body, to produce kinesiology, the science of movement of the body.

With a basic knowledge of these sciences, the Strength Coach or individual athlete will be in a position to comprehend why some exercises work better than others; how to adapt certain movements to meet the individual's needs; and will be better able to develop new exercises for the injured, or otherwise handicapped, player.

The more the Strength Coach knows about the way the body functions the better able he will be to create, adjust, and modify exercise programs for the individual athlete. He especially needs to be well versed on the action of the musculoskeletal system, i.e. the way in which the muscles and joints work.

To rephrase the statement in the negative sense, how can a coach outline a program to build strength in the shoulder girdle without at least a basic understanding of how the muscles and joints work in the shoulder girdle? It is, certainly, rather difficult to summize how this could be done with any degree of success.

SKELETAL STRUCTURE

Man, like the rest of the vertebrates, has a skeleton for support. The size and strength of the bones determine his height and general structure. The bones serve for the attachment of muscles and form protective structures for such delicate organs as the heart, lungs, and brain.

The skeleton of man has more than two hundred separate bones. Those of the skull are made up of those which surround the brain and those which form the skeleton of the face. The spinal column consists of thirty-three segments, or vertebrae. The different vertebrae permit a limited amount of movement which enables the body to turn and bend the trunk in various directions. At the same time these vertebrae, piled one on top of another, constitute a strong support for the weight of the body and head. They also surround and protect the spinal cord.

The seven neck vertebrae (cervical) make it possible to turn the head and change its position to aid in balancing the body. Below these are the twelve chest vertebrae (thoracic) which serve for the attachment of the ribs. The five vertebrae in the lower back (lumbar) make it possible to bend at the waist and twist the body in many directions. The sacrum in the pelvic region consists of five fused vetebrae which are immovable. At the tip end of the spine, also in the

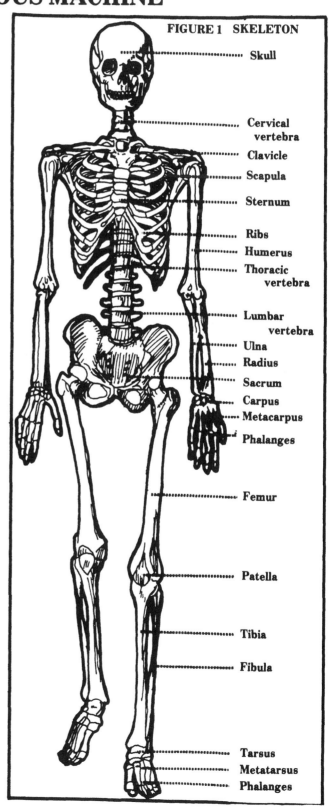

FIGURE 1 SKELETON

Skull

Cervical vertebra

Clavicle

Scapula

Sternum

Ribs

Humerus

Thoracic vertebra

Lumbar vertebra

Ulna

Radius

Sacrum

Carpus

Metacarpus

Phalanges

Femur

Patella

Tibia

Fibula

Tarsus

Metatarsus

Phalanges

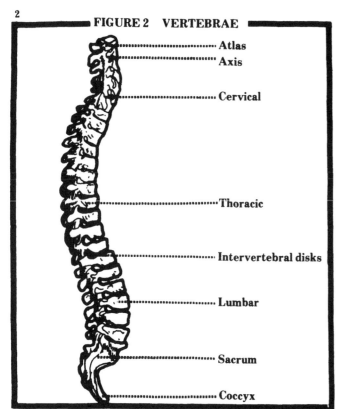

FIGURE 2 VERTEBRAE

- Atlas
- Axis
- Cervical
- Thoracic
- Intervertebral disks
- Lumbar
- Sacrum
- Coccyx

pelvic region, are four more vertebrae fused to form the coccyx. In lower animals the coccyx grows much longer to form a tail.

There are twelve pairs of ribs — all attached to the vertebrae of the spinal column. Of the upper seven pairs, the other ends are attached directly to the breastbone, or sternum, by flexible cartilage. This permits the freedom of movement necessary in breathing. Of the other five, the upper three are indirectly attached, while the two lower, having no cartilages, are called floating ribs.

The breastbone, or sternum, consists of a single piece which serves for the attachment of the ribs and protects the heart. The arm and leg of man are built upon the same plan. In the arm, there is the long bone (humerus), which extends from the shoulder to the elbow, the two bones in the forearm (radius and ulna), the row of small bones in the wrist (carpus) which move freely upon each other, and the bones of the fingers (phalanges). Corresponding to these are the long upper bones of the leg (femur) that extends from hip to knees; the two bones (tibia and fibula) that go from the knee to the ankle; the several bones in the ankle (tarsus); and the bones of the toes (phalanges). The knee-cap (patella) is an extra bone in the leg not duplicated in the arm.

Two bones join the arm at the shoulder. One of these, the collar bone (clavicle) connects the upper end of the sternum with the shoulder. The second bone is the shoulder blade (scapula) which is the large flat bone at the back of the shoulder, serving as a most important surface for the attachment of the powerful muscles that help move the arm.

The hip girdle (pelvis) joins a number of the vertebrae furnishing a firm base of support for the body and at the same time permitting a large range of movement in the legs.

Your skeletal system determines the overall shape of your body. Likewise, the shape of the various bones differ according to the functions they perform. The large bones found in the legs and pelvic girdle are weight supporters; the flatter ones in the cranium, chest and pelvic girdle protect vital areas; and the small ones found in the wrist and instep are compact so that they can move more readily and absorb the shock from the hands and feet and transmit it to many smaller surfaces.

The long bones with expanded articular surfaces deal primarily with motion. Such bones are found in the arms and legs, the humerus and femur being two examples.

THE ARCHITECTURE OF JOINTS

The junction of two bones is called a joint or articulation. There are three general classifications of joints:
1) The **immovable** or **synarthrodial joints.** These include the bones of the cranium and face.
2) The **slightly movable** or **amphiarthrodial joints.** The joining bone surfaces are separated by a pad of elastic fibrocartilage. Movement is effected only by compression of the pad at one or the other side. This type of joint is found in the vertebrae, where the pad serves to cushion shock as well as to allow movement.
3) The **freely movable** or **diarthrodial joints.** The bone surfaces are held in close proximity to one another, the movement being determined by the related shapes of the two surfaces. The elbow is an example of the freely movable joint.

This book will only be concerned with the freely movable or diarthrodial joints, as they are the ones most involved in athletic performance. A typical structure is shown in Figures 2 and 3. The weight-bearing (articular) surfaces of the bones are covered by a layer of cartilage known as the articular cartilage. This cartilage is tough but not brittle and prevents shocks from wearing on the bones, and actually modifies the shape of the bones to insure a better fit. This cartilage has no nerve or blood supply of its own.

The capsular ligament serves as a sleeve and is attached to both bones of the joint enclosing it completely. This capsule is lined internally by a thin membrane called the synovial membrane. The synovial membrane secretes synovial fluid into the joint cavity which provides nourishment to the articular cartilages and serves to lubricate the joint. An injury or irritation to the joint produces an over abundance of this fluid and swelling results.

Some freely movable joints such as the knee have an additional cartilage separating the two adjoining bones called a fibrocartilage disk or interarticular disk. This separating disk is shown in Figure 2 and assists in holding the joints more firmly together.

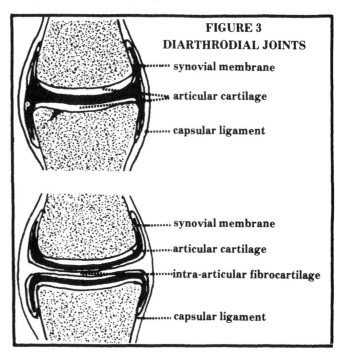

FIGURE 3 DIARTHRODIAL JOINTS
- synovial membrane
- articular cartilage
- capsular ligament
- synovial membrane
- articular cartilage
- intra-articular fibrocartilage
- capsular ligament

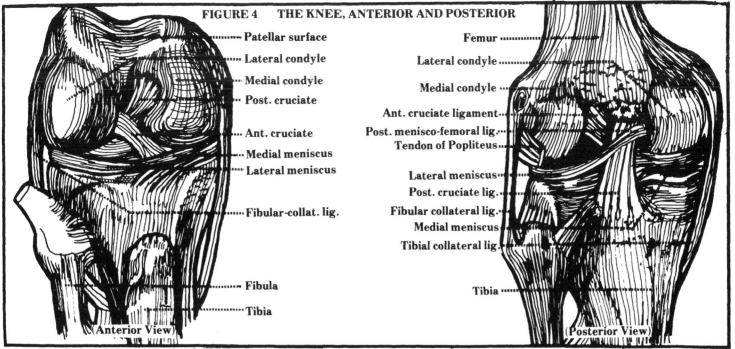

FIGURE 4 THE KNEE, ANTERIOR AND POSTERIOR

Patellar surface
Lateral condyle
Medial condyle
Post. cruciate
Ant. cruciate
Medial meniscus
Lateral meniscus
Fibular-collat. lig.
Fibula
Tibia
(Anterior View)

Femur
Lateral condyle
Medial condyle
Ant. cruciate ligament
Post. menisco-femoral lig.
Tendon of Popliteus
Lateral meniscus
Post. cruciate lig.
Fibular collateral lig.
Medial meniscus
Tibial collateral lig.
Tibia
(Posterior View)

THE KNEE JOINT

All joints of the body are, naturally, extremely important to the Strength Coach and athlete, but none is as important to the football player as the knee. A basic understanding of this complex joint is most critical when dealing with a high contact sport.

The knee joint is the largest and the most complex in the body. It is a hinge-type joint with movements only of flexion and extension. The joint itself is made up of two condyles of the femur (medial and lateral condyles) two rounded shaped structures and the upper end of the tibia on the top of which are two pairs of cartilages which provide accurate fitting of the condyles of the femur. These cartilages, the medial and lateral menisci or semilunar cartilages, serve to adapt the shapes of the femoral condyles to the articular surfaces of the tibia, to cushion the knee while walking, running, or jumping.

The tibial collateral ligament and the fibular collateral ligament are very strong ligaments on either side of the knee joint which prevents lateral movement of the tibia and fibula.

The two cruciate ligaments prevent the knee from moving too far forward or backward. The anterior and posterior cruciate ligaments are two short, strong ligaments, one of which runs from the forward part of the head of the tibia, backwards to become firmly attached posteriorly to the lower end of the femur. This prevents forward movement of the tibia. The other cruciate ligament runs from the posterior aspect of the head of the tibia forward to be inserted into the forward part of the lower head of the femur. This prevents the backward movement of the head of the tibia.

Two additional ligaments which help to stabilize this joint are the oblique popliteal ligament and the arcuate popliteal ligament.

The knee joint is protected in front by a small triangular-shaped bone, the patella. The patella is housed intramembranously within the tendon of the quadriceps femoris muscle group. The patella fits in a groove which lies between the two femoral condyles. The patella ligament is correctly named, since it joins bone to bone, but functionally it is a tendon, since it is made up of fibers which are continuous with those of the quadriceps tendon.

The patella protects the front part of the knee joint and acts as a pulley by increasing the angle of insertion of the patellar ligament upon the tibia. This increases the mechanical advantage of the quadriceps femoris muscle group.

The knee joint is extremely strong, since it is made up of heavy bones above and below it and is surrounded by strong ligaments. The knee joint is controlled by very strong muscles, some twelve in number and it can take heavy strains and jolts.

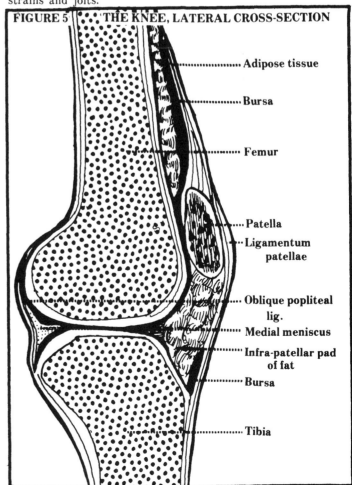

FIGURE 5 THE KNEE, LATERAL CROSS-SECTION

Adipose tissue
Bursa
Femur
Patella
Ligamentum patellae
Oblique popliteal lig.
Medial meniscus
Infra-patellar pad of fat
Bursa
Tibia

TENDONS

Tendons serve to attach muscle to bone and muscle to skin. In order to make a functional distinction between ligaments and tendons you should regard a tendon as a functional extension of the muscle — as a fibrous structure that connects the muscle to other structures, especially to bone.

Tendons also have a role in holding the bones of a joint together. A tendon's primary function is to transfer muscle tension so as to cause movement. The tendons provide a narrow attachment for the muscle, thereby avoiding large, bulky muscle masses from having to function at joints. If the muscle of the forearm, rather than the tendons, were to cross the wrist joint, the hand would not be able to perform such highly skilled mechanisms. The tendons provide certain pulley actions that allow greater efficiency, especially when fine movements are desired.

The stabilization of joints is maintained by the surrounding structures. The ligaments serve as limiting factors to extremes and directions of motion of the bones. The articular capsule functions as a support or "housing" and the tendons and their associated muscles provide movement as well as support and stability of the joint. Of these structures, the muscles and their tendinous attachments are the major stabilizing components of the joints.

LIGAMENTS

The capsular ligament has the job of holding the two bones in place. There are also other ligaments which join the two bones and are separate from the capsular ligament.

The role of the ligaments is to bind bones together, to prevent dislocation, and to limit the kinds and ranges of motion. Ligaments are made of extremely tough material and are practically non-elastic. If a joint is put under constant stress the ligament will often stretch and lengthen, thus reducing its effectiveness.

Not only do ligaments function as limiting components for extremes in range of motion, but the location of the ligaments at each joint largely determines the type of movement that the muscles can perform.

ANATOMICAL MOVEMENTS

In order for the Strength Coach or athlete to fully understand the working of the various muscles and joints he must have a basic knowledge of the various anatomical movements. These terms are used to help facilitate explanations of the various movements. For the purpose of defining joint movements it is always assumed that the body is in the anatomical position, that is, elongated as if suspended by its skull from a hook, with arms, legs, dangling and the palms of the hands facing forward. The skeleton in Figure 1 is in the anatomical position except that its right hand has been turned in towards the thigh.

The following list of anatomical positions and movements with their definitions should be helpful in understanding information in this and other chapters of the book.

1. **Abduction**, movement away from the midline of the body.
2. **Adduction**, movement toward the midline of the body.
3. **Circumduction**, movement of a limb in a manner that describes a cone.
4. **Depression**, downward movement of a body part.
5. **Elevation**, upward movement of a body part.
6. **Extension**, movement resulting in the increase of a joint angle.
7. **Flexion**, movement resulting in a decrease of a joint angle.
8. **Hyperextension**, movement beyond the position of extension.
9. **Lateral flexion**, movement of the trunk sideways from the mid-line of the body.
10. **Prone position**, lying in a face-down position.
11. **Supine position**, lying in a face-up position.

STRUCTURE AND ACTION OF MUSCLES

The muscles are the parts of the body which are responsible for converting energy manufactured by the body into mechanical action. Three different types of muscles, or contractile tissues, are found in the body. They are both similar and different in certain characteristics. They are all affected by the same kind of stimuli; they all produce an action potential soon after stimulation; they all possess the ability to contract; they all have the ability to maintain tone and finally; they all will atrophy (reduce in size) from inadequate circulation and will hypertrophy (enlarge in size) in response to increased work.

The three types of muscles are: smooth, striated, and cardiac.

SMOOTH OR INVOLUNTARY MUSCLE

The smooth, or involuntary muscles are found in the various systems of tubes in the respiratory system (trachea and bronchi), the circulatory system (blood vessels), the digestive tract (stomach), and reproductive organs (genital ducts). These are often referred to as "nonstriated muscles." These muscles contract much more slowly than do skeletal muscles. They also have the power to sustain a longer contraction and are capable of a rhythmic contraction. The smooth muscle is more sensitive to heat and chemical stimuli than the other two types.

The contraction of smooth muscles in a hollow organ, such as the stomach, will cause that organ to empty. Its action is usually involuntary and it can be activated by both the sympathetic and parasympathetic nervous systems.

CARDIAC MUSCLE

The caridac muscle is found only in the heart, hence its name. It displays structural and functional resemblances to both skeletal and smooth muscle. Even though this muscle is made up of many cells, it acts electrically as if it were a single cell. Cardiac action is involuntary, automatic, and rhythmic.

STRIATED, VOLUNTARY, OR SKELETAL MUSCLE

There are approximately 434 skeletal muscles and an estimated 250 million striated muscle fibers in the human body. Of these, some 75 are involved in the movement of the body. The others are small and are concerned with such minute mechanisms as controlling the voice, facial expressions, and swallowing.

Striated muscles are made up of thread-like fibers showing both light and dark fibers. Each muscle contains some fibers of each type, but in general, rapid movements are carried out by muscles in which white fibers predominate, while the slower movements are executed by those in which red fibers predominate.

Each fiber is actually an elongated cell. Each cell is separate. The individual cells are activated by either the cranial or spinal nerves. They are under voluntary control.

The striated muscles are the ones which the coach and athlete are most concerned with and any reference to "muscles" henceforth will mean the skeletal or voluntary ones, unless otherwise specified.

ORGANIZATION OF WHOLE MUSCLES

A bundle of 100 to 150 individual muscle fibers are bound together by a connective tissue. The bundle is termed a **fasciculus**. Then, several of these bundles are further grouped by more connective tissue to form a yet larger unit. These units are then covered by more tissue, called **epimysium**, to form a whole muscle.

The connective tissue, called **perimysium**, join to form the tendon and attach the bundle of muscle fibers to the body surface. The closer a muscle lies to the surface of the body the more connective tissue there is surrounding it in order to provide additional protection.

These sheaths of connective tissue form the structural framework for the various muscles. They are structually strong and relatively elastic, being able to return to their original length even after having been stretched some 40%.

FEEDING THE MUSCLES

The blood flowing through the muscles carries food to the muscle cells. Glycogen is stored in the liver and to a limited extent in muscle tissue. This is changed to glucose and is transported to muscle tissue and there oxidized to furnish energy for muscular contraction. A small amount of fat is present in muscles and may be used up during their contraction. Under ordinary circumstances the protein foods do not furnish energy for contraction, but are used to repair the actual wastes that take place in the muscle cells as they work.

The individual muscle actually receives its oxygen, sugar, and other nutrients by way of an incredible number of capillaries. The walls of these capillaries are extremely thin and allow for easy transfer of nutrients to the muscle fibers themselves.

There is now sufficient evidence to support the fact that the body actually develops additional new capillaries within the muscle in response to the need of a greater blood supply. This need is brought about when the muscle is exercised heavily and regularly. Dr. Jokl in Volume 16 of the 1946 edition of **Research Quarterly**, reported that this increase was about 45%.

The capillaries communicate freely with one another and form interlacing networks of variable form and size in the different tissue. All the tissue, with the exception of the cartilages, hair, nails, cuticle, and corneas of the eye are traversed by these networks of capillary vessels. Their diameter is so small that the blood cells must pass through them in single file, and very frequently the cell is larger than the caliber of the vessel and has to be squeezed to enable it to pass through. They are the most abundant and form the finest networks in those organs where the blood is needed for purposes other than local nutrition, as for example, exertion, secretion, or absorbtion.

During active exercise the rhythmic contraction of the skeletal muscles exert a strong pumping action on the flow of blood. Relaxation follows and allows the veins of the muscle to refill with blood. During contraction the blood is squeezed out of the muscle towards the heart. A series of valves in the veins prevents it from flowing in the wrong direction. If an athlete stops all movement after strenuous exercise this pumping action ceases and there may not be sufficient blood to maintain the cardiac output. It is therefore advisable to reduce activity gradually rather than abruptly after a heavy set of lifting or a tiring run.

THE VALSALVA MANEUVER

Strength Coaches and athletes need to be aware of the phenomenon referred to as the "Valsalva Maneuver" as it comes into play ever so often in the weight room. When a lifter holds his breath while performing a maximum exertion, generally the overhead press, he hinders the return of venous blood from the brain to his heart. This results in the athlete blacking out which, of course, can be quite hazardous if he is holding a loaded barbell overhead or if he falls onto some equipment.

Caution the lifter, when performing a maximum attempt, to breathe immediately after the weight passes the sticking point. Once you either inhale or exhale you open the glottis in your throat and this relieves the pressure on the veins that return from the brain.

ORIGIN AND INSERTION OF MUSCLES

In order to fully understand how the various muscles of the body perform you must understand a few terms associated with the anatomy of muscles.

Two such terms are origin and insertion of skeletal muscles. Skeletal muscles generally pass over joints, some of which are movable, some immovable. If the joint is movable, it is convenient to speak of the origin and insertion

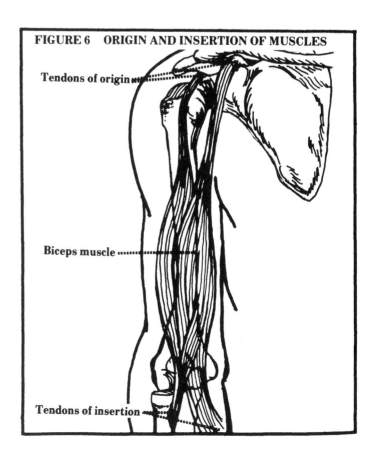

FIGURE 6   ORIGIN AND INSERTION OF MUSCLES

Tendons of origin

Biceps muscle

Tendons of insertion

of the muscle. The origin is the end attached to the less movable bone, while the insertion is the attachment to a bone moving in the ordinary activity of the body. The origin alone is fixed in a small number of muscles such as those of the face, many of which are attached by one end to a bone and by the other to skin.

Figure 6 shows the origin and insertion of the upper arm.

HOW MUSCLES CAN ACT

Muscles can perform only two acts; develop tension within itself or relax. These two actions can be influenced by many factors such as: the size, shape, and number of fibers in the muscle; the type of joint and the angle and place of insertion. Muscles may perform alone or as members of a group in various combinations and patterns of movement.

While the various roles of the muscles have specific technical names attached to them, they vary from textbook to textbook and may or may not be of value to the Strength Coach or athlete to know. I refer you to a suitable text on kinesiology should you be curious about this information.

ACTIVATING THE MUSCLES

Each muscle has within it, along with the abundant circulatory vessels, an ample supply of nerves. The number of muscle fibers activated by a single motor nerve may vary from one to several hundred. Under normal conditions the group of muscle fibers activated by a single nerve unit contracts as a single muscle unit. A nerve cell, its axon with its various branches, and the muscle fibers served are known as motor units. The motor unit is the basic functional unit of a neuro-muscular contraction.

The muscle fibers are housed in a container known as the sarcolemma which aids in preventing the stimulating effect of a nerve impulse from spreading from one muscle fiber to another.

The inter-action of the nervous and the muscular systems are quite involved and beyond the scope of this book. Rather than dig deeper into the anatomy and physiology of the nervous system, I will present an example of how the involuntary muscle is put into action.

When you place your left hand around the upper right arm and raise the right forearm toward the shoulder, you feel the muscle under your hand become shorter, thicker, firmer. This is the biceps muscle, which is made up of approximately 260,000 voluntary muscle cells held in place by connective tissue. These cells must receive a message from the brain if they are to contract. Each cell in a muscle contracts as hard as it can when the order from the brain is given. Thus when we move our forearm slowly or rapidly, the difference seems to depend on the number of muscle cells that we order to contract. We may order 100 to 1000 of the cells in the biceps to contract, and it is possible for us to combine them with as few cells or with as many cells in other muscles as we like. We rarely ask all of the cells in any of our muscles to contract for us at the same time.

TYPES OF MUSCULAR CONTRACTIONS

When the term "contraction" is used in the study and action of muscles it refers merely to the development of tension within the muscle and does not necessarily mean that there is any shortening of the muscle taking place.

STATIC CONTRACTIONS

If the muscle is compelled to contract against some resistance which it cannot move, the tension in the fibers increases, but the muscle length remains unaltered. Since the length of the fibers is unchanged, such contractions are called **static** or **isometric**.

An example would be the pulling on a bar which is stabilized in a power rack. It should be noted that no muscle action is purely isometric in nature as even under the most rigid conditions the contractile elements shorten as much as 5 to 10% by stretching elastic components.

CONCENTRIC CONTRACTIONS

If the muscle actually becomes shorter as a result of developing sufficient tension to overcome a resistance, it is said to be in **concentric** contraction. In performing a dumbell curl, the dumbell is moved from a straight-arm position to a bent-arm position as the muscle contracts. This is a **concentric** contraction and is **isotonic** in nature.

ECCENTRIC CONTRACTIONS

When a given resistance, such as the same dumbell, overcomes the muscle so that the muscle actually lengthens, the muscle is said to be in **eccentric contraction**. While the muscle does contract, it is still overpowered by the resistance. This is also a form of isotonic contraction and is the basis to the negative training used by some strength athletes. If the dumbell were loaded with such poundage that it forced the contracted biceps to lengthen, the muscle said to be in **eccentric** contraction. **Eccentric** and **concentric** contractions are both **isotonic** in nature.

THE ALL-OR-NONE LAW

It has been found that if a stimulus applied to a single muscle fiber is strong enough to produce a response it will give a contraction which is 100%, or maximal, no matter what the strength of the stimulus. This is known as the all-or-none law. This does not mean that the excitability of the cell cannot be changed, but merely that it must be accomplished by other means than an increase in this stimulus. In other words, each muscle fiber gives a maximal response or none at all. Other factors, such as fatigue or varying conditions of nutrition may alter the cell's response, but increasing the strength of the stimulus will not do so.

To fully understand the principle behind the contraction of skeletal muscles, however, a distinction must be made between the contraction of a whole muscle and the contraction of its individual fibers. The all-or-none law only applies to individual fibers, the whole muscle cannot contract maximally.

The height of contraction of a skeletal muscle is in direct proportion to the strength of the stimulus applied. This is not a contradiction of the all-or-none law. It is explained by the fact that voluntary muscle cells are separate units insulated from each other by connective tissue. On account of environmental conditions the minimal stimulus of these separate fibers may vary. Thus the minimal stimulus of a skeletal muscle trunk is one which evokes contraction from a single fiber; the maximal stimulus is one which will cause the contraction of every fiber present.

It is helpful to distinguish between the conductile mechanism and the contractile mechanism of a muscle fiber in order to further understand this action. The conductile processes, like those of the nerve fibers, do follow the all-or-none law. That is, if the stimulus is strong enough to elicit a response, the response is 100%. The contractile processes, on the other hand, do not follow strictly the all-or-none law. The contraction is in direct proportion to the strength of the stimulus.

GRADUATION OF CONTRACTION

It is quite obvious to anyone who has ever contracted a muscle that whole muscles do not follow the all-or-none law. Graded contractions, from very weak to very strong, are an outstanding characteristic of the muscular system.

The central nervous system has the ability to send stimuli to a greater or lesser number of motor units. When greater tension is desired in the muscle, more motor units are activated. This is known as **recruitment**. While it is true that a single neuron cannot activate more than the total number of muscle fibers than it actually innervates, it does not necessarily follow that it must activate all of the muscle fibers it innervates.

Perhaps a further clarification is necessary. Various muscle fibers differ from each other in such things as temperature, accumulation of fatigue products, or adequacy of circulation. Because of these factors a stimulus may not be sufficient to activate those muscles whose thresholds are at the moment relatively high.

The contraction of single muscle fibers can be graded by the rapidity of stimuli. Even though the successive stimuli are equal in strength, very rapid volleys of impulses will cause a maximum response while slightly spaced impulses will result in a submaximum response on the part of the individual fibers. This trait, applies to whole muscles as well as to the individual fibers and is known as **summation.**

The gradation in both the speed and total force of contraction of the voluntary muscle depends on both the number of motor units in action and the frequency of response in each of the individual units. The frequency of response increased quite evenly.

It should be emphasized that the threshold levels of individual muscle and nerve fibers are quite different from one another and can often change due to certain factors, body temperature being but one example.

The Russian researcher, A.S. Stepanov postulated in **Sechenov Physiological Journal of the USSR** that one of the benefits of training with near-maximal weights in progressive resistive exercises is that it brings some of the high-threshold neurons within the range of voluntary activity.

AEROBIC AND ANAEROBIC TRAINING

Physiologists often distinguish between the types of training that develop a high rate of cardiovascular, respiratory fitness and those which merely stimulate muscle tone or muscle growth. **Aerobic** training is of the nature that causes a prolonged strain on the heart and lungs, thus producing a relatively high pulse and respiratory rate. This type of training produces a high rate of cardiovascular, respiratory fitness and includes such activities as long-distance running, distance swimming, and distance bicycling, plus other activity which is prolonged and vigorous enough to produce a sustained pulse rate of 150 beats per minute and last a minimum of twenty minutes.

Kenneth Cooper, author of **Aerobics** added that aerobic benefits could also be gained even if the exercise was not vigorous enough to elevate the pulse rate to 150, then the total time must exceed five minutes (Cooper prescribes an exercise duration of with a minimum of five minutes but most other fitness authorities advise for a bout of no less than twenty minutes) and is totally dependent on the amount of oxygen consumed during the exercise period.

Anaerobic training, on the other hand, is of the type which is not sustained. **Anaerobic** training does demand a quick surge of oxygen, more in fact than the circulatory system can provide and actually creates an "oxygen debt." This debt must be repaid quickly so the exercise is not usually prolonged in nature.

Weight training is generally listed in the anaerobic category along with sprinting. Weight training does, of course, build other facets of fitness such as muscular strength and overall tone but the exercises are generally not sustained so that the pulse rate will remain at a high level.

There are, however, exceptions to this general rule. Weight training, if done in a prescribed manner, can be a form of aerobic training. The squat program outlined on page 83 is but one example of aerobic weight training. It is, as this program demonstrates, quite possible to elevate the pulse rate to 150 and to hold it above that level for 20, 30, or even 45 minutes. When this is done, exercises performed with weights or other resistive equipment meet all the criteria of aerobic training. As far as we know weight training is the only physical activity whereby a participant can build strength and cardiovascular fitness of the highest order simultaneously.

The circuit program as recommended in the Programming the "Big Three" chapter is yet another example of how weight training can produce aerobic fitness.

Aerobic weight training is possible as was empirically pointed out by Pat O'Shea in his book, **Scientific Principles and Methods of Strength Fitness.** He summarized his finding on the subject as follows: "The results of aerobic weight training are: 1) cardiac output is greatly increased, 2) respiratory efficiency is improved and 3) the muscle fatigue factor in training is reduced."

The utilization of aerobic weight training should be of special interest to the Strength Coach and athlete who resides in the northern latitudes. You can, by utilizing the information contained in this book, set up a weight training program which combines a high level of strength fitness plus an equally high level of cardiovascular, respiratory fitness. The players would not even need to run except to keep their strides loose. This has been demonstrated on many players from all skill levels with a high degree of success. More about this particular type of training is included in later chapters.

THE PHENOMENA OF MUSCLE FATIGUE

In muscles undergoing contraction, the first effect of the formation of two waste products, carbon dioxide and lactic acid, is to increase irritability. If a muscle is continuously stimulated, the strength of the contraction becomes progressively less until the muscle refuses to respond at all. This phenomena is termed fatigue and has been experienced by every athlete.

Fatigue is caused, in part, by the toxic effects of the waste products which accumulate during exercise. The loss of nutritive materials is also a contributing factor in fatigue. In moderate exercise the system is able to rid itself of these waste products rather easily. If the exercise is of the pro-

FIGURE 7   TYPES OF LEVERS

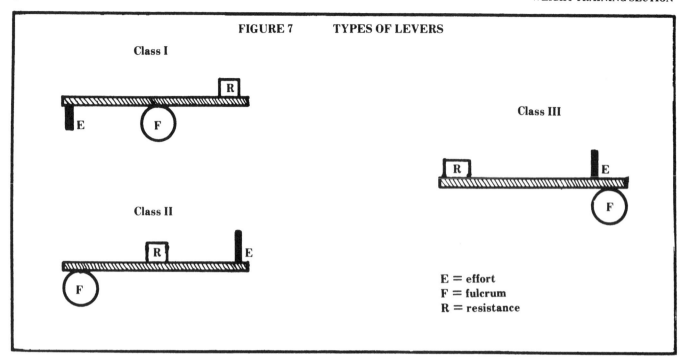

Class I

Class II

Class III

E = effort
F = fulcrum
R = resistance

longed nature, a period of rest is necessary in order to furnish the blood with the opportunity to carry away the fatigue products and also to supply the muscle with more nutritive material.

The body is susceptible to other fatigue than that of muscles. The nerve cells are, in fact, the most easily fatigued; next comes the junctions between the nerves and the muscle fibers; then the muscles themselves; and lastly, the connecting nerve fibers.

It should be mentioned that the state which we refer to as fatigue is not always purely physiological. The sense of fatigue is quite complex and is often brought on by such mental states as lack of interest, lack of motivation, and laziness.

Exercise stimulates circulation and thereby brings about a change in conditions for cells in all locations throughout the body. Exercise has been shown to increase the size, strength, and tone of the muscle fibers. Massage and passive exercise may, if necessary, be used as a partial substitute for active, resistive exercise. While some form of exercise is most desirable for aiding metabolic processes, continued use of fatigued muscles is often injurious if, during such conditions, the muscles exhaust their energy (glycogen) supply and begin utilizing the protein of their own cells. The state of fatigue then, actually protects us from overdoing the extremes of exercise.

MUSCLES AND BONY LEVERS

Direct muscular contraction alone is not generally responsible for our bodily motions. Intermediate action of bony levers is usually essential. In the body cooperative functioning of bones and muscles form levers. A basic knowledge of levers gives a basis for understanding the principles underlying such things as good posture and the basic positions of the body when lifting weights.

A **simple lever** is a rigid rod which is free to move about on some fixed point or support called **fulcrum**. It is acted upon at two different points by 1) the **resistance** (weight) which may be thought of as something to be overcome or balanced, and 2) by the **force** (effort) which is exerted to overcome the resistance. In the body, bones of varying shapes are levers,

and the resistance may be a part of the body to be moved or a barbell to be lifted, or a combination of both of these. In performing a squat, the lifter has to move the weight of his own body plus the weight on the barbell. The muscular effort is applied to the bone at the insertion of the muscle and brings about the motion or work.

For example, in performing a dumbell curl, when the forearm is raised the elbow acts as the fulcrum, the weight of the forearm plus the weight on the dumbell is the resistance, and the pull due to contraction of the biceps muscle is the effort.

Levers act according to a law which may be stated thus: When the lever is in equilibrium, the effort times the effort arm equals the resistance time the resistance arm ($E \times EA = R \times RA$). This is not really as complicated as it may sound. For example, if the distance from the effort to the fulcrum is the same as the distance from the resistance to the fulcrum, the effort of five pounds will balance a resistance of five pounds.

Levers may be divided into three classes according to the relative position of the fulcrum, the effort, and the resistance. In levers of the **first class** the fulcrum lies between the effort and the resistance as in a set of scales. The action of the skull is an example of this class of lever. As the head is raised, the facial portion of the skull is the resistance, moving upon the axis as a fulcrum, while the muscles of the back produce the effort.

In levers of the **second class** the resistance lies between the fulcrum and the effort and moves, therefore, in the same direction as that in which the effort is applied, as in the raising of a wheelbarrow. Raising the body on tiptoe is sometimes cited as a physiological example, the weight of the body acting as the resistance, the toes on the floor as the fulcrum, and the calf muscles as the effort. W.H. Lewis in **Gray's Anatomy**, however, states that there are no levers of the second class represented in the body.

In levers of the **third class** the effort is exerted between the fulcrum and the resistance. Levers in which the resistance arm is thus longer than the effort arm produce rapid delicate movements wherein the effort used must be greater than the resistance. The flexing of the forearm is a lever of this type, as are most of the levers of the body. The Strength

Coach and the athlete need only be concerned with the third class type of lever.

The law of levers is especially pertinent in maintaining a correct posture. The head held erect in correct standing posture rests on the atlas (vertebrae at the top of the spinal column) as the fulcrum with little or no muscular effort being exerted to maintain this position. The head in this position is in the line of gravity which passes through the hip-joints, knee-joints, and the balls of the feet.

When a person stands with his shoulders stooped, his head bent forward, there is a constant muscular effort exerted against this pull of gravity on the head. Back aches, muscle tension plus a variety of related ailments result when poor posture is practiced. Figure 7 will help further explain the action of these three types of levers.

THE OVERLOAD PRINCIPLE

All exercise does not develop strength and endurance in a muscle. It is only when a muscle works with greater intensity than normally or when it works for a longer period of time than normally that it acquires strength or endurance. Development occurs in a muscle only when it is pushed beyond its usual performance — in other words, when it is "overloaded."

This phenomenon of the body adapting to the demands of stresses placed upon it is known as the Law of Use and Disuse: function begets function. Increased physical activity of the right kind and amount will bring about improvements in the range of joint motion, strength, tone, size, and endurance of skeletal muscles and give the cardiovascular, respiratory system the ability to sustain stress without undue fatigue.

To "overload" a muscle means just what the name implies, i.e. that there must be an overloading or pushing beyond the normal limits if a muscle is to be developed beyond its present state.

In the book **Movement Fundamentals**, authoress Janet Wessel points out the following, concerning this physiological principle. "To produce physical and physiological changes that improve strength you must progressively increase the demands or intensity of the overload by increasing the:
1) amount of resistance (lift heavier loads or apply greater force).
2) rate of work (perform the exercise in a shorter period of time).
3) duration of work (lengthen the work period while maintaining the rate of work).
4) duration of rest intervals (shorten the rest periods between exercises).

"The rate of improvement is directly related to the intensity of the workload. This means that the closer the overload is to maximum, the faster the rate of improvement. Overload, however, should be applied gradually; it takes time for the body to adapt without excessive muscle soreness or fatigue."

SUMMARY

This brief encounter with the workings of the "Marvelous Machine" is meant to be a review for some and an introduction for others. I hope to either rekindle an interest in kinesiology for those coaches and athletes who have had training in this science or to initiate a curiosity for all those who have not. I believe that the more you understand about the various ways in which your body functions, the better able you will be to develop it to its fullest strength potential.

★

2

CHAPTER TWO
YOUR MUSCLES AND THEIR FUNCTION

AN INTRODUCTION OR REVIEW

FOR THOSE WHO ARE well versed in the science of kinesiology, this chapter will in all likelihood be quite elementary. For those who have not been exposed to the muscular system and the functions of the various muscles, this chapter might seem a bit too technical. It is an attempt to familiarize each person who is interested in gaining strength, either for himself or for a team he coaches, with the basic terminology and kinesiology of some of the muscles involved in the sport of football.

This chapter does not attempt to encompass the entire muscular system, but rather is selective in that it highlights those muscles which are of the greatest concern to the Strength Coach or football player. I do not, for example, explain the location or action of all of the muscles of the lower leg, although they are certainly all very important. I selected those which can be most influenced in the weight room.

This chapter, while not a complete treatise of the total muscular system, will enable you to better understand the ways in which many of the major muscles function. With this knowledge you should be better able to formulate, adapt, adjust, and modify training programs to stimulate growth and strength gains in specific muscles. It is quite impossible to set up a program to strengthen the thigh muscles, for example, without actually knowing how the muscles function.

I am often asked at clinics such questions as "what exercise works the trapezius?" or "how can we strengthen the back of the arm?" If you understand, even on a basic level, how the various muscles function, then you can devise an exercise to successfully work that muscle. Once you have the exercise that directly stimulates the muscle in question, then all you need to add is the correct number of sets of reps. This I provide later on in the book.

Again, I must reiterate that this chapter on the muscular system is meant to be but an introduction to the highly technical science of kinesiology. For those who seek more information on this subject, I refer you to one of the many excellent texts recommended in the reference list at the end of this section.

MUSCLES OF THE BACK

Trapezius
Latissimus dorsi
Sacrospinalis (spinae erector)

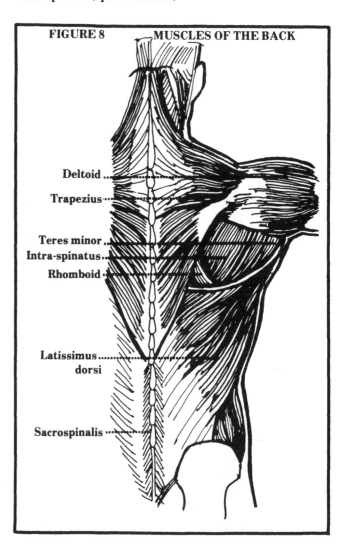

FIGURE 8   MUSCLES OF THE BACK

Deltoid
Trapezius
Teres minor
Intra-spinatus
Rhomboid
Latissimus dorsi
Sacrospinalis

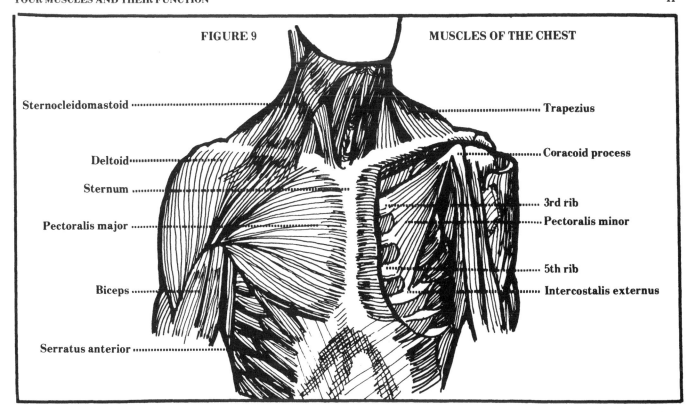

FIGURE 9   MUSCLES OF THE CHEST

Sternocleidomastoid ··· Trapezius

Deltoid ································· ····················· Coracoid process

Sternum ······························· ······················ 3rd rib

Pectoralis major ··················· ······················ Pectoralis minor

······················· 5th rib

Biceps ··························· ······················ Intercostalis externus

Serratus anterior ·····················

The muscles of the back are disposed in five layers. For our purposes I include only two large muscles, the trapezius and latissimus dorsi, which form the superficial layers, and the sacrospinalis, which forms one of the deeper layers.

The **trapezius** derives its name from the fact that the right and left sides together make a large diamond-shaped sheet. It arises from the occipital bone high on the skull. Its line of origin continues down the spine from the seventh cervical vertebrae all the way to the twelfth thoracic vertebrae (see Figure 2 . From this extended line, the muscles converge to their insertion in the clavicle (collar bone), the acromion process (the large triangular projection on the scapula which articulates with the clavicle) and the spine of the scapula (see Figure 11).

The trapezius is a very large muscle and covers the other muscles of the back and neck, as well as the upper portion of the latissimus dorsi.

The trapezius can lower the back of the skull and turn it to the side and elevate the shoulder girdle. This muscle is of special interest to weight trainers because it comes into play anytime a weight is lifted past the waist. These are the muscles, when developed thoroughly, that assist the barbell in moving from waist level to chest level. Since they are seldom used in ordinary, everyday activities, they are often quite weak initially, but they respond rapidly to any high pulling or shrugging exercises.

The trapezius plays a most important role in protecting the upper portion of the vertebrae, especially at the base of the skull. All football players can help prevent neck injuries by making certain that they strengthen this vital protective muscle.

The **latissimus dorsi** or "lats" originate at the sixth thoracic vertebrae, continue to the crest of the ilium (hip bones) and from the lower three or four ribs. From this rather extensive origin which covers a large portion of the lower back the fibers join at the humerus (bone of the upper arm, Figure 13).

The latissimus dorsi is responsible for pulling the humerus to the body, drawing it backward and rotating it inward. The lat machine enables the trainee to isolate this particular muscle and to develop it to a high degree. Chinning of all forms also involves the lats to a large extent.

The **sacrospinalis**, ordinarily referred to as the "spinal erectors" attaches to the ribs and vertebrae from the lower portion of the spine as well as to the pelvic bones all the way up to the back of the skull at the occipital bone.

As this muscle climbs up the back it does not relinquish one foothold before it establishes another. The result is not merely a continuity of structure but an overlapping effect. The spinal erectors have the primary responsibility of holding the vertebrae in place. They are, therefore, most critical to the athlete as it is impossible to engage in any sport with an injured vertebrae. The stronger these muscles become the better protected you are against back problems.

All pulling motions involve these muscles. When a barbell is pulled off the floor, the lower spinal erectors situated over the lumbar vertebrae are utilized. As the bar passes the knees the spinal erectors in the thoracic vertebrae region become more involved and finally the erectors at the cervical vertebrae region assist in the final uplifting of the bar to the chest.

MUSCLES OF THE CHEST

Pectoralis major
Pectoralis minor
Serratus anterior (serratus magnus)

These three muscles make up the layers of the chest. The **serratus anterior** lies the deepest and is attached to the ribs and inserted in the scapula. It helps move the scapula forward, assists the trapezius muscle in raising the shoulders and in supporting weight on the shoulders. It also assists the deltoids in raising the arms.

The **pectoralis minor** is the middle layer of muscle of the chest and arises from the outer surfaces of the third, fourth, and fifth ribs and is inserted in the scapula. The pectoralis minor pulls the point of the shoulder downward and rotates the scapula downward. In forced breathing, which results from heavy squats or distance running, these muscles help in drawing the ribs upward and expanding the chest.

The **pectoralis major** forms the surface muscles of the chest. It arises from that portion of the clavicle closest to the sternum, the front of the sternum, and the cartilages of the ribs. The muscle fibers converge and form a thick mass which is inserted into the humerus.

This muscle brings the arms into the body and draws them across the chest. It also rotates the arm inward. If the arm has been raised the pectoralis major, acting with the latissimus dorsi plus other muscles, draws the arm down to the side of the chest.

The muscles of the chest are rather easy to develop through weight training and there are a variety of exercises designed to stimulate growth and strength development in these muscles. Pressing movements while lying on a bench, pull-overs while lying on a bench, lateral flying motions with resistance on a bench all bring the pectorals into action. They are an important group of muscles to the football player as they give the power for the inward pulling motion of the arms, as in tackling and pulling an opponent in toward the body.

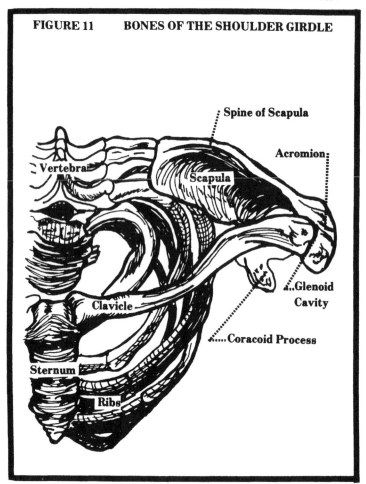

FIGURE 11   BONES OF THE SHOULDER GIRDLE

Spine of Scapula

Acromion

Vertebra

Scapula

Glenoid Cavity

Clavicle

Coracoid Process

Sternum

Ribs

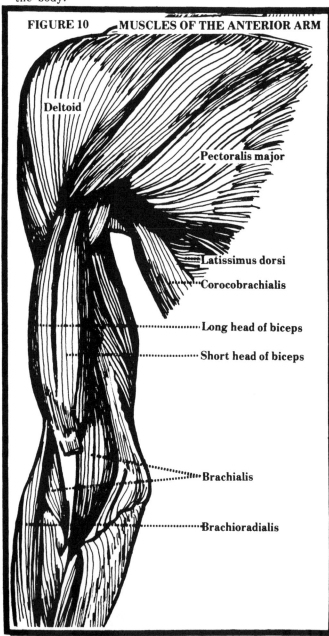

FIGURE 10   MUSCLES OF THE ANTERIOR ARM

Deltoid

Pectoralis major

Latissimus dorsi

Corocobrachialis

Long head of biceps

Short head of biceps

Brachialis

Brachioradialis

MUSCLES OF THE ARM

Deltoid
Biceps brachii
Triceps brachii
Brachialis
Brachioradialis

While it is technically more correct to separate the deltoid from the muscles of the arm, I will include it in this section for the sake of simplicity.

The **deltoid** is a thick triangular muscle which covers the shoulder joint. It is, basically, the cap of the shoulder (see Figure 10). It arises from the clavicle, the scapula, and is inserted in the side of the humerus. It is divided into three parts: anterior (front), lateral (side), and posterior (rear).

The basic action of the deltoid is raising the arm to the side so that it is at a right angle to the trunk. The frontal deltoid assists in lifting the arm upward towards the front, the lateral has primary responsibility for the side movement, and the rear deltoid assists in lifting the arm up and back.

The deltoid plays a most important role in stabilizing the shoulder joint and athletes need to strengthen it for preventive measures. Any exercise that involves the shoulders utilizes the deltoids to some degree. All pressing movements, dipping, lateral and frontal raises with dumbells, and even pulling motions utilize the deltoids.

The **biceps brachii** is the most well-known and most prominent muscle on the front side of the upper arm. It has two places of origin, hence its name. The longer head starts from the scapula at the glenoid cavity (the socket where the humerus fits into the scapula) and the short head from the coracoid process (upper extremity of the scapula). The two muscles are separate until within about ½ inch from the elbow joint where they unite and form a flat tendon which is inserted in the radius (smaller bone of the forearm on the thumb side, Figure 13).

The biceps act to flex the elbow and to a lesser extent the shoulder. The biceps also play a role in turning the palm forward and upward (supination).

This is a muscle which is worked religiously by all beginning trainees because it is so visible. When a player first starts training he always seems preoccupied with bigger arms and since he views the front of his arms more easily than he does the rear he usually spends an unproportionate amount of time exercising the biceps. Unfortunately, there are many other muscles which serve more functions for the athlete and the biceps exercises, such as curls, should be kept in proper perspective to the overall strength program.

The **triceps brachii** is located on the back of the upper arm and arises from three places of origin, hence its name (Figure 12). The long head arises from the scapula, just below the shoulder joint; the lateral head from the higher part of the humerus, and the medial head from the lower part of the humerus. The muscle fibers join together just above the elbow and are inserted into the olecranon process (upper extremity of the ulna which forms the prominence of the elbow,) (Figure 13), of the ulna (larger bone in the forearm at the little finger side).

The triceps acts to extend the forearm and is the direct antagonist of the biceps. The great number of short fibers in its structure together with its large angle of pull gives the triceps great power as well as speed.

The triceps is a most important muscle for the athlete as it is involved in so many functions connected with the sport of football. Weight training enables the player to develop this muscle quickly and as a result not only arm size, but arm strength increases rapidly.

All pressing movements involve the triceps. The various heads can be isolated with specialized exercises. Straight-arm pullovers, for example, stimulates growth in the long head while French presses, or triceps extensions involve the lateral and medial heads more specifically. Most of the size of the upper arm comes from the triceps, so any trainee who is eager to possess a larger upper arm must concentrate on the triceps, rather than the biceps.

The **brachioradialis** is located on the outer border of the forearm (Figure 10) and is responsible for the shape of the forearm from the elbow to the base of the thumb. The muscle is attached to the humerus, extends across the inner portion of the elbow, and is inserted to the radius at the styloid process (see Figure 13) which is at the wrist joint. The brachioradialis forms the outer curve of the forearm, from the elbow to the base of the thumb.

The brachioradialis is a flexor of the elbow and because its leverage is long and the angle of pull is small, it has better mechanical advantage than the biceps in flexing the elbow.

This muscle becomes highly developed on those who do a great deal of reverse curling or high-pulling motions. When the elbows bend to pull a heavy weight to the chest the brachioradialis contracts and assists in this upward lifting movement.

The **brachialis** lies between the biceps and the humerus near the elbow (Figure 10). It originates at the lower portion of the humerus and is inserted at the ulna just below the elbow.

The brachialis has been called "the workhorse among the flexor muscles of the elbow" and, like the biceps and brachioradialis, flexes the elbow. Because of its position in the arm, its line of pull does not change with the rotation of the elbow. This makes the brachialis equally effective in flexing the arm regardless of whether the forearm is in a supine, prone, or middle position.

The brachialis is involved in all curling and high-pulling movements. Anytime the elbow bends, the brachialis is exercised.

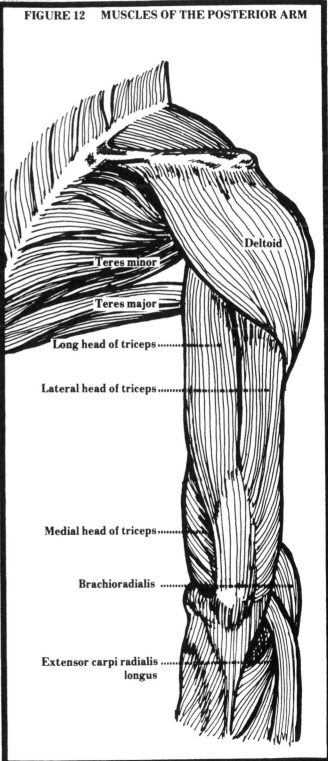

FIGURE 12   MUSCLES OF THE POSTERIOR ARM

Deltoid

Teres minor

Teres major

Long head of triceps

Lateral head of triceps

Medial head of triceps

Brachioradialis

Extensor carpi radialis longus

MUSCLES OF THE HIP

Psoas major
Iliacus
Gluteus Maximus

The **psoas major** arises from the last thoracic and all of the lumbar vertebrae and extends downward and forward, then downward and backward to its insertion in the femur.

The **iliacus** arises at the top of the ilium. The fibers converge and are inserted into the lateral side of the tendon of the psoas major and the body of the femur. Figure 14 shows these muscles and their interrelationship very well.

The iliacus and psoas major act together as one muscle and are generally referred to as the **iliopsoas**. They flex the thigh to the pelvis and rotate the upper leg outward. These muscles are utilized in a variety of athletic activities and are especially well suited to action where the hip joint and spinal column are fixed at the same time, as in rope climbing.

The value of these muscles are usually not realized until they are injured. Without full benefit of the iliopsoas it is difficult to advance the leg to walk or run, so they are extremely important to the football player. Squatting and some pulling motions help strengthen these muscles.

The **gluteus maximus** is the large fleshy muscle at the back of the hip. It arises from the outer portion of the ilium, the rear surface of the lower part of the sacrum close to the ilium, the side of the coccyx, and the lumbar region of the vertebrae. It is inserted on a line about four inches long on the rear of the femur, beginning at the greater tochanter (see Figure 15) and extending downward.

The gluteus maximus is responsible for the extension and outward rotation of the hip joint. When the knees are fully bent, as in a squatting position, it is the gluteus maximus which brings the body out of the bottom-most position. It ceases to act before the erect position is achieved, however.

This is the muscle which raises the body from a sitting position and is brought into play when walking up stairs or in jumping.

The gluteus maximus is not called into action in the extension of the hip unless the hip is flexed in excess of about 45 degrees. This is one reason I strongly recommend full squats as the full range affords a complete development of this powerful and most important muscle. Those who are interested in being able to jump higher, such as defensive and offensive backs, tight ends and wide receivers, and those who want to be able to come out of a crouched position strongly such as offensive and defensive linemen, and anyone else who has to make a tackle, need to make certain that they strengthen the "glutes."

ANTERIOR THIGH	POSTERIOR THIGH
Sartorius	**Biceps femoris**
Quadriceps femoris	**Semitendinosus**
Rectus femoris	**Semimembranosus**
Vastus lateralis	
Vastus medialis	
Vastus intermedius	

The **sartorius** is the longest muscle in the body and is capable of a greater extent of contraction than any other muscle. It originates in the anterior superior iliac spine (see Figure 16) and is inserted in the upper part of the tibia (larger bone of lower leg on big toe side, Figure 15).

This muscle, quite obviously, is very much involved in all forms of running, both in straight ahead and lateral

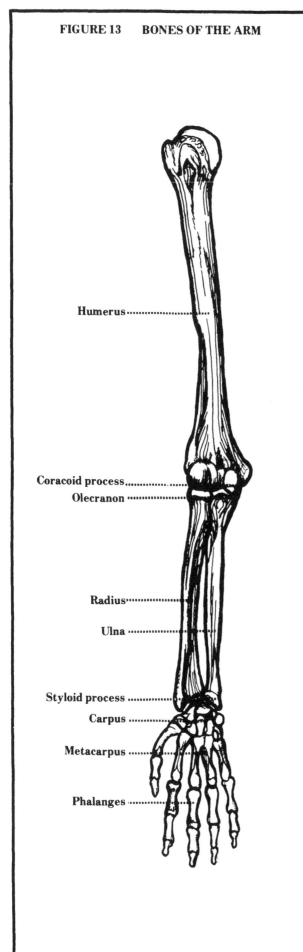

FIGURE 13   BONES OF THE ARM

Humerus

Coracoid process

Olecranon

Radius

Ulna

Styloid process

Carpus

Metacarpus

Phalanges

FIGURE 14   BONES AND MUSCLES OF THE PELVIC GIRDLE

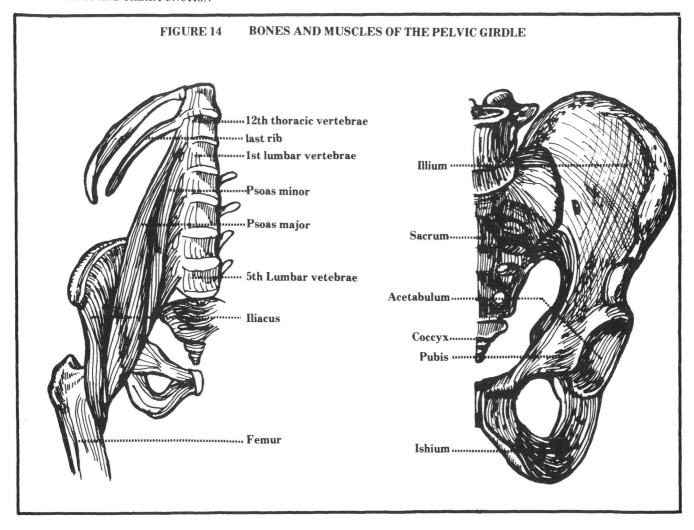

movements. It is developed by various squatting and pulling movements, especially dead lifts, high pulls, and power cleans.

Figure 16 shows the relationship of the quadriceps groups of muscles in the front of the thigh. The **rectus femoris** arises from two tendons, one from the anterior inferior iliac spine (see Figure 14) and the other from a groove just above the base of the ilium. This is the "kicking muscle."

The rectus fibers of the rectus femoris along with the **vastus lateralis, vastus medialis,** and the **vastus intermedius** converge at the lower portion of the thigh and form a strong tendon which passes in front of the knee joint. It is inserted in the tibia. The patella (knee cap) is developed within this tendon.

These four muscles have responsibility for hip joint flexion. They extend the leg upon the thigh and flex the thigh.

To better understand the action of a full contraction of these muscles, visualize the motion employed in kicking a football. These are the only muscles which could do this action alone. Isolated action of the rectus femoris causes a flexion of the hip and extension of the knee with great speed and power.

The quadriceps can be seen quite easily when the athlete performs leg extensions on the leg extension machine. Their value in protecting the knee should be most obvious and they are extremely important for all forms of running and jumping.

The **biceps femoris** is very similar to the biceps brachii of the upper arm. The biceps femoris also has two heads, one arising from the ischium and the other from the linea aspera (see Figure 16 of the femur. It is inserted in the head of the fibula and the lateral condyle of the tibia .

The tendons of insertion of the biceps femoris, along with those of the **semimembranosus** and **semitendinosus** muscles are called the hamstrings, hence the muscles are often referred to collectively as the "hamstrings." They derive their rather odd name from the fact that butchers hang hams on hooks from these particular tendons.

The leg biceps group, or hamstrings, extend the leg upon the thigh and extend the thigh. The biceps femoris is responsible for the outward rotation of the knee and the semitendinosus and semimembranosus rotate the knee inward.

In football players, these muscles are very often quite weak in comparison with the stronger quadriceps group. Since the hamstrings cross the back of the knee joint and help support the knee, it is most critical for the athlete to keep these muscles strong. Some form of specific strengthening exercise is most important to prevent injury. Pulled hamstrings are unusually common in football players because these muscles are often neglected. Many trainers feel that the weakness in this muscle group is largely responsible for many knee injuries since the knee joint is only as strong as its weakest supporting muscle.

This muscle can be worked directly with leg biceps curls on the leg extension machine. Development of the hamstrings also benefit the athlete because these muscles, while not as powerful as the gluteus maximus, do aid in running and jumping.

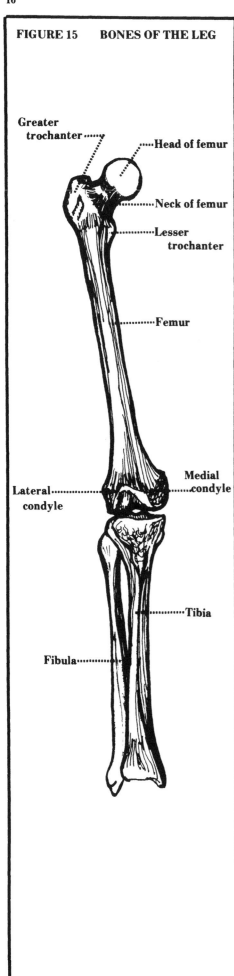

FIGURE 15   **BONES OF THE LEG**

Greater trochanter

Head of femur

Neck of femur

Lesser trochanter

Femur

Medial condyle

Lateral condyle

Tibia

Fibula

MUSCLES OF THE ANTERIOR LOWER LEG

Tibialis anterior
Extensor digitorum longus
Peroneus tertius
Extensor hallucis longus

The four muscles which make up the anterior (front) of the leg are called the "flexors of the foot." The largest of the group is the **tibialis anterior**, a slender muscle situated in front of and to the outside of the tibia. It originates high on the tibia and inserts at the base of the foot. When this muscle is damaged the athlete cannot lift his foot properly and will constantly stub his toes.

The **extensor digitorum longus** is very similar to the tibialis anterior, although it is a bit smaller in size. It begins on the lateral condyle of the tibia and fibula and attaches to the four lesser toes. It is, therefore, the prime mover for the toes in all directions.

The **peroneus tertius** has often been described as a portion of the extensor digitorum longus. Evolutionists are fond of remarking that this muscle is only found in the feet of man and the gorilla. It is the prime mover for dorsiflexion and eversion of the foot.

The **extensor hallucis longus** is a smaller muscle beneath the tibialis anterior and the peroneus tertius. It begins approximately midway down the fibula and is inserted at the base of the big toe. Therefore, it is the prime mover for the big toes.

The four flexors of the foot are all brought into action in any movement such as walking, running, and jumping which necessitates the raising of the toes and the front of the foot.

MUSCLES OF THE POSTERIOR LOWER LEG

Gastrocnemius
Soleus

The **gastrocnemius** and **soleus** form the calf muscle of the leg. The gastrocnemius arises from two heads from the medial and lateral condyles of the femur (see Figure **16**). The soleus arises from the back of the head of the fibula and the middle of the tibia (see Figure **15**). Both go downward and insert into a common tendon known as the tendon calcaneus or the Achilles tendon. The Achilles tendon is the thickest and strongest tendon in the body and is finally inserted into the calcaneus (heel bone).

The gastrocnemius and soleus lift the heel and extend the foot at the ankle. The gastrocnemius also flexes the femur upon the tibia. The calf muscles are most valuable to the football player as they give him lift and spring when jumping and running.

When the calf muscle is injured, the player is hobbled and has to shuffle around as he cannot come up on his toes. Movement in all directions is quicker if the athlete has an abundance of strength in these muscles and is able to "stay on his toes."

These muscles can be directly stimulated in the weight room with a wide variety of calf raises. A proper program of calf development has been shown to add as much as 4 inches to the jumping ability of the athlete.

FIGURE 16   MUSCLES OF ANTERIOR AND POSTERIOR LEG

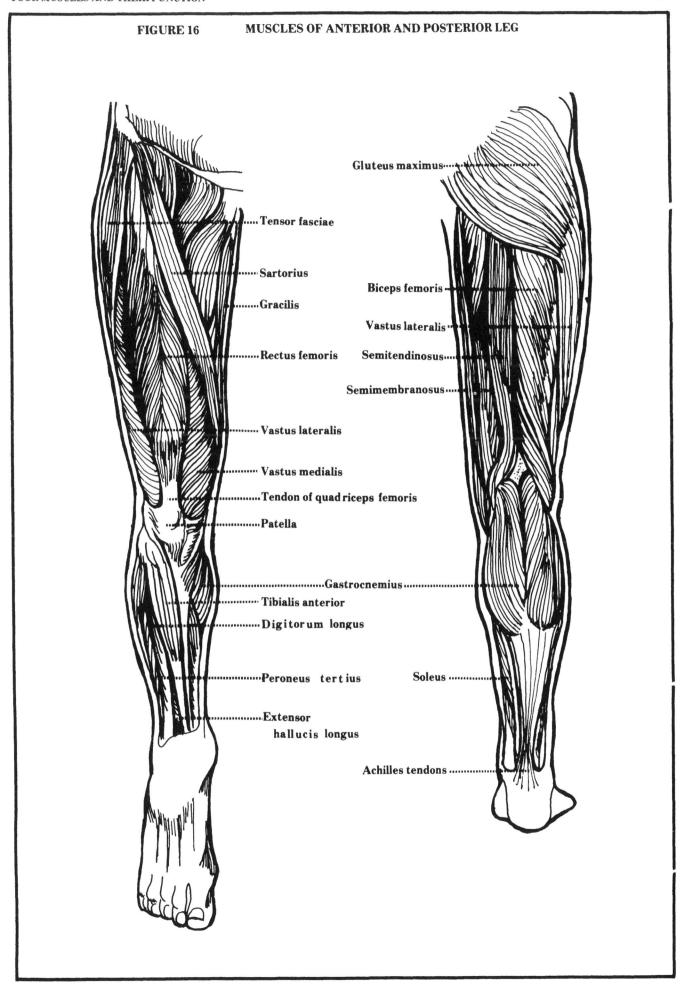

Tensor fasciae

Sartorius

Gracilis

Rectus femoris

Vastus lateralis

Vastus medialis

Tendon of quadriceps femoris

Patella

Gastrocnemius

Tibialis anterior

Digitorum longus

Peroneus tertius

Extensor hallucis longus

Gluteus maximus

Biceps femoris

Vastus lateralis

Semitendinosus

Semimembranosus

Soleus

Achilles tendons

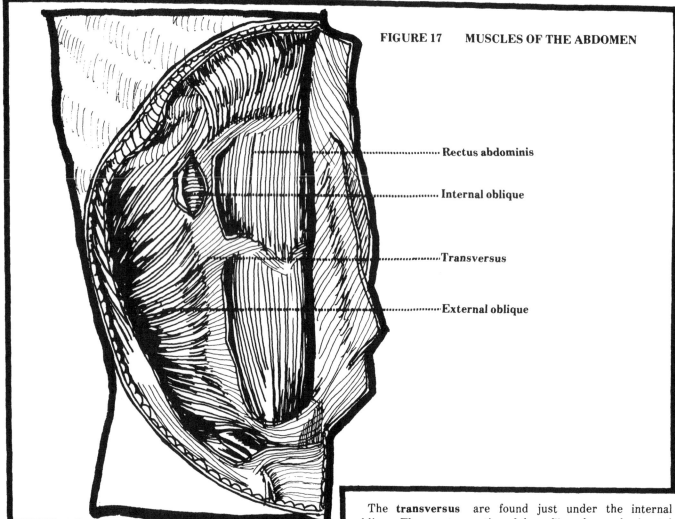

FIGURE 17   MUSCLES OF THE ABDOMEN

.... Rectus abdominis

.... Internal oblique

.... Transversus

.... External oblique

THE ABDOMINAL MUSCLES

Rectus abdominis
External oblique
Internal oblique
Transversus

The **rectus abdominis** is a long flat muscle consisting of vertical fibers situated at the front of the abdomen. A right and left recti muscle is separated by a thin tendinous strip about an inch wide. The rectus abdominis arises from the crest of the pubis (Figure 17) and is inserted in the cartilages of the fifth, sixth, and seventh ribs.

The rectus abdominis is responsible for spinal flexion. If but one side is flexed the body will bend to that side.

The **external or descending obliques** are the strongest and most superficial of the abdominal muscles. They cover the front and side of the abdomen from the rectus abdominis to the latissimus dorsi muscle.

They arise from the external surface to the lower eight ribs. The fibers travel downward and attach to the ilium, the upper edge of the thigh and the pubis.

The external obliques are primarily responsible for flexion of the trunk. They are also responsible for lateral flexion to the same side and rotation of the trunk to the opposite side.

The **internal oblique** lies just under the external oblique and its muscle fibers are at right angles to the ones above.

The internal oblique originates at the ilium, the lumbar region and attaches to the cartilages of the eighth, ninth, and tenth ribs.

The **transversus** are found just under the internal oblique. The greater portion of these fibers have a horizontal direction.

The four layers of muscles in the abdomen act together in all movements of vigorous flexion of the trunk. If the movement, such as sitting up from a lying position, begins slowly, then the rectus abdominis acts alone in lifting the head. When the shoulders begin to rise then the obliques join in the flexion.

These four layers of abdominal muscles run cross-pattern to each other, sort of nature's own version of plywood, to give added strength to this critical region of the body. Since there are no bony structures protecting the abdomen, the strength in these muscles is most critical to the athlete to protect himself from injury.

These muscles can be strengthened in a wide variety of ways. Sit-ups of all types, leg raises, trunk rotation movements all involve the abdominal muscles to different degrees. Football players need to be aware of the importance of these muscles and spend time in each training period exercising them.

SUMMARY

If you are seriously interested in strength training, then knowing your muscles and how they function is not a luxury, but an absolute necessity. This chapter is designed to give you a brief introduction to this knowledge, but any serious Strength Coach or weight training athlete will want to know more about the human machine. I refer you to the list of references at the end of this section and especially recommend **Kinesiology and Applied Anatomy** by Drs. Rasch and Burke.   ★

FIGURE 18   MUSCLES OF THE BODY, ANTERIOR VIEW

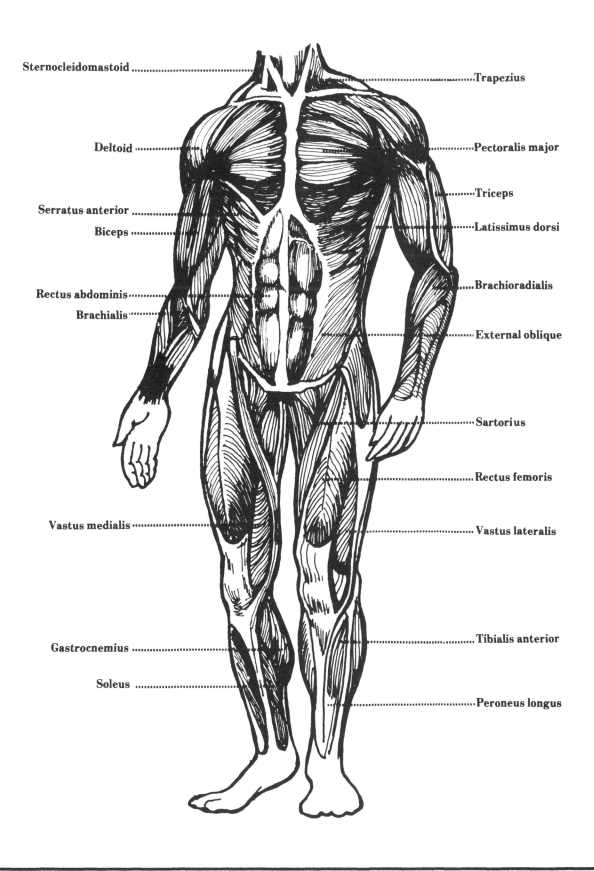

Sternocleidomastoid

Deltoid

Serratus anterior

Biceps

Rectus abdominis

Brachialis

Vastus medialis

Gastrocnemius

Soleus

Trapezius

Pectoralis major

Triceps

Latissimus dorsi

Brachioradialis

External oblique

Sartorius

Rectus femoris

Vastus lateralis

Tibialis anterior

Peroneus longus

3

CHAPTER THREE
STRENGTH —
THE CRITICAL INGREDIENT

THE ATHLETIC ATTRIBUTES

THERE ARE A NUMBER of physical attributes which make up the complete athlete. These include: speed, coordination, flexibility, and strength. Increase any of these qualities, without adversely affecting the others, and you will have a more improved physical specimen. There are numerous speed programs which are designed to improve the ability of the athlete in this department without making him weaker or less coordinated. Likewise, there are plenty of coordination drills which can enhance this physical variable while keeping the strength and speed of the athlete constant. These facts are accepted by all coaches, but the fact that strength can be increased while keeping the other variables constant is always a topic of debate.

One of the most frequent arguments the author faces when presenting football coaches with a proposed strength program is that the athletes are already strong enough and if they become any stronger their performance in the sport would be limited. The logic behind such statements is suspect, at best. This would be exactly like saying that if a player becomes faster he is therefore less effective on the playing field. Or, if a player increases his overall flexibility his playing ability would be affected adversely. How is it possible that being stronger can be a handicap to a football player? The obvious answer is that it cannot, keeping in mind the fact that the other athletic attributes must remain the same.

What is being said should not be misconstrued. While it is a fact that a stronger athlete is a sounder physical specimen, it does not always follow that he will be a better performer just because he is stronger. This would indicate that strength is a panacea for all athletic ills and this certainly is not the case. To perform better in any physical activity requires a honing and a perfecting of certain mental and physical skills involved directly in that sport and this is especially true in the game of football. This same reasoning, however, can be applied to those other attributes as well as to the factor of strength. For example, a faster athlete is not always a better performer merely because of his speed. If he does not practice his sport correctly so that he can apply his speed in an effective way, then his speed may be a hinderance rather than a help.

THE IMPORTANCE OF STRENGTH

"Muscular strength is perhaps the most important of all factors in athletic performance." This quote would seem to be taken from a Strength Coach's manual, but it is not. It is, rather, an opinion based on research by Drs. Rasch and Burke. The authors of **Kinesiology and Applied Anatomy** go on to contend that a general strength test gives the best single index of ability to learn an unfamiliar or new activity. This final statement was brought home very implicitly when the author was indoctrinating each new draft choice for the Baltimore Colts during the 1971 season. As the records of the comparative strength levels of each new rookie were reviewed it was discovered that the relative strength of each new rookie was in direct proportion to the rank in which they were drafted. Don McCauley, the number one choice was the strongest of the group. Bill Attessis of the University of Texas was the second strongest. He was the number two draft choice and the pattern followed all the way to the tenth man. It may be a wise variable for the General Managers to contemplate at draft time.

Professor Gene Logan of Southwestern Missouri State and noted author in the field of physiology goes even further in his book **Adaptations of Muscular Activity** to state that, "Strength undergirds all other factors when one considers the total functioning of the body movements. Without sufficient strength, factors such as endurance, flexibility, and skill cannot be used effectively."

STRENGTH ALONE IS NOT ENOUGH

Total body strength has to be kept in context to the total sum of the athletic ability of the football player. Should a linebacker increase his strength by 50%, but fail to practice the necessary mental and physical skills inherent to his position, then he will not be a better linebacker, but a less effective one. If, on the other hand, he can continue to practice those skills and become stronger at the same time, then he will be more effective at his position. And this is the principle point. Through strength training, the objective is to increase this one variable while keeping all the others at least constant. It has been found, time after time, that as the strength of the athlete increases then so does his speed,

John Woodcock (77) is congratulated by University of Hawaii teammate Cliff LaBoy. Both of these athletes had outstanding collegiate football careers due to their exceptional strength. John is now doing duty with the Detroit Lions.

flexibility, and coordination.

A negative point has to be mentioned as it is a consideration in the mind of every coach contemplating a strength program. It cannot be denied that it is possible to limit an athlete's performance with the use of resistive training. Short-range exercise motions will certainly limit the range of motion of that muscle group. For example, should the trainee be doing partial curls for his upper arm, then he will soon discover that he cannot call upon that muscle group to respond in a full-range of performance.

In a nutshell, this is why so many football coaches have not wholly endorsed a strength program. They have had too many bad experiences with some players or some strength programs that hurt rather than helped their cause. An assistant coach at Baltimore was very apprehensive about including a strength program in the conditioning phase for the Colts because of an experience he had at Michigan State.

OVERTRAINING IS THE GREATEST FAULT

Some programs overwork the athlete to the point where he cannot practice his sport skills adequately. Each person only has so much energy and a sensible program must be geared to this fact. Overtraining, as a matter of record, is the one greatest fault of almost every strength program the author was asked to analyze and correct. The experience at the Naval Academy is a perfect case in point.

THE NAVAL ACADEMY STORY

The author and Tommy Suggs, who were co-editors of **Strength and Health** magazine at the time, were asked to come to Annapolis and to offer any suggestions for improvements on the proposed strength program for the Midshipmen by Captain Ed Schantz, the officer in charge of conditioning. Captain Schantz had, admittedly, little experience in this sort of conditioning so he researched as best he could and came up with a program which he felt covered every possible body part.

He presented us with a list of sixteen exercises and we had to admit that they did cover every body part from the calves to the forearms, but the catch was that all of these exercises were supposed to be performed by forty men in about an hour. Our first recommendation shocked the Marine Captain as we reduced the sixteen exercises to three. We then proceeded to give a rationale as to why these three exercises could get the same work done — in fact, much more accomplished — and why sixteen exercises were really quite impossible in the limited time. Happily, the Captain was a logical sort and saw the reasoning behind the proposal. He installed the "Big Three" and reported glowing success throughout the training period. One sidelight to this story is that the Captain had been doing the sixteen exercises himself so that he would be better able to teach them more effectively to his players. He said that he would try the "Big Three" and see if he could see any difference in the way his body felt the following day as he believed himself to be in tip-top condition. He called us in York the following day to inform us that after just 30 minutes on the three movements he was barely able to get out of bed the next morning. We obviously had a convert.

MORE IS NOT ALWAYS BETTER

The point of this tale is, stated simply, because some resistive exercise is good, it does not necessarily follow that more is always better. The Strength Coach has to be constantly aware of the fact that the football player only has so much energy to spread among his many interests. If he taps off too much of this energy in the weight room, then he will have a little less for his gridiron activities. Also, it has been confirmed through both practical and empirical research that the body responds best to a limited amount of physical stimulation. Too much of a good thing often results in less than favorable results.

THE FACTOR OF SPEED

One of the classical criticisms a number of football coaches have of a strength program is that it slows their men down. Like all other axioms that have grown up around strength training, there is a fragment of truth lingering in the background. The unadulterated truth is this: a poorly applied strength program can slow a player down; a correctly administered strength program can only improve the athlete's speed.

For empirical validation, the reader can note these three studies: 1) "The Effect of Weightlifting Upon the Speed of Muscular Contraction," by William Zorbas and Peter Karpovich, **Research Quarterly**, May, 1951, 2) "The Effect of Weight Training on Speed of Movement" by Bruce Wilken, **Research Quarterly**, October, 1952, and 3) "Weight Training in Relation to Strength, Speed, and Coordination" by John Masley, Ara Hairabedian, and Donald Donaldson, **Research Quarterly**, October, 1953. All of these studies, plus numerous others, support the hypothesis that a sound weight program can increase speed in an athlete.

THE BILLY NEWSOME STORY

Perhaps more importantly to the coaches and players are the real life examples. Here is but one rather dramatic case in point. Billy Newsome of the Baltimore Colts, out of Grambling College, was one of my most conscientious trainees in the spring of 1971. Bill worked diligently on the strength program outlined from March to the start of summer camp in early July. At the beginning of the program Billy weighed 235 and at the conclusion, he was a very muscular 270. There was not a trace of fat on his frame. In fact, he looked as if he had been weight training for four years rather than just four months. His overall body strength had increased 50% in those four months. He could bench press 360, squat 385, and power clean 300.

When Billy showed up at Westminster College for the Colt's summer camp the coaches were a bit alarmed. They felt that the weight program had been too excessive. Billy was too big, in their opinion and, therefore he must be slower. But when they put the clock on him for the 40-yard-dash, their lower jaws dropped. He did the 40 in 4.6 seconds, a drop of some .25 seconds over the previous year when he weighed 35 pounds less. He had increased his total body strength as well as his speed. It should also be noted that Billy did not include running in his program until just three weeks before going to camp and then just enough to loosen his stride. The increase in speed was a very direct result of the strength he had gained in his legs from doing full squats.

It is, therefore, not resistive training per se that is the villain in slowing a player down, but the manner in which the movements are applied. Strength training, quite realistically, is a double-edged sword. The concerned Strength Coach must be constantly aware of the dangers of doing exercises incorrectly, of doing too many exercises, or of doing the wrong exercises, and finally, of doing the right exercises at the wrong times.

THE FACTOR OF FLEXIBILITY

What about flexibility? Can a strength program possibly aid the athlete's flexibility? As a matter of fact, it can. Again, the key is a soundly organized program which is properly administered. By performing full-range movements with resistive equipment, the trainee can actually increase his range of motion in that particular muscle group.

The resistance, whether it be free weights or machines, extends the muscle past the point where it would go normally if there were no added pressure from the resistance. As an example, examine an exercise which is familiar to everyone, the curl. If the curl is performed correctly, the biceps are stretched beyond the range that they would normally extend because the added weight forces them to do so. Obviously, it is most important to be aware of this fact and insist that each and every exercise be performed in its fullest possible range.

Again, the research supports this contention. Benjamin Massey and Norman Chaudet in the March, 1956 edition of the **Research Quarterly** concluded that weight training, when properly conducted, did not have a detrimental effect upon the range of joint movement throughout the body, but rather enhanced it.

Any sound strength program builds flexibility movements into the total program. The importance of flexibility in this program has been noted as I have included a full chapter on flexibility exercises. It's really just a matter of being aware of the situation. Including towel stretching after each set of

Levi Stanley, University of Hawaii, the Hawaiians, and the San Francisco 49ers, incorporates the principles of flexibility into his total training program as well as any professional football player in the nation. A conscientious and alert athlete, Levi spends thirty minutes before and after each weight room session performing a complete program of flexibility exercises. At a bodyweight of 255 pounds, he is able to perform flexibility movements generally reserved for gymnasts. He is a prime example of an athlete who pays attention to detail and success has been his reward.

bench presses, for example, insures the trainee of more flexible shoulders. Every sensible strength program also begins and ends each session with numerous stretching exercises.

So the fact is that flexibility can be enhanced via a solid strength program. Many players are as amazed at their new flexibility as they are their new-found strength. It is basically a matter of building all of these important factors into the program. Take nothing for granted. Make sure flexibility movements are a vital part of the total strength concept.

THE FACTOR OF COORDINATION

Coordination is greatly improved as strength improves. In fact, total body coordination is very dependent on the factor of strength. As the muscles, tendons, and ligaments grow stronger they are better able to perform the functions for which they were designed. Physical therapists are quite aware of this fact. They know that a patient must have sufficient strength in his legs, hips, and back before he can be expected to relearn to walk. The gymnast and dancer will also bear testimony to the importance of strength for the sake of coordination. Before a gymnast becomes accomplished in that highly skilled sport of coordination, balance, and timing, he must have a solid base of strength. As that strength increases, then so does the coordination — assuming of course, that the athlete is practicing the intricate skills of the sport.

A great volume of research backs up this hypothesis. Sidney Calvin, in the December 1959 edition of **Research Quarterly** in a piece of research entitled, "Effects of Progressive Resistive Exercises on the Motor Coordination of Boys" reports that the "weight-trained group improved in motor coordination more significantly statistically than the non-training group."

Another classical study on the subject, mentioned earlier in the section on speed is that one conducted by Masley, Hairabedian, and Donaldson. These investigators reported that increased strength gained through weight training was associated with increased muscular coordination.

INCLUDE HIGH COORDINATION MOVEMENTS

It is wise to include one or two movements that entail a high degree of coordination as well as some designed just for increasing raw strength. This is why the power clean has been tabbed the "athlete's exercise." Some coaches even use the power clean to judge the player's overall athletic potential. A coach from North Carolina told me that he could pick his best athlete just by observing his players during their first introduction to the power clean.

Some exercises are designed primarily to increase pure, raw power. The bench press and squat would fall into this category. Others need a much higher degree of coordination to perform. The Olympic lifts, power clean, power snatch, and shrug are examples of the latter. It is important to include at least one exercise that utilizes a higher degree of coordination in a strength program so that this athletic quality remains at least constant while the player becomes stronger.

Helping an athlete to obtain increased strength is really quite simple. This just requires doing lots of work on a systematic series of exercises. Getting athletes stronger while increasing all their other athletic attributes is a different trick. It can be done, most certainly, but not without sound application of all the principles of athletic strength training.

THE ASSET OF STRENGTH

Strength, it must be concluded, is a most valuable asset to the football player. Only the uninformed will argue against such a statement in the light of the available facts. A stronger athlete will always be a better athlete if for no other reason than he is able to practice his sport longer. Keep all the other athletic attributes constant, such as: speed, coordination, flexibility, and increase the player's strength level by 40-50%, and the result is a superior physical being.

Increase muscular strength in the player's legs and he is able to cover the same distance in a shorter period of time, i.e. he is faster. Strengthen the muscles in his shoulder girdle and it is guaranteed that he will hit harder as he will have more power to hit with — a definite advantage in any position on the gridiron.

Increase his total body strength and he will be better able to get through a game without experiencing fatigue. A factor some call endurance is very dependent on total body strength. Make a player stronger overall, with special attention to those critical joint areas and he will be less prone to injury for it is the muscular system, along with the strength in the ligaments and the tendons that literally hold the joints together. A physically stronger football player will also be much better able to get back on the field after an injury — a fact often overlooked by coaches, team doctors, and trainers. A well-conditioned body will respond to therapy much more rapidly than a weaker one.

STRENGTH IS NEVER A NEGATIVE

So, in no instance is strength a handicap or an attribute to be avoided. It is, rather implicity, a most desirable commodity that should be sought after by every football player who wishes to improve his performance. The key to success is a soundly organized and properly administered strength program.

Any football player who desires to improve his ability must list strength training as his number one objective. Any coach who desires a better team must be aware of the advantage of a strength program. This book could be filled with glowing examples of coaches who have made their teams into champions by way of a sound strength program. One will serve the purpose.

TWO TESTIMONIALS

I could provide scores of testimonials from outstanding professionals concerning the merits of weight training as outlined in **The Strongest Shall Survive . . . Strength Training for Football**, but I have selected Mike Curtis and John Williams as representatives for them all.

Mike trained with me during the spring of 1971 and made very rapid progress during that time. A most intent and dedicated athlete, the All-Pro linebacker was able to power clean 275 x 5 and overhead press 300 with less than three months of training. Here is what a member of the 1971 World Champion Baltimore Colts has to say on the subject of weight training: "I have found that lifting weights has not only increased my strength significantly, but has also increased my speed. Also, by continuing a planned lifting schedule, I can extend my playing career beyond the average retirement period. There has been no loss in coordination due to lifting."

John Williams, formerly a Baltimore Colt and now with the Los Angeles Rams, blows open a hole in the Kansas City line. His overall strength has enabled him to become a highly-respected professional.

John Williams was the first player on the Colts team to seek me out about a strength program. He was a skeptic as to the value of weight training but wanted to drop a lot of extra pounds and was willing to give anything a try. He became a most reliable trainee, never missing a workout and always on schedule. He made progress quickly as he is an exceptional athlete and recently gained some well-deserved recognition for his fine play with the Los Angeles Rams.

John wrote me the following: "I'm still basically on the same weight program you put me on five years ago. I have found the results to be superb. My stamina and endurance improved greatly. Also, my recovery time was reduced considerably. My progress is most noticeable during training camp and the latter part of the season. This is important because these two times are injury-prone periods. These factors and my over-all strength development give me the confidence to compete with anyone."

THE KODAK STORY

A junior high coach from Virginia approached Tommy Suggs and I at the Washington, D.C. version of the Kodak Coach of the Year Clinic. He had just concluded a 1-9 season and was concerned that he would be replaced if he could not make a better showing the following year. This fact was made rather clear by his athletic director. He believed and hoped that a strength program might be a start in the proper direction and asked us for some assistance. We outlined a strength program centered around the "Big Three" and provided him with some nutritional information.

We didn't hear from him until the same convention the next winter. He bounced into our booth shaking our hands as if we were long-lost and very rich relatives. He sat us down, opened a thoroughly documented scrapbook, and happily related his past season. After leaving the convention, he told us, he immediately put into operation the strength program we had suggested and started many of the smaller players on a high protein supplement at his own expense. This was in mid-February. When his players took the field for the opening game in September, the opposing coach nearly choked. Our coach had transformed 165-pounders into 200-pounders that looked like Sons of Hercules. His former 190-pounders now weighed in at 220 and 230. To shorten a sensational story, our coach and his weight-trained team crushed everyone for a perfect 10-0 record and undisputed honor of being the hottest team in the entire state. Opposing coaches screamed that he was bringing in overage boys, but all he had done was to transform a mediocre group of athletes into superior ones by way of some weight training and sound nutrition.

The rest of the convention was cake for us. If a coach began doubting our assertions — and there were many doing so in the sixties — then we merely referred them to our young coach and his scrapbook. He was so enthusiastic and had all the tangible proof he needed right in his hands. Needless to say, he made lots of converts during the three-day convention. The best and most useful research in this field is really the practical kind. The best testing ground is on the playing field in the final analysis. When results are produced on the scoreboard then it is certain that the information being conveyed is most useful.

The episode mentioned above is not an isolated case by any means. The number of teams and individual players who have gained success by virtue of the recommended strength program is now legion.

THE SCIENCE OF STRENGTH TRAINING

Strength training has slowly evolved into a complete and rather complex science although no one carries a degree of any sort of this particular field of physical education. The competitive weightlifter comes the closest to understanding the many intricate facets of this activity. He has had to learn most of his information from personal trial-and-error experience. He has taken the time to talk to any and all who pretend to know or who actually do know something about the subject of strength. He has read every magazine, book, and article available to him on the topic of strength training. And he has made his own body a laboratory in which to test the theories he came across.

This is why, after some 10 or 15 years of training, the competitive weightlifter pretty well knows just what does work and what is a waste of time. The professional teams have realized this fact and have turned to the experts on strength, former competitive lifters, in order to gain the answers to the myriad of problems revolving around getting their players stronger. Quite obviously, not all competitive weightlifters fill the bill, but those who can apply what they have learned from their sport to that of football and who are interested in teaching are certainly most valuable to a football team.

STRENGTH — THE BASE OF
ATHLETIC IMPROVEMENT

A team can definitely turn itself around if the coach puts his full effort behind a strength program. The coach, however, must thoroughly believe in the program or it will not be effective. I have worked with teams, through the

general manager, where the head coach did not encourage strength training. The results are much harder to come by in this situation. I always recommend that the coach actually do the program himself. He will feel it work on his own body and be in a much better position to analyze the problems encountered as the program progresses.

It would not be amiss to mention that a coach who weight trains with his players also deserves a higher degree of respect from those players. It is also visible evidence that the coach believes in what he says. It certainly doesn't hurt to set a physical example for the players. A little respect gained in the sweat and pain in the weight room can go a long way on the football field. Besides, fat, out-of-condition football coaches seem to make a sham of the sport.

Now that it has been established that a strength program is desirable — no, let's say essential — for every football player on every football team in the country, let's move on to the meat of the subject. The trick is to put the theories into practice.   ★

All-Pro linebacker, Mike Curtis of the Baltimore Colts carried the strength he gained in the weight room onto the playing field.

4

CHAPTER FOUR
FLEXIBILITY AND WARMING-UP

FLEXIBILITY CAN BE IMPROVED

WHILE IT IS A FACT that the primary goal of any strength program is to increase the athlete's overall strength, we are also very interested in enhancing as many of the other athletic attributes of the trainee as possible. Flexibility is one such variable which can be improved in a properly-administered strength program. For many, many years proponents of weight training for football were confronted with the objections of coaches on the grounds that weight training restricted the range of motion of the players, i.e. their flexibility. I have spent quite a few hours convincing coaches of the fact that this is not necessarily so. A properly administered program will enhance, rather than restrict, flexibility.

As far back as the early 1950's researchers in the field of physical education proved through scientific testing methods that individuals who use weights properly become more flexible, rather than less flexible. Jim Counsilman revealed the findings of one such study in the January, 1955 edition of the **Journal of Health, Physical Education, and Recreation**. He tested three competitive weightlifters and found that they were considerably above average in the tests of flexibility devised by Dr. Thomas Cureton. Since the N was so low he proceeded to test fifteen more weightlifters and found similar results. He concluded that, "weight training seems to improve power, speed, strength, and flexibility." These tests have never been refuted.

When I speak of flexibility in the athlete, I am defining flexibility as the range of possible movement in a joint or a series of joints involved in a movement. It is rather difficult to state that an individual is flexible or inflexible unless you specify a given joint or combination of joints. One individual may be extremely flexible in the shoulder girdle, for example, but at the same time be quite inflexible in the lower back or leg biceps.

THE ROLE OF JOINTS IN FLEXIBILITY

Each individual has many joints in his body and some of these quite obviously are more flexible than are others. Much of this relative flexibility is simply due to heredity. If you happen to be born with a limited range of motion in your leg biceps, then you will have to spend much more time working that area than someone who is blessed with a fuller range of motion.

Another reason that some joints of the body are less flexible than others is simply because they have not been utilized through a full range of motion during the athlete's particular activity. For example, a great many football players lack flexibility in their ankles because they seldom stretch those particular muscles and tendons. A gymnast has to have flexibility in these joints in order to be successful in the sport, so he spends much time keeping these joints loose and supple.

It was felt for quite some time that one's body-build largely determined his potential flexibility as an athlete. It was believed that an individual who is tall and rather lean should have a greater range of motion because of smaller joints, longer more slender muscles and ligaments which are more lax. Conversely, it was assumed that a person who possesses a high degree of muscularity would be less flexible. Several investigators have since discovered, however, that "there is not significant relationship between flexibility and various body measurements."

You will recall from Chapter I that the shape of the various joints of your body determines what kind and what degree of movement is possible in that joint. Using this information as your basis, you can then proceed to understand why I recommend these various flexibility movements later in this chapter.

One of the goals of every Strength Coach is to provide movements in the weight room which will enhance and improve total flexibility of the athlete. There are a few basic rules of thumb regarding flexibility which apply to all exercise programs. The first is to warm-up and stretch thoroughly before commencing training; secondly, insist on full range movements in all exercises and, finally, stretch out before, during, and after each workout.

THE IMPORTANCE OF THE WARM-UP

Warming-up refers to any activity which prepares the trainee for more strenuous movements. A warm-up activity should influence the body in the following ways:
1) increase the pulse rate
2) increase respiratory rate
3) increase body temperature
4) increase range of joint mobility
5) produce a condition of readiness in the athlete

This physiological preparation gives the body time to prepare itself for the more strenuous activities which lie ahead. Equally important is the fact that psychological preparation. You must provide your mind with time to get ready for the program of the day.

A brief period of exercise which involves the entire body followed by a series of stretching movements appears to be the most beneficial to the participant. Activities such as rope skipping, running in place, jogging, jumping jacks, free-hand squats, or squat thrusts activate the total body and raise the pulse rate, respiratory rate, and body temperature. Any exercise or activity which involves cardiovascular, respiratory fitness provides a fine warm-up. This warm-up should take approximately five-to-fifteen minutes or until your body temperature begins to rise.

Once you feel sufficiently warmed up you should go immediately to your specific stretching exercises. It is very important for the weight trainer to stretch all the various joints in his body prior to handling the barbell. Each of the joints should be attended to individually. Do a movement for the wrist, the elbows, the shoulders, the lower back, the hips, knees, and ankles before commencing your weight program.

When I speak of stretching specific joints I am really referring to stretching the muscles and tendons which are involved in that particular joint. Before describing some specific stretching movements for each joint mentioned I would first like to introduce you to some of the more technical aspects of flexibility so that you may better understand the "whys" as well as the "hows."

THREE FACTORS OF FLEXIBILITY

Flexibility is based on three factors: elasticity, extensibility, and the stretch reflex. The **elasticity** of the muscle refers to the fact that it can stretch beyond its normal resting length and return to it once again after the force has been removed.

When I speak of the **extensibility** of a muscle I mean that length which a muscle can be stretched and still not be damaged. The extensibility of most muscles is approximately 50% its resting length. Muscles and tendons rupture or tear when forced past this margin of safety.

THE STRETCH REFLEX

One of the basic rules of warming-up muscles revolves around an understanding of the **stretch reflex.** To better understand this principle, do this movement. Stretch your lower arm so that your arm is fully extended. In order for

this action to take place the muscle spindle in the biceps is stimulated and an impulse is generated. The impulse is relayed on up the line through nerve fibers to a junction in the spinal cord, with a motor neuron that inverts the action of the muscle fibers of the biceps. When the motor neuron is stimulated, impulses are conducted over its nerve fibers to the muscle fibers, which then contract. In other words, it is extremely difficult to stretch out a muscle because it will tend to contract and shorten when it is fully extended.

In order to successfully stretch a muscle you must avoid triggering this stretch reflex response. This can be accomplished by performing slow, steady stretching movements rather than quick bouncy ones. The slow movements appear to inhibit a reflex response of the muscle and a lengthening of the entire muscle group can take place.

Whenever you perform a stretching movement be certain to do it slowly. No jerky, fast motions. Tease the muscles into stretching. Don't force them. One of the exercises recommended for stretching the shoulder girdle is the towel dislocates. When performing this movement, never snap the towel back and forth over your head in a rapid motion. Move into any stretching exercise very slowly and deliberately or they can actually cause more harm than good.

DYNAMIC AND PASSIVE MOVEMENTS

A brief period of active (dynamic) stretching exercise followed by passive (static) movements seems to be most beneficial to athletes. By active exercises I do not mean rapid, but merely the opposite of static. There is movement in active exercises, there is none in the static ones.

The hurdler exercise for the lower back and leg biceps can be used as an example. Place your leg on a bench. Fully extend it and slowly reach forward with your head and try to place it on your knee. Lean forward slowly, come back upright. Go forward a bit deeper each time until you finally reach the deepest position. Hold that position momentarily. Come back erect; now lean forward going a bit deeper yet. Do this for about 10-12 repetitions until you have reached your furthest point of stretch. Then hold that position for 10, 15, 20, or 30 seconds. Try to build up the time to ½ minute. This static hold just after the dynamic stretches allows you to increase your range of motion considerably.

Doing a static move without a few dynamic stretches does not work quite as well. The dynamic stretches help to further warm the muscle and enable you to go deeper further into a stretch. Remember the importance of slow, deliberate movements. Fast, snappy movements can be quite dangerous. The quick, jerky motions often result in very sore muscles or even injuries to the muscles or tendons.

START WITH A LIGHT WEIGHT

The next step in a complete flexibility program is to take a light weight for the initial set of any lift and to go through the first set very slowly. Allow the muscles to warm up for that specific movement before trying to build speed into the lift. Even though you have spent 10-15 minutes preparing your body for an exercise, there are still muscles involved that have not been reached exactly. Some trainees often complain when it is suggested that they start an exercise with as little as 135 pounds, yet it is always wise to start with a very light weight in any exercise, regardless of your strength level.

It is recommended that you go through some shadow movements of the exercises you are about to perform. For example, before squatting with a barbell, perform a few free squats. Before starting in on power cleans, take a broomstick and do a few power clean movements.

This is the procedure you will see demonstrated in an international level weightlifting competition — where the strongest men in the world congregate. Weightlifters take their initial warm-up and go through the lift in slow motion. As they slowly loosen up the muscles to be used in that lift they begin moving faster and faster until they are literally exploding under the barbell. But speed follows the flexibility and warming up exercises.

PROGRESSIVELY ADD RESISTANCE

One of the purposes of staggering each set in progression is to allow the body to warm-up thoroughly before you put it under the maximum stress for the day. The steady progression also allows your mind to prepare for the higher weights. There are a few prescribed strength building routines available which advocate starting with a maximum weight and then working downward towards a lighter poundage. This procedure is not only against the entire philosophy of progressive weight training but is a royal invitation to injury. Those who get away with this type of program can consider themselves lucky and most pay up for their lack of understanding of how the body functions sooner or later. Of all the cases of injuries in the weight room, these are usually the most severe.

I often find that less experienced trainees complain because they are scheduled to start with as little as 135 pounds when they know that they will be doing 225 in that exercise for the day. I must remind all those anxious athletes that there is a sound physiological reason behind commencing an exercise with a light weight and also that even the strongest man in the world starts with 135 pounds.

I was in the warm-up room that historic night in Columbus, Ohio, when the Russian Super Heavyweight, Aleexev, became the first man to elevate 500 pounds overhead. This giant strongman warmed up with 135 pounds. And — he had already performed clean and presses and snatches, but since the clean and jerk involved certain different muscles he wanted to make certain that these new muscles had a chance to be warmed-up thoroughly before attempting a heavier poundage. If the procedure is good enough for the strongest man in the world, it should be good enough for all who train with weights.

BUILDING FLEXIBILITY INTO THE PROGRAM

I believe that flexibility can be built directly into each and every exercise. By insisting on full range movements you can be certain that the flexibility of a specific joint will be enhanced. It has been shown that full range movements performed with resistance can further the total range of motion of that joint. This is possible because the added weight of the resistance forces the muscles and tendons past their normal range of motion. Try this exercise so you will see what I mean. Stretch your elbow to complete extension with your palm facing upward. Note how far it is extended. Now place a 35-pound dumbbell in your hand and repeat the same movement. You will find that your arm extends a fraction further than it did without the added weight. The same principle applies for all exercises. You'll find many athletes utilizing this principle without being aware of it.

They will push and pull each other as part of their warm-up past the normal range of motion in order to warm-up and stretch a joint. This is but another form of applying resistance to the body.

FLEXIBILITY DURING THE EXERCISE

The next step in our total flexibility program is to emphasize stretching movements during the exercise period itself. As the athlete moves from station to station he should be encouraged to perform some flexibility work. This can be accomplished quite simply and adds a great deal to the athlete's overall flexibility.

As the trainee gets up from the bench press he should take a towel and perform a half dozen shoulder dislocates while walking to the squat rack. As he is waiting for the barbell at the power clean station he can be loosening his wrist or shoulders. While resting prior to the bench press or leg extension he can stretch his ankles and hamstrings. It can become a matter of practice to be stretching between sets rather than just standing around doing nothing. The stretching also serves a dual purpose in that it keeps the muscles warm between exercises as sometimes the stations back up long enough for the athlete to cool off slightly.

STRETCHING AFTER THE WORKOUT

The final phase of the flexibility program comes after the exercise session. Stretching after the workout is extremely important to the athlete. At this time the muscles are thoroughly warmed up and most conducive to stretching movements. They are, at the same time, most congested with blood and have a tendency to assume a shortened position if they are not stretched sufficiently.

Go through the same flexibility program following a workout as you do prior to lifting. Do a stretching exercise for your wrist, elbows, shoulders, lower back, hips, knees, and ankles. Spend about five to ten minutes stretching as you cool down. You'll find that this practice eliminates much of the muscle soreness encountered in the weight room (especially in the first few weeks of training) and enables you to gain a bit in your overall flexibility program. The time spent between your last exercise and the shower room can be most beneficial to increasing your overall flexibility.

There are numerous flexibility exercises that will be helpful to the football player and each athlete would do well to investigate as many varieties of stretching movements as possible. Sports which require a great deal of flexibility are the ones to examine most closely. Gymnastics heads the list. Judo and karate incorporate some excellent flexibility exercises in their sports. Track athletes and swimmers also utilize many excellent stretching movements. Competitive weightlifters must also be extremely flexible so I will turn to this sport for some timely exercises since I am most concerned with flexibility as it pertains to lifting weights.

From these various sports activities I have selected a sampling of flexibility movements. These are not meant to be all encompassing, but rather representative of the many exercises available. They are presented so that you will have some program to put into practice immediately. As you learn more about flexibility you may well discover another movement to replace the ones recommended. Feel free to incorporate it into your program. My hope is not that you adhere to these suggested exercises, but rather that you perform some flexibility work for every body part.

FLEXIBILITY MOVEMENTS

WRIST

A simple but effective stretching movement for the wrist entails applying pressure to your finger tips with your other hand. Push your hand backward towards your forearm and then turn your hand downward and press the back of your fingers. Repeat this movement back and forth until you feel the wrists loosen up thoroughly. Then push in each direction gently and hold the final position for 10-15 seconds.

ELBOWS

1) Bend your arm and reach back over your shoulder with your palm facing upward. Use your other hand and grasp under your elbow and lift it up and back. Force the arm back slowly and then hold in the final position once it is warmed-up thoroughly. Repeat on the other arm.

2) Another effective stretching movement for both the wrists and elbows is to take a light barbell or even a broomstick and rest it on your frontal deltoids. Have a training partner lift up under both elbows pushing them as high as possible. As you become warmed up, use a fairly heavy weight. The added weight will help keep the bar on your chest and frontal deltoids so that the wrists and elbows take all the stretch. Ease into this one as it is a rather advanced exercise.

SHOULDERS

Towel stretches are most beneficial for loosening the shoulder, but caution is the order of the day when doing this movement. Grasp a towel as wide as you can and extend your arms fully overhead. Lock one arm while bending the other and rotate your shoulders so that the towel passes over your head and on down to your lower back. Bring it back in similar fashion. Now lock the opposite elbow and repeat.

Do this movement very slowly and as you feel your shoulders becoming warmer, bend the off-side elbow less and less until, finally, both elbows are locked and you are performing dislocates. Do them slowly, repeat s-l-o-w-l-y. A snappy motion, especially before the shoulders are completely warmed-up, can be dangerous.

As your shoulders become loose, begin moving your hands closer together on the towel. In a brief 2-3 minute stretching bout you may be able to move your grip in as much as 3-4 inches.

I encourage all trainees to use this exercise before, during, and after each workout because the one area most prone to becoming tight from weight training is the shoulder girdle. This is because the bench press thickens the higher portion of the pectoral region and if flexibility exercises are not incorporated into the program some overhead flexibility can be lost.

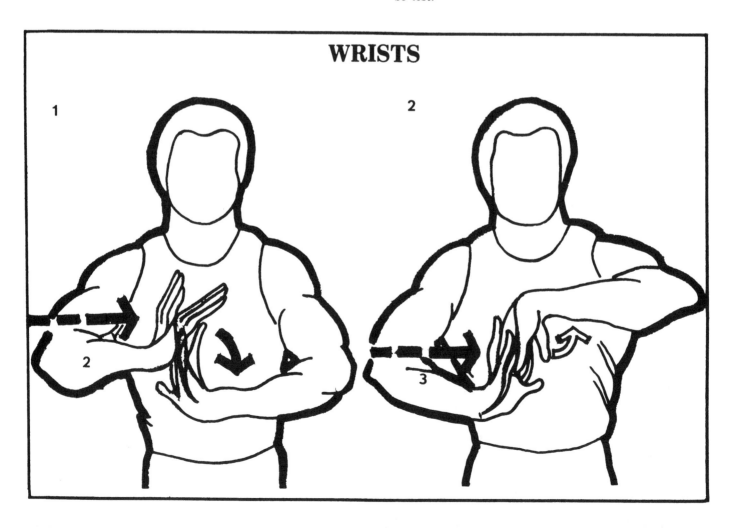

WRISTS

1

2

2

3

ELBOWS

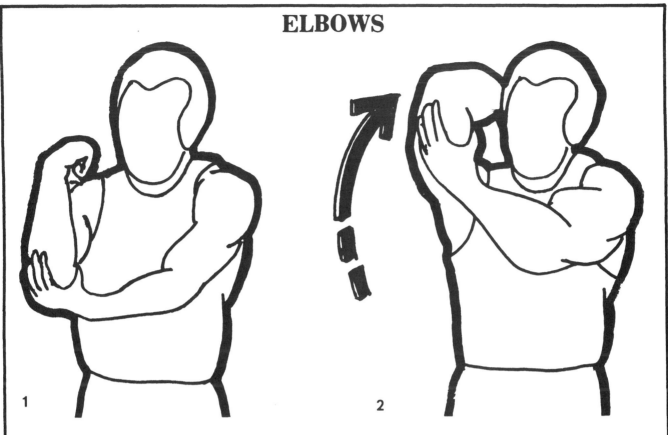

SHOULDERS

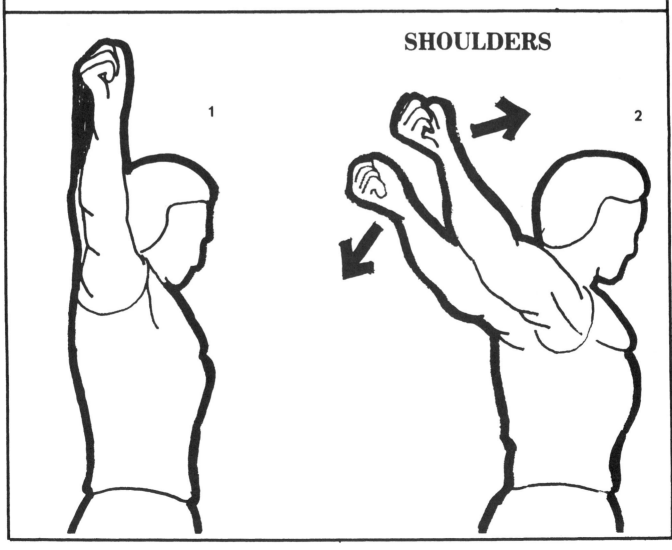

LOWER BACK

Since nearly all stretching movements for the lower back also involve the muscles of the leg biceps group, these movements are grouped together.

1) The standard **toe touching** exercise can be most useful in helping to stretch the lower back and leg biceps, but it must be done with care. You must be aware, once again, of the importance of a slowly regulated movement when stretching any muscle group. Stand erect, lock your knees, and slowly reach down with your hands towards your feet. On the first repetition just go to your knees then come back erect. Then go lower, and lower and lower until you are finally touching your toes. After you feel completely warmed-up, reach to your toes and hold that position for 10-15 seconds.

HURDLER EXERCISE-
SINGLE LEG

TOE TOUCHES

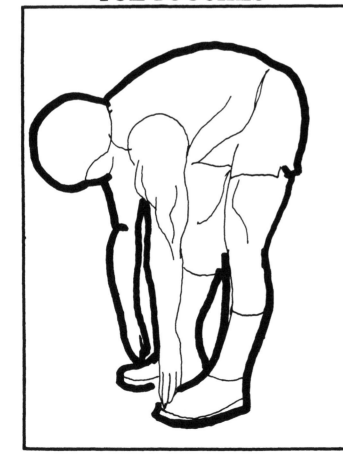

1

2

LOWER BACK

HURDLER EXERCISE-
DOUBLE LEG

2) The **hurdler exercise** is another excellent stretching movement for the lower back and leg biceps. Sit on a bench with one leg extended and the other on the floor. This can be done on the floor also. Lock your knee and lean forward slowly so as to place your forehead on your knee. Don't force your head down, but rather go deeper on each repetition until you are able to reach your lowest position for the day. Then hold that deepest position momentarily for 10-15 seconds. Repeat on the other leg.

After you feel that each leg is sufficiently warm, place both legs together, lock your knees and bend forward in the same fashion. This exercise does a fine job of stretching the lower back and leg biceps.

A more advanced version of this same exercise has the trainee being pushed over further and held in the deepest position by a training partner. This movement should only be performed when the athlete feels completely warmed up and stretched out. Caution should be practiced. Do not forcefully push the trainee. Rapid, jerky thrusts can cause severe injury to the muscles and tendons and should be avoided. Ease down and hold the final position for as long as possible.

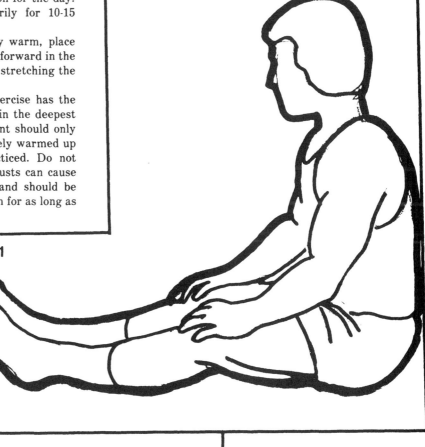

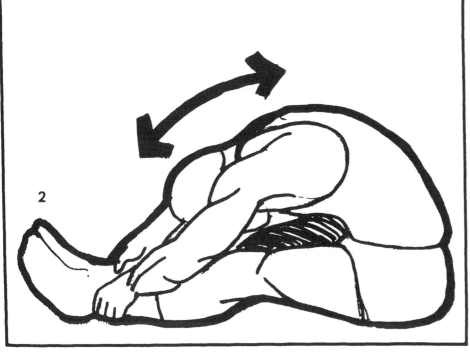

HIPS

1) Simple **hip rotations** are most effective in loosening and warming up the hip girdle. While standing erect with your hands on your hips begin making a slow circular motion with your hips. Exaggerate this movement so that you are swinging wider and wider on each rotation. Accentuate the forward and backward thrust as this is much the same motion as will be later utilized in the power clean.

2) The **snatch split** receives its name from one of the competitive Olympic lifts. The weightlifters who utilize the split style of snatching have to be able to stretch out in a deep split position while supporting a heavy weight overhead so they do plenty of these. It gives an excellent stretch to the muscles of the hips, and especially the gluteus maximus.

Stand erect and place your hands on your hips. Step forward with your left foot and backward with your right one. Keep the rear knee locked and bend the front knee forward so that your front knee is out in front of your toe. Keep your trunk erect and force your body down into a deeper and deeper position.

Reverse to the other leg and do the same movement. Go back and forth from one leg to the other trying to stretch the trailing leg more and more on each set.

3) Another fine stretching exercise for the hips and the legs is the **side stretches.** Stand erect and spread your feet wide apart. While keeping your trunk in a vertical position, lock your left knee and bend your right leg so that your gluteus maximus is moving toward your heel. Come back erect and go down to the other side. Continue this motion until you are able to put your glutes against your calf and then hold that position momentarily.

This is the exercise done by many track athletes before they do any running and is an especially good warm-up movement to use before and after performing deep squats.

HIP ROTATIONS

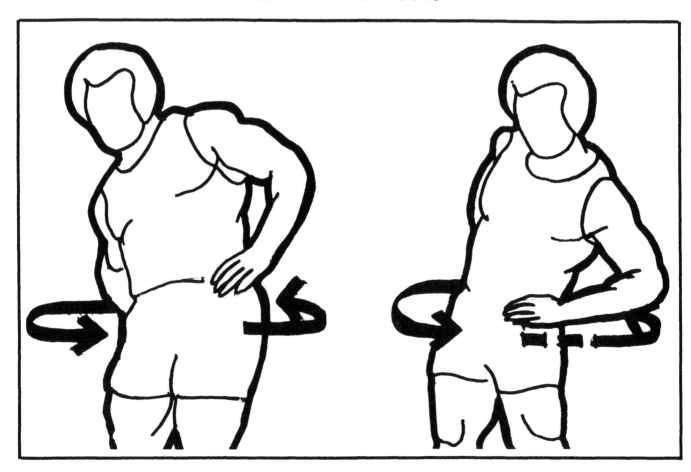

HIPS

SNATCH SPLITS

SIDE STRETCHES

KNEES

SQUATS

Many of the flexibility movements already recommended, do involve the knee joint, but it is always wise to do at least one specific movement just for that area to be certain that it is warmed up sufficiently.

It is a good idea to do a few free squats before doing any with resistance. Go deep and rock a bit at the deep position. Do a few with your feet set rather wide apart, a few with your feet very close together and, finally, some in your regular squatting position.

ANKLES

Find a board or something which is elevated some 2-3 inches. Place the ball of your foot on the board and lock your knee. Lean forward so that the gastrocnemius is being stretched thoroughly. These are valuable to do prior to and following squats.

A variation of this same exercise is for you to place your foot about four feet from a wall. Lock your knee and keep your foot flat against the floor. Place your hands against the wall and lean toward it. Stretch the muscle out slowly. As it loosens up move back a few inches and repeat. Alternate each foot until you feel it stretch way out, then hold the final position for 10-15 seconds.

After a thorough flexibility warm-up prior to training, it is a wise idea to perform a few abdominal exercises before starting to work with the bar. These serve to warm the critical lower back and abdominal region and also stimulate the internal organs.

One set of sit-ups, some twists, and a set of leg raises will be sufficient. If you conclude your workout in the same manner you will soon discover that your midsection will begin to firm up considerably and since everyone dislikes abdominal exercises, this seems to be the most palatable way to slip them into your program.

It should be reiterated that these recommended exercises constitute but a small sampling of the many that can be used. If you have a flexibility program for a few stretching movements that have worked well for you in the past, then by all means continue to use them in your program.

Jaris White began training on the "Big Three" in his senior year at the University of Hawaii. He diligently worked on his strength, speed, and flexibility and adhered to a sound nutritional program. The five-year NFL veteran is now performing for the Tampa Bay Buccaneers.

IN SUMMARY

To summarize, a proper warm-up program should influence your body in the following ways:
1) increase the pulse rate
2) increase respiratory rate
3) increase body temperature
4) increase range of joint mobility
5) to produce a condition of readiness in the athlete.

It could safely be stated that nothing stops progress in athletics like an injury. There is no way that you will get stronger if you have an injured ligament, muscle, or tendon. It could also be stated without fear of contradiction that more athletes have been injured in an athletic program because they have failed to warm up properly than for any other reason. And this certainly applies to a weight program as much as it does to any sport.

A thorough warm-up period will insure you of a more successful workout and leave you less prone to injury. These two facts should make it quite clear just how important a warm-up period should be to every conscientious athlete.

Don't make the mistake of being in such a hurry to train that you do not take time to prepare your body properly. The famous trainer for the York Weightlifting Team, Dick Smith, constantly preaches to all his lifters, "If you don't have time to warm-up then you don't have time to train." I concur and hope that all athletes take to heart the necessity of warming up thoroughly and the importance of flexibility exercises to the overall strength program.   ★

5

CHAPTER FIVE
THE BIG THREE OF WEIGHT TRAINING

THE KEY IS SIMPLICITY

THE KEY TO ANY successful strength program is simplicity. Coaches are invariably pressed for time, space, and equipment. They simply do not have the time to learn a dozen or so different exercises correctly no matter how important they might be. They cannot spend two hours a day supervising weight training activities and they cannot appropriate thousands of dollars to this segment of conditioning.

By utilizing the knowledge of strength building that has been accumulated over the past 20 years in the sport of competitive weightlifting and by applying that knowledge to the particular needs of the sport of football, "The Big Three" have been chosen as the core of my strength training program. The "Big Three" consists of: the bench press, the squat, and the power clean. These three simple, but effective exercises meet this all-important criteria of total simplicity in all ways.

RATIONALE BEHIND THE "BIG THREE"

The rationale behind choosing these three exercises over all the others available was really quite basic and simple once the problems of strength training were thoroughly analyzed. These are the three basic exercises used by weightlifters to increase their strength. Competitive weightlifters add to them, naturally, bringing in various movements to strengthen weaker points and also they practice skill movements such as the snatch and the clean and jerk so that they can apply the power to the sport.

The same general rule, it was theorized, should apply to football players. They, too, need overall body strength and they, too, need to practice the skills inherent to their particular sport. It was also realized that the football player, like the competitive weightlifter, must work for overall body strength as opposed to specific strengthening exercises — unless, of course, the football player is trying to build up a weak muscle or overcoming an injury. In other words, the athlete should be building total leg strength rather than just stronger hamstrings. He should be seeking overall strength

in this shoulder girdle rather than just stronger deltoids.

It was also obvious that the football player must have exercise that would not limit his other athletic attributes, such as speed, flexibility, and coordination. This is not a foreign problem to the competitive weightlifter as anyone could testify who has watched the Olympic lifter in action. He, too, must increase his strength while at the same time, increase those before-mentioned qualities through the use of weights. So, by taking the principles available from the sport of weightlifting, it was felt that this goal could be accomplished.

WHY ONLY THREE EXERCISES?

The question is often asked, "Why only three exercises? Isn't the bent-over row a good exercise for the lower back?" Or, "Isn't the curl great for upper arm strength?" Since these same questions may be on the reader's mind, they will be answered up front. Of course these exercises are good. There are terrific individual movements for each and every muscle in the body, but again, simplicity is the key to success in a systematic strength program for athletes. A program that attempts to cover every body part by way of specific individual exercises is more difficult to put into effect in a school situation. This is why this program is built around three basic exercises.

The pure researcher lends support for selecting these three over all others. Through various studies, it has been shown that in order to increase strength, an individual has to overload the muscles involved for a short period of time. Once that individual muscle group has been worked thoroughly and sufficiently, then more work not only does not help, it actually detracts from progress. Too much work, then, on a particular muscle group literally weakens rather than strengthens.

The "Big Three" stimulates all the major muscle groups in the body without overly tiring any of them. The bench press involves the triceps, deltoids, pectorals, and to a lesser degree, the lats. The power clean brings into play the legs, hip girdle, lower, middle and upper back as well as the biceps and deltoids. The back squat: all the muscles of the leg, the hip and lower back. Only the abdominals have been missed and these are exercised in the pre-workout warm-up. So it is contended, if these three exercises can do the entire job, why add more? The only answer deals with variety and there are provisions for that variable further along in the program. But the "Big Three" can get the job done and it meets the basic criterion of simplicity very nicely.

The program is fast, simple, and, most importantly, effective. It requires very little space and a minimum of equipment. The circuit method is utilized and it has been found that a group of 40 players can go through the entire series in less than an hour. An individual can do his program in 20 minutes on the light days and in 45 minutes on the heavy days. Only three stations are required which makes it possible for small schools on tight budgets to finally inaugurate a strength program. A small amount of space is required and this is a relief as every school is cramped for extra space. Finally, it is simple to supervise. The coach can keep his eye on all three stations, encourage his players and spot them for safety. The program meets all requirements for individual and group training.

RESULTS ARE QUITE POSITIVE

The program has been tested in hundreds of schools and colleges over a ten-year span. Some programs were adapted to meet the individual requirements of time and space in various schools, but basically the program remained the same. Apart from personally setting up numerous programs, I also directed many other coaches from all over the country who inquired by phone or mail or talked with me at demonstrations and clinics. I simply lost count with this category as it was done on an almost daily basis.

I always asked the coaches to report back to me and they always seemed more than happy to do so. The results were even more fantastic than I had expected. There were no failures. Some had limited success, due mainly to the fact that they were handicapped in time or equipment to implement the program to its fullest, but all reported some degree of progress. Some came back with reports of 60-70% strength increases. Losing seasons became winning seasons. Weight training athletes become All-Staters. Some coaches were most pleased with the way their team sustained their hustle throughout the entire game. Their margin of victory came in the fourth quarter as the less-conditioned opponents gave out. Yet other coaches commented that injuries had been cut in half as a result of the strength program.

I feel that this is the first totally sensible strength program which is flexible enough to be applied to any situation. Junior high school players could use it right alongside the pro teams. Only the poundage lifted woud be changed.

THE "BEST" WAY TO INCREASE STRENGTH

I believe The "Big Three" to be the best way to increase over-all body strength for the sport of football. This does not mean it is the only way — only the best way. There are other methods which will get the job done, but they will either take more time, equipment, or supervision to get the same goal. The chapters on machine training will explain my position on the universal machine and the Nautilus equipment. There is no question that any form of resistive training will result in strength gains, but the free weights, when used properly, are still the **best** method of gaining strength.

THE FULL SQUAT CONTROVERSY

This, perhaps, is the ideal spot in the book to discuss the full squat as opposed to the half or partial squat. Every coach, every trainer, weight trainer, parent, and grandmother has heard that full squats damage the knees. People who do not know the difference between a barbell and kitchen stove still know that full squats injure the knees.

So why do I advocate full squats. Am I in league with the local orthopedic surgeons? Maybe I own stock in ace bandages. In truth, I recommend full squats because I believe that they are better for overall strength development and also because they help to protect the knees better than half squats. Unbelievable?

DR. KLEIN'S STUDY

A bit of history is in order. In the early sixties, Dr. Karl K. Klein of the University of Texas, published a piece of research which concluded that full squats loosened the knee joint and, therefore, the exercise was harmful to the knees — especially to those engaged in contact sports such as football. As a result, coaches across the nation forbid their players from doing full squats. Some states, such as New Jersey, even outlawed full squats in secondary schools — a rather absurd ruling in the light of the other problems inherent in secondary schools. If coaches allowed their trainees to squat at all, they only gave their ok to half or quarter squats.

Dr. Klein tested a group of 128 competitive weightlifters who had done full squats against 386 college students who had no such experience. He concluded that the weightlifting group had unstable collateral and anterior cruciate ligaments as a result of the squatting and advised against performing the full-range movement.

I was a member of the Southern Methodist University weightlifting team during this time and served as a subject for Dr. Klein's testing on two separate occasions. I have always contended that this study needs to be examined more closely as it was not conducted under rigid testing procedures. Dr. Klein used an aluminum gadget for his test which covered the upper and lower leg much like a leg cast. He exerted pressure from each side of the knee and took a reading on a dial similar to a blood pressure gauge. Dr. Klein always inquired whether the subject did full squats before he conducted his test.

OBJECTIONS TO DR. KLEIN'S RESEARCH

My dispute with the testing procedures centers around two main objections. One, the applying of the pressure was far too subjective. The tester could push harder and harder on the knee joint and secure a pre-determined reading. Many athletes complained that the tester actually hurt their knees because he pushed so hard. Did he push equally hard on each subject? Two, the tester always had the subject classified as a squatter or non-squatter **before** he tested him, rather than after. This certainly gave the tester the opportunity to have a built-in prejudice and eliminates the testing procedure from the pure, controlled category.

By applying the same testing procedure, another researcher, with an eye to reversing the findings, could quite easily do so. A pure piece of research should not have this wide margin of testing subjectivity unless it is specifically spelled out in the conclusion, which it definitely was not in this case.

COMPETITIVE WEIGHTLIFTERS WERE SUBJECTS

Another objection I voice against this study is that Dr. Klein used competitive weightlifters as his full squatting subjects. It certainly is true, of course, that weightlifters do perform full squats. What was not recorded, however, was that these athletes also perform heavy squat cleans, squat snatches, and jerks — all of which put a greater stress on the ligaments and tendons of the knees than do full squats. These Olympic lifting movements are snappy and quick. The lifter jams into a deep squatting position in cleaning a heavy weight. This combination of hitting the bottom position of the squat clean rapidly, along with the great resistance applied by the barbell, could certainly cause tendon stretching. It is a hazard of the sport which every lifter knowingly recognizes.

The full squat, when performed as I recommend for football players does not entail: 1) hitting a deep position or, 2) going to the bottom-most position quickly. In effect, the wrong exercise has been given the villian's role. Dr. Klein missed this point because he knew too little about the sport of Olympic weightlifting, or he merely overlooked this important fact.

Ironically enough, Dr. Klein followed up his study of the effect of full squats on the knees of weightlifters by testing 95 paratroopers who performed squat jump exercises. Ligamentous instability was found in the knees of the paratroopers similar to that found in weightlifters. No doubt. It's the jamming motion, rather than the squat itself doing the damage. Strange that the researcher did not see the connection.

It is a recognized fact that joint stability can be increased through resistive exercises of the supporting musculature. If this basic fact holds true, then certainly exercises which strengthen the muscles, tendons, and ligaments of the knee will make that joint more secure.

FULL-RANGE MOVEMENTS

Another point worth mentioning. It is equally recognized that full-range movements build more strength in the muscles and tendons simply because more fibers become involved. It logically follows that full squats work more muscles than do half squats, just as a full-range curling motion brings into play more muscles of the upper arm than does a partial curling movement.

The culprit is not the full-range movements but the stretching of the tendons and ligaments that results when the trainee bounces at the bottom-most position. I know that the more muscles an athlete involves in a single exercise, the better the exercise for over-all development. Full squats involve more muscles than half squats. Should you doubt this assertion, merely try a few sets of high repetition full squats after a period of only performing half squats. The insides of your thighs, your gluteus maximus and your lower back will all experience a new soreness, after doing full squats.

A MORE RECENT STUDY SUPPORTS FULL SQUATS

Earle Meyers performed a rather involved study on the "Effect of selected exercise variable on ligament stability and flexibility of the knee" and reported his findings in the **Research Quarterly** (42:4, 1971).

He found that flexibility was greater in the full squat group as compared to those who used the half squat. He also found that lateral collateral ligament stretch **decreased** after both full and half squats and medial collateral ligament stretch **decreased** after the deep squat. Deep squatting with light and maximum poundages also brought about equal quadriceps strength gains as maximum half squats.

These findings, along with others done on the subject of full squats, were in direct conflict with the Texas professor. The later scientists concluded that full squats, when performed correctly, were actually beneficial to the knee joint as they built up the muscles, tendons, and ligaments that support the knee. In fact, strength around the knee joint was the best protection against injury and this could best be developed by full-range motions like the full squat. When used in conjunction with leg extensions and leg bicep curls, full squats served to protect, rather than damage that crucial area.

Dan Audick, now with the St. Louis Cardinals, built tremendous hip and leg power with the full squat.

THE DANGERS OF BOUNCING OFF THE BOTTOM

All researchers agreed, however, that any bouncing or rebounding would stretch the tendons and ligaments and cause damage to the joint. This was not news to the weightlifter. He had been advocating full squats right through the controversy and insisting that full squats, correctly performed, were far superior than partial movements. The sound reasoning is that any joint will be damaged if a jamming or rebounding occurs in an exercise. Start bouncing a curl at full extension and the elbow will soon become sore. So what the researcher has found is that the full squat per se was not the villian, but rather the improper manner in which it was performed.

As a result, the full squat once again found its way into the athlete's training schedule and rightfully so since no other single exercise can do so much for hip and leg power.

SUMMARY OF THE FULL SQUAT CONTROVERSY

In summary, I must reemphasize the fact that deep squats work more muscles than any form of partial squats since they involve a full-range motion. Since the full squats work more muscles, they enable the trainee to become stronger faster than through partial movements. Full squats are safe for the knees if they are performed correctly. The correctness in this case means specifically that the athlete does not bounce or rebound from the deep position. Research has shown that full squats actually helps to stabilize and secure the knee joint.

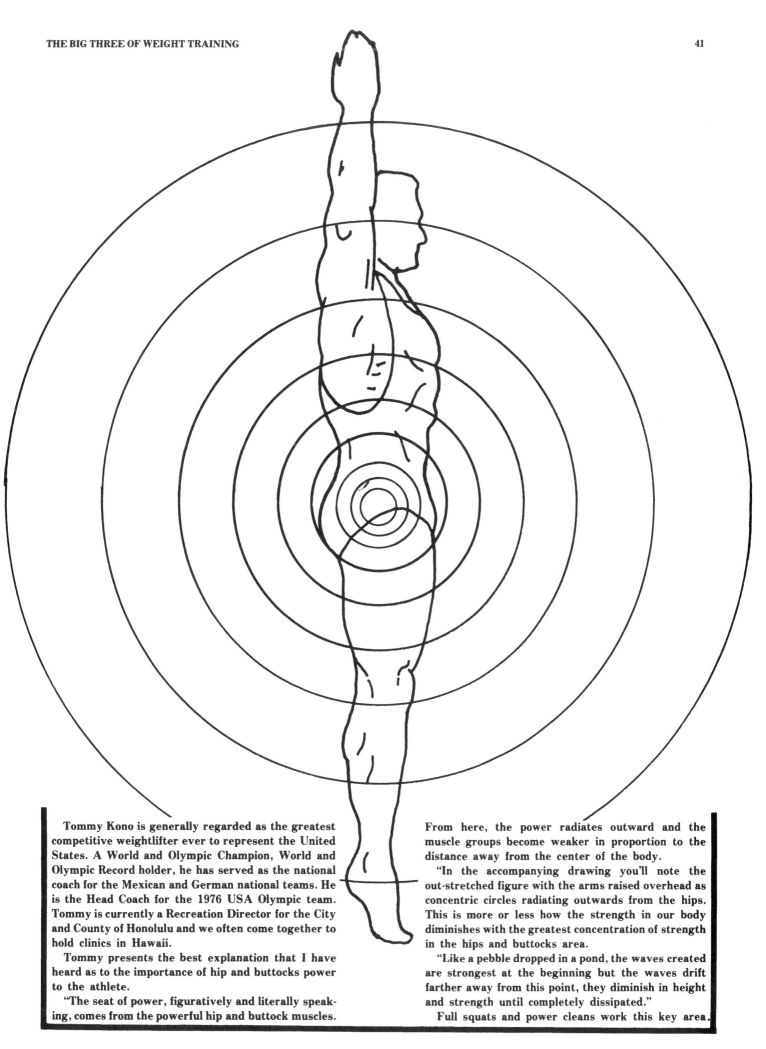

Tommy Kono is generally regarded as the greatest competitive weightlifter ever to represent the United States. A World and Olympic Champion, World and Olympic Record holder, he has served as the national coach for the Mexican and German national teams. He is the Head Coach for the 1976 USA Olympic team. Tommy is currently a Recreation Director for the City and County of Honolulu and we often come together to hold clinics in Hawaii.

Tommy presents the best explanation that I have heard as to the importance of hip and buttocks power to the athlete.

"The seat of power, figuratively and literally speaking, comes from the powerful hip and buttock muscles.

From here, the power radiates outward and the muscle groups become weaker in proportion to the distance away from the center of the body.

"In the accompanying drawing you'll note the out-stretched figure with the arms raised overhead as concentric circles radiating outwards from the hips. This is more or less how the strength in our body diminishes with the greatest concentration of strength in the hips and buttocks area.

"Like a pebble dropped in a pond, the waves created are strongest at the beginning but the waves drift farther away from this point, they diminish in height and strength until completely dissipated."

Full squats and power cleans work this key area.

THE BIG THREE — THE BENCH PRESS

Exercises modeled by Arnold Morgado

EXPLANATION OF EXERCISES

The Bench Press

The bench press involves the muscles of the chest (pectorals), the upper arm (triceps), and shoulder caps (frontal and lateral deltoids). In other words, the muscles that make up the shoulder girdle. Some anatomy writers do not like the term shoulder girdle since it isn't really a girdle, but it adequately and simply explains my point and that is the purpose of this book, to convey uncluttered information in an understandable way, so I will utilize this term.

Lie on the bench in a supine position, that is, lying with your back on the bench facing upward. Strangely enough, the bench press has been referred to as the prone press for years, but obviously someone forgot to check their physiology handbook as the prone position is facing downward and this would make the lift exceedingly tough. Grip the bar at approximately shoulder width. This grip can be varied to suit individual preference and need. It should be remembered that the grip somewhat determines what portion of the pectorals is stimulated.

The grip recommended for football players is a close grip just about two inches wider than were the knurl begins on the Olympic bar. Keep the arms tucked to the sides rather than allowing them to point out to the sides. This motion more closely duplicates the movement used by the football player when he is delivering a blow to his opponent. A wider grip with the elbows outward will not as closely emulate this motion. The muscles developed in the weight room are to be utilized in the sport, so the closer you come to the actual movement you wish to strengthen for the game, the better.

Lower the loaded barbell slowly to a point just below the center of the chest at a point at the end of your sternum. The

closer grip forces you to touch this low on your chest. Touch the chest to insure a full range of motion and extend the bar in a quick motion back to arms' length. The bar, to reiterate, should be lowered slowly and extended rapidly. There is a reason for this. By lowering the bar slowly you can be sure of keeping it in the same groove on each and every repetition. This is critical for long-range progress. You should not be bouncing the weight off your chest. Down, pause and explode upward.

The quick upward thrust builds speed directly into the muscle. You are, in effect, teaching the muscles to react quickly. This is essentially how the body learns. You "think" speed into every exercise and the muscles of the body literally "learn" to react in this manner. This learning carries over to any and all athletic endeavors. Conversely, if the movements are performed slowly, then those muscles only know how to react in a slow manner so they cannot be expected to move quickly on the gridiron. Teach them to explode in the workout room and they will explode on the playing field.

Keep your hips and back on the bench throughout the exercise. No bridging. You might be able to handle more weight initially but, you can never determine whether your improvement is a result of new strength or just better bridging technique. Concentrate the work directly on the muscles. Keep your hips flat from the very first and you will soon discover that the progress will come quicker because you are building pure muscle strength.

As the bar leaves your chest, you should try to move it in a slight arch so that it finishes just over your eyes. The bar, then, does not move in a true straight vertical course. It

THE BIG THREE — THE BENCH PRESS

moves from a point from the center of your chest to a point at the center of your head. There's a good reason for this curving motion. The muscles that move the bar off your chest are the frontal deltoids and the pectorals. They are responsible for 75% of the lift. That portion of the lift is straight upward, but once the bar has passed ¾ of its route, the triceps must come into play in order to complete a heavy lift. (Lighter weights are often handled incorrectly but few succeed with a maximum poundage with incorrect form.) By moving the bar slightly backward the triceps can be utilized to their fullest and the bar can be successfully locked out.

Inhale and exhale only while the bar is at the locked arms position. Hold your breath while performing the movement. Actually, for the warm-up poundages it really isn't necessary to breathe at all until the last rep is finished as it only takes a matter of 5-6 seconds to do the required repetitions. On maximum lifts, hold your breath during exertion and breathe as soon as the bar is securely past the sticking points.

As soon as you get up from the bench, grab that piece of rope mentioned earlier or if that is not available a towel will do. Grip it as wide as necessary and hold it directly over your head with your arms straight and elbows locked. Now do some shoulder dislocates, about a dozen will be sufficient. This little exercise keeps the shoulders loose throughout the training period. Many players have found that their shoulder flexibility was greatly increased by the addition of this simple stretching exercise. It's an ideal time to do it because the shoulders are warmed up very thoroughly. Make it a part of the exercise itself and you'll never have to worry about tightness in this area.

THE BIG THREE — THE POWER CLEAN

The Power Clean

The "athlete's exercise." If your program only allowed you to do one exercise, this would be the best. The muscles involved are: upper and lower leg, hip girdle, lower, middle and upper back, the upper arm and the forearms. In fact, there are so many muscles involved in this movement that if they were listed this section would read like an anatomy chart. Suffice it to say that the power clean is a most complete single exercise.

Step up to the loaded barbell so that your legs are just about touching the bar. Push your chest out, look straight ahead and reach down and grip the barbell. Your grip will naturally fall at about shoulder width. Keep your lower back very flat and your arms perfectly straight. Ease the bar off the floor slowly. Do not try to pull it off the floor quickly as this will make you break the proper position. As the bar passes your knees, bring the hips forward very rapidly. Almost at the same time, perhaps merely a fraction of a second later, pull with the muscles of the upper back (trapezius) and the arms (biceps and brachioradialis).This will bring the bar to shoulder level. Now bring the elbows

under the bar and let it rack on your pectorals and frontal deltoids. Lower the bar cautiously, making sure that you keep the same flat back on the downward route. Stop. Reset your body position and repeat the movement.

Breathe both at the start and finish of the power clean but hold your breath during the exertion. On lighter warm-up weights, you will be able to do all the reps on a single breath.

You will quickly discover just how important the factor of speed is once you begin this exercise. You must move the bar quickly once it clears the floor. The hips snap towards the bar, the traps contract violently and the arms finish the motion — all in a flash. A loaded barbell does not stay suspended in the air for very long. This speed developed in this lift is carried over onto the playing field. Since the motion of the power clean is very akin to the motion of the player coming off the line and striking his opponent, it has a special merit for football players. The upward snap of the bar almost duplicates the thrust of the forearm shiver. The striking blow delivered by the lineman is strengthened tremendously by this single exercise as identical muscles are

THE BIG THREE — THE POWER CLEAN

involved.

The bar needs to be pulled close to the body in order to achieve maximum performance. The mechanics of the body levers favor the bar being next to the body on its complete route. It should be against the shins at the start, pass just over the knees, brush the stomach and chest as it passes them. If the bar hangs too far from the body, even so much as an inch or two, the big muscles of the upper back are not in as favorable a positon to contract completely and this, naturally, limits the amount of weight that can be used in the exercise.

As the bar passes the hips and you are about to give the final lift with your arms, do not let your elbows float backward. The elbows should lift directly to the sides and be pointed upward at the conclusion of the lift. If you begin pulling backward you will limit the poundage used once again because you are not using the best possible body leverage. If you find the bar knocking you slightly backward at the end of each lift, you can rest assured that you are pulling back rather than up on the bar.

Another by-product of the power clean is the terrific cardiovascular work it gives to your body. A few, quick sets with a heavy weight (relatively speaking) leaves even the most conditioned athlete sucking for oxygen. When used in a circuit, this exercise can do wonders for an overall conditioning program. It has, in short, great fitness value along with being a most excellent strength building exercise.

THE BIG THREE — THE BACK SQUAT

THE BACK SQUAT

The squat, or deep-knee bend, works all of the muscles of the leg (leg biceps, quadriceps, gastrocnemius), hip girdle, gluetus maximus and lower back. These various muscles can be almost pinpointed on your body after the first workout involving this exercise.

Place the loaded barbell across the back of your neck. If the bar lays heavy on your neck and creates a great deal of discomfort, then wrap a towel or piece of rubber tubing around it until you become accustomed to the pressure.

Spread your feet slightly wider than shoulder width with your toes pointed slightly outward. Keep your head pointed upward and an arch in your lower back. Go down slowly to a just below parallel position. Stop momentarily. This is an important point to always remember, for if a pause is built into every rep, there can be no rebounding. Do not relax when you stop, however, but stay tight so that you do not round your lower back and break position.

There is a certain amount of flexibility involved in going into a full squat, although it may appear to be a simple movement. Most players are not flexible enough in the ankles to go to the bottom without rounding over at first. After a time, they will be able to sink lower and lower and still keep a perfectly flat back. This is the key point, as long as the trainee keeps his back flat he can go as low as he likes. If he starts rounding, that's the place to stop.

If you find that you cannot hold your balance in the bottom position without tipping forward, place a block under your

heels until you obtain the flexibility in your hips and ankles to do so. You will find that squats stretch the calf muscles and actually allow you more range of motion than previously. Use the block only as long as you have to, as this flexibility in the back of the leg is most desirable.

Come out of the bottom position quickly. Think of exploding upward. Make the plates rattle at the top of the thrust. It is this upward thrust that builds the quick starts off the line and as was mentioned previously, you teach the muscles to react quickly by "thinking" speed into every single exercise.

Breathe only at the standing position. Inhale, holding your breath throughout the movement, and exhale as you come back erect. When you are handling the heaviest weight, your maximum, you may want to take two or three good, deep breaths before going down.

As you come out of the bottom, lift your head upward. This flattens the lower back and keeps you from rounding over. It puts the full stress on the legs and this, of course, is the purpose of the exercise.

I have the players go as low as they can just so long as their backs remain flat. Once the lower back rotates under, I feel that they are too deep and I caution them to cut it off just a bit higher on the next rep.

Some coaches, in the light of the anti-full squat controversy, decided that bench squats would serve as an adequate substitute, but it has been found that bench squats **can be**

THE BIG THREE — THE BACK SQUAT

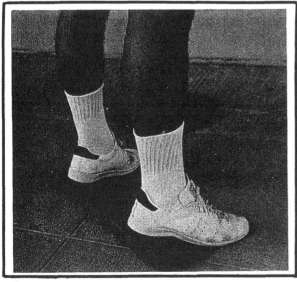

harmful if not closely supervised. The trainee should never sit on the bench and relax with the weight on his back. If a bench is used the trainee should just touch and come back up. The relaxing tends to put a great deal of pressure on the lower back and this is to be avoided.

The power rack is ideal for squats since the pins can be set at the exact lower position for each athlete. This is much better than a bench as every person is of a different height and hence, his bottom position is going to be different also. The pins also act as a perfect safeguard in case the trainee gets stuck under the weight. In that case, he merely lets the bar settle on the pins and walks out from under the rack.

THE OVERHEAD PRESS

THE IMPORTANT OTHERS

While it was firmly stated that this program only entails three exercises, it might seem a bit contradictory to explain more specific exercises in the program. Actually, however, I am not going back on our original declaration.

The "Big Three" are the core exercises of the program. They are not, however, the only exercises in the total program. There are many, many other exercises to build strength. Some specific ones are used very rarely, while others are used most frequently. A number of these will be described further along in the book. All have a role to play in the acquisition of strength.

The overhead press is used in place of the bench press in certain circumstances. It serves as a change of pace from the bench press. Once the athlete reaches a certain level of proficiency he should not do bench pressing every workout. Rather, he should overhead press once a week and bench press twice. This allows the muscles involved in benching to rest a bit, but they still receive stimulation as a result of the overhead pressing movement. Sort of a case of having your cake and eating it too.

Then, too, the overhead press is recommended to replace the bench press for some particular positions and some individual players. Defensive backs and linebackers, for example, need the overhead work more than the interior linemen, so they usually work overhead presses into their programs from the very onset, alternating them with benches.

The leg hyperextensions and leg bicep curls are quite important as was mentioned in the section on full squats. They can insure stronger muscles that protect the knee joint. If a hyperextension machine is available, these two exercises will conclude every session, but they are not major energy movements and are done only after the large muscle groups have been exercised. They are, quite obviously, preventive exercises.

The same holds true for the sit-up and/or leg raise. These exercises serve as warm-ups and do not tap into the energy level of the trainee. They are described specifically as it is important to do each and every exercise correctly.

THE OVERHEAD PRESS

The Overhead Press

The overhead press, sometimes referred to as the military press, works the shoulder caps (deltoids), back of the upper arm (triceps) and upper portions of the back (trapezius) and chest (pectorals). This exercise can be done either standing or while seated.

Once again you will be utilizing the squat or power rack for this exercise. Grip the bar 1" wider than shoulder width. Take the loaded barbell off the rack so that it lies across your frontal deltoids and high portion of your pectorals. Assume a firm, upright body position. Your feet, if you stand, should be set at shoulder width and your body perfectly erect. Do not bow backward as you want the stress to be placed on the muscles of the shoulders, not the lower back. Push the bar directly overhead, keeping the head pointed straight ahead.

Breathe at the lock-out position, lower the bar slowly so that it touches your deltoids once again and repeat. As in the bench press, the downward motion of the bar should be slow and the upward one explosive.

The important point to learn in this exercise is to keep everything very, very tight, i.e. your thighs, hips, buttocks, lower and middle back. If any point relaxes, you will experience the "accordion effect" and not be able to push with a 100% effort.

Do not "jump" the weight with your legs at the start of the press. Make the muscles of the shoulders do all the work, not the legs. Keep the bar very close to your face. It has to pass right next to your nose so that the triceps can take over and lock the bar out overhead. If it travels away from your face you will have to bow out to bring the bar back over the center of your head and this is not recommended, as this movement puts an undue strain on the lower back.

Use the lifting belt in this exercise. It keeps the back warm and does serve to protect the lower back. Regardless of whether a belt is worn or not, do not bow under the bar. The body should be kept vertical so that the shoulders do all the work.

THE LEG EXTENSION

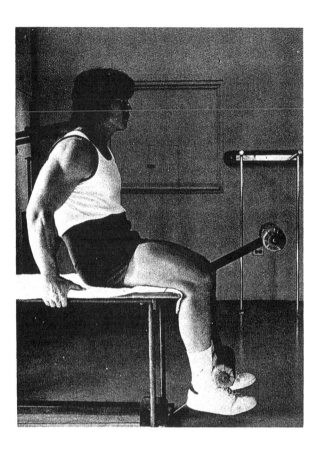
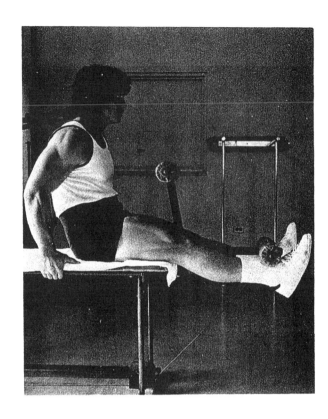

Leg Extensions

The specific muscles, tendons and ligaments worked in the knee joint itself are worth mentioning once again, as they are the ones that really hold this joint together. The gastrocnemius, hamstrings and quadriceps attach themselves to bones after they cross the knee. The gastrocnemius attaches just above the knee joint and slightly behind and laterally to it. The hamstrings attach just below, behind and laterally and the quadriceps below and in front. Also involved in stabilizing the knees are the: lateral collateral ligament, biceps femoris tendon, posterior cruciate ligament, anterior cruciate ligament, medial collateral ligament, anterior and posterior cruciate ligaments. The patella ligament, running from bone to bone, is actually a tendon of the quadriceps muscle group.

The leg hyperextension works those tendons, ligaments and muscles that lift the lower leg upward. They extend the lower leg so that the knee locks into position. By adding resistance to this simple movement, the muscles, tendons, and ligaments involved are strengthened and hence are better able to perform their function.

PERFORMANCE

Sit erect on the hyperextension machine (actually a table with weight bearing padded bars attached for the feet to hook under) and place your feet under the padded extension. Be sure that you are stable and comfortable. Hold onto the sides of the table for balance. If the extension hurts your feet, add something for padding, like a towel or piece of foam rubber.

Lift the bar upward in a quick motion until you have achieved full extension of the leg. Now resist momentarily at that top-most position before returning the bar to the starting position. Lower the weight slowly. Do not rebound the bar off the machine. Let it dead stop before doing the next rep. On the final rep, resist as long at that top, full hyperextended position as possible.

THE LEG BICEPS CURL

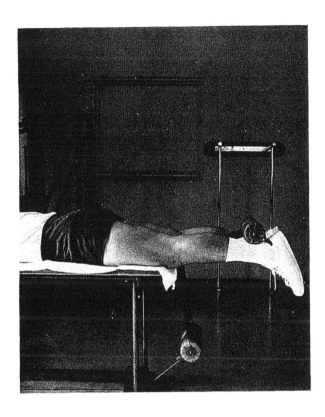
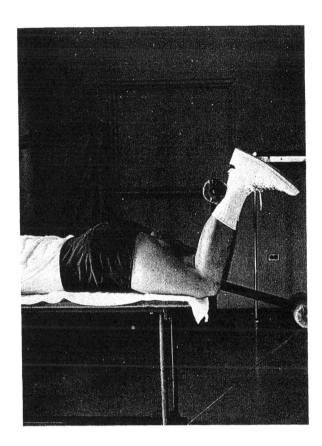

Leg Biceps Curls

As the name so implies, the leg biceps curls work the back portion of the leg involving the biceps femoris, semitendinosus, semimembranosus and other muscles generally referred to as the hamstring group. This exercise also involves the gluteus maximus. The leg biceps curls may appear to be merely a token exercise, but actually it is a most critical one for football players. It has been found that many knee injuries occur because the leg biceps were so relatively weak in proportion to the frontal portion of the thighs. The quadriceps got stronger from constant running, but the hamstrings do not get enough full action in simple running to sufficiently strengthen them. It's the old tale of the weakest link.

Most football players can handle twice the poundage in the leg hyperextensions than they can in the leg biceps curls. Some were found to be so weak in that area that they could barely do 25 pounds for 10 repetitions. Most do twice as much in the hyperextensions as they do in the leg biceps curls. This degree in disparity is certainly not healthy. Ideally, you should work for a 3 to 2 ratio. When this difference drops below 50%, the chance of knee injury greatly increases.

PERFORMANCE

Lie in the prone position on the leg hyperextension machine and hook the back of your heels under the padded bar. This position varies somewhat depending on the height of the trainee and the particular make of the machine. Bring your heels up towards your lower back until your leg is in a vertical position. Try to keep your hips flat against the bench as the stress needs to be placed primarily on the leg biceps rather than on the buttocks and lower back. Lower the bar back to the starting position slowly and do not allow the weight to bounce off the bottom position.

Resist the bar as it is lowered so that the leg biceps get the full benefit of the movement. As the repetitions get more difficult and you find you cannot do as many reps as you are scheduled for, still continue to pull the bar up with your legs as far as possible. Work for a complete flush as this increased circulation in the specific area will do much to tone and strengthen the muscle.

THE SIT-UP

Sit-Ups

The sit-up works the muscles of the midsection: rectus abdominis, external obliques, internal obliques and transverse abdominis. All of these are brought into some degree of play although the primary work is for the higher portion of the abdominal muscles, those nestled just under the chest. The sit-up and leg raises are ideal exercises to use to warm up the all-important midsection and the internal organs.

If a sit-up board is available, you're way ahead because it's much easier to do them on this piece of equipment. If you have to do them flat, then they are not as strenuous so you will have to do quite a few more to achieve the same result, but they will still serve the purpose of a warm-up.

Two very important points to remember while performing this simple exercise: 1) Keep your knees bent at all times, and 2) keep a constant tension on the abdominal muscles. The bent knees keeps the stress off the lower back and directly on the muscles concerned. The constant tension insures total work in less time. Squeeze the muscles tight at the conclusion of each repetition and do not let them relax at any point. Do not set yourself any specific number of reps. Rather, do as many as you can and add to this each week. If you do, say 25, the first week, try to do 30 the second week and 35 the third and so forth until you are soon able to do 100 in a single set.

Do not use any resistance at all. You want to keep them toned, but you do not want to build them up so that they are thick and bulgy. This gives you a pot-bellied appearance. As you become more proficient in this exercise just add reps and increase the angle of the sit-up board, do not add weight.

THE LEG RAISE

Leg Raises

The leg raise is the companion exercise to the sit-up and works the lower portion of the abdominals, those which attach directly to the pubis. Lie on the sit-up board with it set at about a 30 degree slant, if this is possible. Grasp the board with your hands behind your head securely, bend your knees and lift your feet to a vertical position. Do not let your feet come all the way back over your head as this allows the abdominals to relax. Keep a constant tension on the muscles and do not let your feet rest back to the floor or the board. If you are doing these on a flat surface, only lift your legs to a 45 degree angle and do not let your heels touch the floor.

Together, the leg raise and sit-up enable the trainee to begin each work out with a thoroughly warm trunk — an extremely important measure. The two abdominal exercises do, in fact, tone the midsection but they should not be utilized exclusively to lose extra inches from around the midsection. This is better accomplished through diet. Check the section on losing weight in the nutritional chapter for more specifics on this subject. By doing midsection exercises, you can assure yourself of having toned muscles once the excess poundage is eliminated from around the middle, but diet is the key in this particular problem, not exercise.

EQUIPMENT REQUIREMENTS

In describing the equipment which is needed for this program I will begin with the ideal and work back to the less than ideal. In other words, if the school budget allows the privilege of spending the money for the preferred equipment — fine and dandy. If not, improvisation is necessary and I have some tips on that too.

To implement the program to perfection, you should have three Olympic sets, a bench, a squat or power rack, a leg hyperextension machine and a sit-up board. The Olympic sets are the absolute best of the free weights and almost a necessity for movements such as the power clean for the simple reason that the inner bar revolves while the outside plates do not. On standard bars, the lifter has to turn the plates over as he rotates the bar and this cuts down considerably on the amount of weight that can be used in the exercise. The Olympic set enables the athlete to handle more poundage in the bench and squat as well, and, obviously, the more weight handled, the stronger the athlete becomes.

There have been occasions, at clinics and demonstrations, where coaches who trained themselves stepped forward so that they could benefit from our supervision. Almost to the man, they increased the weight they were using in any given lift because of the convenience of the Olympic bar. This personal awareness was usually testimony enough to get them to spend the few extra dollars on an Olympic set.

The bench selected for this program ideally should be an extra-heavy duty one, with the supports set wide apart rather than close together. Oftentimes, coaches will economize and purchase a less than adequate bench only to find that it becomes extremely shaky and actually dangerous. The benches with the close uprights also seem to have the

nasty habit of pinching fingers at regular intervals. The advantage of the wide supports is that a variety of gripping positions can be utilized. Smaller players as well as the larger ones can grip the bar in the most preferred position.

A strong solid bench is not a luxury, but rather a necessity if safety is honestly considered. It should be realized from the very onset that eventually many of the larger players will be handling over 300 pounds in the bench press and in all likelihood some will exceed 400 pounds. Add their bodyweight from anywhere between 200 and 250+ and it can be quickly calculated that the bench must support as much as 650+ pounds. To suggest having an individual, regardless of his value to the team, lie on his back on a shaky bench while attempting to lift a maximum weight says something about the basic concern of the coach for the player.

A sturdy squat or power rack is also necessary for heavy squats. While it is possible to have fellow trainees assist the athlete in placing the loaded barbell on his back, it is exceedingly awkward and, once again, limits the poundage used in the exercise. There are a number of good choices for the squat rack. The two most popular are the stair-case type and the power rack. Both serve somewhat the same purpose and coaches like them because they allow the trainee to walk out from under the weight safely if he should get stuck at the bottom-most position. A power rack can be used for a wide variety of movements from squatting, bench pressing, overhead pressing, and many advanced exercises.

The leg hyperextension machine should also be selected for durability. There are a number on the market and nearly all are alike. The primary criterion is that it is functional for the entire team — some are only suitable for one leg length — and that it's able to hold up under lots of wear and tear as football players are rough on equipment. I personally stay

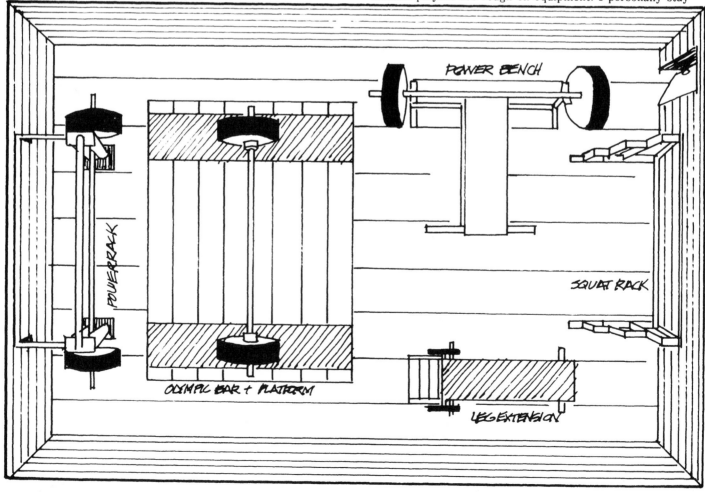

POWER RACK

OLYMPIC BAR + PLATFORM

POWER BENCH

SQUAT RACK

LEG EXTENSION

away from all which utilize cables as, regardless of their test strength, they all break in a heavy training gym. I prefer the type which are mechanically simple, the type which standard or Olympic weights can be added to directly.

The same rule holds true for the sit-up board, or boards if possible. It should be of the stair-case type so that the angle can be varied. The sit-up board should be made out of a strong piece of timber as the players really give it a workout. Try to check on the various types at a sporting goods dealer or a sporting goods show before selecting as it's extremely difficult to judge true quality in a catalog. A sit-up board should be padded so that it is comfortable and not rough at the point of contact.

The total cost of setting up an ideal facility with three 320-pound Olympic sets, an extra-heavy-duty bench, a squat rack, a leg hyperextension machine, and a sit-up board is just at $1750 depending somewhat on the quality of merchandise selected. The individual breakdown looks like this:

3 Olympic sets (320 pounds) @ $325 each	$ 975
1 Heavy duty bench press	150
1 Squat rack (stair-case or power rack)	150
1 Leg hyperextension machine	200
1 Sit-up board	75
	$1550
approximate shipping	110
sales tax (where applicable)	90
TOTAL	$1750

Since I mentioned earlier that the program outlined could apply to smaller schools with limited budgets, I have included a few suggestions for implementing a weight program when the dollars are tight.

Advertise in the school or local paper for used weights. It is amazing how many tons of barbells and barbell plates are sitting in garages and attics gathering dust and rust. A small town in central Indiana gathered together six Olympic sets and 2,000 pounds of standard plates with a simple notice on the sports page that the football team wanted to start a weight program but could not afford to buy the weights. The town responded remarkably well. Naturally, such fantastic success in every case cannot be guaranteed but you can be assured that you will come up with some amount of equipment if you really dig around.

Much of this prescribed equipment can be made. If there is a school shop it can be done there. If not, locate a welder and design the equipment. Some of the finest sit-up boards are homemade. Likewise, homemade benches, squat racks and power racks are generally as durable as the purchased ones. I have been able to make everything, but the actual bars and weights, and they served the purpose as well as purchased equipment. Fitness equipment carries healthy mark-up, so even if you have to carry the cost of the material you are still way ahead dollar-wise. Oftentimes, too, the homemade equipment can be specifically tailored to meet your team's needs perfectly and could be really better for your program than the standard designed merchandise.

Either design your own bench, squat rack, power rack, or sit-up board or go to a facility that has such equipment (YMCA, health club, sporting goods store) and check that design.

The only items that are nearly impossible to duplicate are the Olympic sets and the leg hyperextension machine. You may, however, substitute a standard bar for the Olympic set in the program if the budget is just too tight. If you can squeeze in just one Olympic set, use it for the power cleans and utilize the standard bars for the benches and the squats.

I have discovered that people are very ingenious once they become determined to have a weight program. They usually come up with the equipment they need by hook or crook. A coach who has his eyes on a winning season or a player who desires to improve his lot generally gets the needed tools together to accomplish his goal.

THOSE IMPORTANT EXTRAS

There are a few other pieces of equipment that should be in every training room as they are quite useful for a strength program, but I have separated them from the weights, benches and so forth because they really do not belong in that same category. Two strips of rubber serve to act as a cushion for the barbell plates on the power clean station. They reduce the noise, protect the floor and the barbell set from damage. Used rubber conveyor belt, the kind used on farm machinery, works nicely. So do old tires, cut into thin strips. Interlocking rubber squares can also be purchased from sporting goods companies. These have proven to be most effective in YMCA weight rooms. Rubber plates which fit the Olympic set are also useful and many schools find these worthwhile investments. They cost about twice as much as the metal ones.

Two other training aids which will prove to be useful are chalk and pieces of rope. The chalk (magnesium carbonate) is the same type used by gymnasts and helps absorb the sweat so that the bar can be held more securely. This item can be ordered through sporting goods distributors or purchased at the drug store.

The ropes will be used for stretching exercises. They can be of clothesline or the thicker variety. Cut pieces about four feet in length and tie 10 to 12 knots in them.

It is also recommended that you have a weightlifting belt in the weight room. This protective piece of equipment is most valuable for the athletes when they are performing heavy squats and any form of overhead work. The belt helps to keep the lower back warm and does give some degree of support.

The belt gives the beginning trainee a feeling of security and is well worth the investment for your program. They usually cost somewhere around $20. Be sure that you purchase one that is large enough to fit every player, or if possible, buy two or three of various sizes so that there is a belt that fits everyone fairly snug.

Straps will be needed for some of the advanced pulling exercises. These can be made quite easily from military belt, seat belt, or other similar material. They should be long enough to go around the wrist with an additional 6-10 inches to spare.

Before I leave the subject of equipment, let me mention a fact often overlooked by the uninformed concerning the Olympic weights. They do not get stolen as readily as standard plates. Standard plates are gathered up greedily to add to everyone's home gym, Olympic weights are not. There is a reasonable explanation for this strange fact: 1) Olympic plates only fit Olympic barbells, so there is no use stealing the plates unless you have an Olympic set at home, and 2) there is a certain fascination with the Olympic set. It spells quality and players seem to show their appreciation of this quality by leaving the weights where they belong. This fact has been confirmed to us over and over by coaches who direct such programs. The same reports come from YMCAs and health clubs. The standard plates go, but the Olympic plates stay. It's a fact worth remembering when making a procurement.   ★

CHAPTER SIX
PROGRAMMING THE "BIG THREE"

PROGRAMMING THE "BIG THREE"

ONCE I HAD SORTED out the specific exercises that would do the job most effectively, my next task was to assemble them into a working order. It was back to the research library to see what the pure scientists had uncovered on the subject. Surprisingly enough, the research was rather easy to come by and the conclusions were almost universally alike concerning the acquisition of strength.

SETS AND REPS

The researchers found that 4-6 repetitions of 4-6 sets, increasing the weight on each successive set, produced the most significant increase in strength. Terrific. I simplified the formula to five sets of five reps as that was the exact median and it was easy to remember. So the program would consist of five sets of five on each of the "Big Three" including the warm-up. For preventive exercises, such as the leg hyperextensions and leg biceps curls, three sets of 10-15 repetitions utilizing the same weight was found most beneficial. For midsection exercises, high reps with no resistance would fill the bill.

THREE DAYS A WEEK

Another look at the data and it revealed that three workouts a week was most sufficient for athletes as they should be engaged in skill practice of a particular sport on at least two days and at least two other days should be essentially rest days. So, three workout days a week is enough for the program to produce the desired results.

HEAVY, MEDIUM, LIGHT

It was also found that the trainee made faster progress if he did not handle maximum poundages at every work-out session. I merely installed the heavy-medium-light system that had been used by competitive weightlifters since Mark Berry came forth with this concept in the early '30's.

CIRCUIT METHOD

The circuit method of training is not a new concept either, but it fit perfectly into the total conditioning plan. It is also so much easier to train large groups of athletes with the circuit system. The circuit system simply means that the trainee does one set of an exercise and then moves on to the next exercise, and then to the next, before performing his second set of the initial movement. It is a preferred method because it insures all the major muscles of obtaining equal attention and an equal work load. A more specific example may be in order. The trainee does one set of power cleans, one set of bench presses, one set of squats and then goes through a second set of each in the same order. So on and so forth until the required five sets are completed.

If, on the other hand, all the bench presses are done before the trainee moves on to the power cleans and squats, then the shoulder girdle would receive the greatest effort as the energy level is much higher at the onset of training. Hence the bench press would improve much faster than the squats. This latter method is called the "Priority System" and is useful when a trainee needs to improve one area much more than the others. If, for example, the athlete is grossly deficient in leg power, it might be wise to have him do all five sets of squats before doing the other movements in the program. Priority training is just what the name implies, it enables you to place a priority on the muscles you want to develop the most. It is an advanced system and should only be used by advanced trainees.

CARDIOVASCULAR BENEFITS

Generally speaking, however, I recommend the circuit method for more equal total development. It has been found that moving from one exercise to another in rapid succession was the most beneficial for athletes. It not only enables them to become much stronger overall faster, but it also has a great deal of cardiovascular, respiratory rewards. Fitness experts tell us that in order to achieve a high level of cardiovascular, respiratory fitness an individual must get his pulse rate above 120 and keep it above that level for a minimum of 22 minutes. This can be accomplished quite simply with the "Big Three" performed in a circuit and moving from one station to the next very rapidly.

My basic philosophy revolves around the following training principles:
1) "Big Three" exercises
2) Five sets of five repetitions
3) Three-days a week training
4) Heavy-Medium-Light System
5) Circuit Training Method
6) Working Rapidly

ORGANIZING THE OFF-SEASON STRENGTH PROGRAM

It is assumed that you have a minimum of three stations set up, one each for the bench press, squat, and power clean. You designate Monday, Wednesday, and Friday as training days. Monday is to be the heavy day each week, Wednesday the light day, and Friday the medium one. The order of exercises, after warm-up is as follows: power cleans, bench press, and squat. The leg hyperextensions and leg biceps curls are performed after the "Big Three" are completed. There are two reasons for this order. First, the power clean takes longer to do than the other two primary exercises and secondly, the power clean is most demanding on the entire body so should be placed right up front. Also, since it involves more muscles than the other two movements it serves as a better opening exercise because it tends to warm the entire body up much better than the other two.

You should attempt to group your trainees according to strength level, rather than by height, weight, or position. This will eliminate a lot of changing of weights which cause unnecessary time delays. It is never possible to group fellows exactly because of the relative strength within the same individual. One player may be among the top five in bench pressing and in the bottom five in squatting. You are dealing with three separate segments of the body: shoulder strength, leg strength, and back strength. Very rarely are all three equally proportioned in the unexperienced trainee.

Break your group into as many equal parts as you have stations. If you have 30 boys and only three stations, then there's ten to a group. Obviously, the more stations the better, but with organization you can hustle the players through quickly with the minimum of equipment. If the group is too large for the available equipment you might be forced to break them into two sections. One section may train from 4-5 and the other from 5-6. If, because of bussing schedules or other demands in the school, this is not possible, then section "A" might be assigned Monday, Wednesday, Friday, and section "B" Tuesday, Thursday, and Saturday.

Safety is the number one watchword for all supervisors of the strength program.

SPOTTING

Three men should be involved on each exercise, one lifting the weight and two others to load and spot. Have them spot each other quite closely, especially on the bench press and the squat. Even a minor bit of carelessness on the part of a spotter could result in an injury and much undue criticism of the strength program. Safety is the number one watchword for all supervisors of the program. Take nothing for granted. Spotters should keep their hands just under the moving bar — without touching it — on both the bench press and the squat. In all of my experience in directing strength programs with large groups I have never had an accident primarily because I always stress safety from the very beginning.

As soon as the weight is returned to the platform or rack at the conclusion of the exercise the two spotters should quickly change the weights, if necessary, and one of the spotters then becomes the active lifter. A new player steps forward to become the spotter/loader. In this way, more people stay involved in the actual program and it definitely facilitates movement.

As the group finishes at one station they go, as a group, to the next and so on down the line. Around and around they go until they have done all five sets of five. Then, they all go to the hyperextension machine and do their leg hyperextensions and leg biceps curls, one immediately behind the other without any rest in between in "super set" fashion. That is, as soon as you finish the final rep on the leg hyperextensions, roll over on the machine and do your set of leg biceps curls. Wait about two to three minutes and do your second set in the same manner. Of course, if there is a large group the wait may be a bit longer, but many players can be put through very quickly. This method really flushes the blood into the desired area and this is exactly what is sought.

SAMPLE PROGRAM

It might be helpful to the reader if I outline one player's weekly schedule. I'll use our hypothetical offensive guard, Charlie West. Charlie's best bench for five repetitions is 200, for the power clean 165, and for the squat 225. This was determined via the test the very first workout. Charlie's heavy day, which is Monday in this case, would look like this:

warm-up: sit-up, leg raises, stretching
power clean: 115 x 5, 135 x 5, 145 x 5, 155 x 5, 165 x 5
bench press: 135 x 5, 155 x 5, 175 x 5, 190 x 5, 200 x 5
squat: 135 x 5, 165 x 5, 185 x 5, 205 x 5, 225 x 5
leg hyperextensions: 60 x 20, 120 x 10
leg biceps curls: 30 x 20, 60 x 10

You will notice that the weight moves progressively towards the final heavy set. At first, until the lifter gets used to the program, he may give out a bit by the time he gets to the fifth set. But in time, he will find that his strongest set is his fifth. The warm-up can be staggered in almost any order, although it is wise to break the jumps up into constant levels. If Charlie is working in a group where others are doing, let's say 205, 210, or 215 as their tops for the bench, then all of them could take the same lead-up attempts to save time in changing weights. The warm-ups are to prepare the lifter for the final heavy set. They help him learn the positioning of the weight and, of course, warm up the muscle so as to prevent injury.

Charlie's light day is on Wednesday and he worked with 80% of his maximum.

warm-up: sit-up, leg raises, stretching
power clean: 115 x 5, 115 x 5, 115 x 5, 125 x 5, 135 x 5
bench press: 135 x 5, 135 x 5, 145 x 5, 155 x 5, 160 x 5
squats: 135 x 5, 150 x 5, 160 x 5, 170 x 5, 180 x 5
leg hyperextensions: 60 x 20, 120 x 10
leg biceps curls: 30 x 20, 60 x 10

The light day is based on 80% of the maximum of five reps on your heavy day and refers to the final set of five reps only. As the heavy day increases, which it should each week, then so do the light and medium days. You will note that the lifter might be handling the same weight for two or three successive sets. This will change as he gets stronger, but it has to be remembered that the light day is employed to allow the muscles to rest to a degree. They are to be stimulated just enough and the five light sets are enough.

Charlie should be able to go through this light day very rapidly — he is encouraged to move from one station to another just as quickly as possible. Billy Newsome, while with the Baltimore Colts, went through the entire five sets of five in just less than 15 minutes. Even though the weights were light, he got a thorough work-out and was quite winded at the end. An extra bonus is the cardiovascular, respiratory fitness. Move as rapidly as possible as there is a method to this madness.

You will also note that the weight, sets, and reps remain constant for the leg hyperextensions and leg biceps curls. These two exercises are to be increased weekly and held constant throughout the week. The weight is to be increased, however, only if the trainee does all the required reps successfully. Then, and only then, is the weight to be increased. Move it up slowly, in ten pound jumps.

Charlie's medium day falls on Friday and is 90% of his maximum.

warm-up: sit-up, leg raise, and stretching
power clean: 115 x 5, 125 x 5, 135 x 5, 145 x 5, 150 x 5
bench press: 135 x 5, 150 x 5, 160 x 5, 170 x 5, 180 x 5
squats: 135 x 5, 155 x 5, 175 x 5, 190 x 5, 205 x 5
leg hyperextensions: 60 x 20, 120 x 10
leg biceps curls: 30 x 20, 60 x 10

When the figuring on the percentage comes out to an odd number, such as 90% of 165 is 148, then merely round it off to the next highest number that can go on the bar, 150 in this instance. The medium day is a bit more taxing than the light day but it is essentially a lead-in day to the heavy day.

INCORPORATING THE OVERHEAD PRESS

Many coaches and players find that by including the overhead press into the strength routine, their overall shoulder power increases considerably. As was mentioned previously, the overhead press is definitely recommended for linebackers, offensive backs, defensive backs, and all receivers as all the overhead movements help to insure complete shoulder flexibility. The overhead press (I am using this term to include both the military press and the behind-the-neck press) helps to increase the poundage used on the bench press so quite often it is incorporated into everyone's total program. Whether it is used or not depends a great deal on the time and equipment available to the coaching staff.

There are a wide variety of ways in which the overhead press can be used in a strength program. It can be used as a substitute for the bench press. Since the bench press builds more total shoulder strength than the overhead press this usually isn't preferred, but in some instances it meets the need of the individual player better than the bench press. He may, for example, have an injury that prevents him from doing bench presses or he may have an individual aversion to building the pectorals. The latter may appear to be a strange bit of reasoning to the reader, but I have encountered it on more than one occasion.

If the overhead press is to be used in place of the bench then the trainee merely follows the same program that is outlined for the bench press, i.e. heavy, light, medium, three-days-a-week. If he should want a bit of variety, then he could substitute the behind-the-neck press on the medium day. When this is done, go ahead and work the behind-the-neck press to 100% rather than the usual 90% medium-day-routine, since not nearly as much weight can be handled in this particular exercise and you don't want to have two light days back-to-back.

The more typical method of utilizing the military press is to work it in conjunction with the bench press routine, doing militaries once a week and bench presses twice. This serves a couple of specific purposes: 1) it allows the shoulder girdle muscles to rest since not as much weight is handled in the military version of the press and 2) it stimulates strength gains in a slightly different angle.

If the trainee begins making steady gains in the bench and climbs up to a fairly heavy poundage for five repetitions, 250 for 5 for example, then he is handling just at 5,000 pounds on his heavy day. This is demanding and even though he does drop off on his light and medium days, it still proves to be fatiguing **to some trainees**. By substituting the military or behind-the-neck press on the medium days it will, in effect, give the bench pressing muscles some rest while at the same time work the muscles of the shoulder girdle in a slightly different angle.

The overhead pressing should be done on the medium day if it is incorporated as a substitute lift for the bench press. The reasoning behind this is basic to the total concept I have been presenting. The light day is needed after the maximum effort day to afford the shoulder girdle a bit of rest. Since the trainee is to go 100% of the overhead pressing movement, this would be too taxing for some trainees immediately following the maximum bench pressing day. So it falls in proper order on the medium day and although it is a 100% day, the poundage is still light enough so that it does not tire the shoulder girdle for the next heavy bench press workout. The trainee doing 250 x 5 in the bench, for example, will be doing somewhere around 165-175 x 5 in the military press and 140-145 in the behind-the-neck press. So even though the trainee is putting out 100%, he is not taxing the muscle groups nearly so much as he would if he did three successive days of bench pressing.

WHEN TO USE THE BEHIND-THE-NECK PRESS

Perhaps you have been wondering why I have been using the **terms** military press and behind-the-neck press as a substitute for the bench press. Why not just one or the other? There's a reason. The military press is the most preferred substitute for the bench press since more weight can be handled than in the behind-the-neck press, but it is not the best for everyone, so provisions must be made for the exceptions to the rule. At this point I refer you to one of the essential Laws of Learning that the Strength Coach must keep constantly in mind: "Each individual is different from every other individual." The truth in this law comes home quickly in the weight room.

The lower back and knees are the two danger zones in weightlifting.

The exception in this particular case is the trainee who cannot keep his body erect while performing the military press. When the Strength Coach notices a trainee constantly leaning back and placing more and more stress on his lower back, then he should immediately correct his form and if this is not possible, switch him over to the behind-the-neck press. The lower back is one of the two danger zones in weightlifting (the other being the knee) so special care must be exercised so that injuries do not occur as a result of faulty form or poor body mechanics. The weightlifting belt will serve some bit of protection, but it is not to be depended upon to keep the player from fatiguing and injuring this critical area through improper lifting technique.

The behind-the-neck press is the most pure form of over-head pressing and can be done while either standing or seated. Not as much weight can be handled as in the military, but the risk of lower back injury is also greatly reduced. As long as the trainee keeps a firm upright position, however, there's no valid reason why he shouldn't go ahead and use the military press. Since more weight can be handled in the military, it is going to build overall shoulder strength faster and this is the goal of the program.

But correct body position is critical. Just as I commented on the subject of bridging in the bench press, excessive lay-back in the military press may increase the weight used, but it does not necessarily follow that the trainee is getting stronger. It may only indicate that he is laying back faster and further, thereby changing the angle of thrust and making the lift easier. The risk to the lower back is definitely not worth it to the football player.

GAUGING THE INCREASE

The goal is to increase the poundage on each heavy day. The rule of thumb to follow, however, so that you do not get too greedy is: you can only increase the poundage if you successfully do the five sets of five with the designated weight. For example, if your program shows that you are to bench press 185 x 5 and you make all five as a top weight, then the following week you should go ahead and schedule 195 x 5. If, however, you make but four reps, then you need to stay with the 185 another time. Patience is always rewarded in strength training. A simple but effective formula: Patience + Persistence = Progress, so don't rush the order of things. Progress will follow if you apply the first two P's.

A simple, but effective formula: Patience + Persistence = Progress.

The amount of weight to add to each exercise is also a concern of many coaches. As the players get stronger they naturally want to increase as rapidly as possible, but at the same time, it is recognized that too large an increase results in a slowing down of total progress. Typically, the greatest gains come early in the program since a good portion of the increase is due more to learning the technique and form of the individual lifts than it is to an actual increase in strength. Merely learning how to balance the barbell on your shoulders correctly helps improve the squat before any appreciable strength occurs.

Since the biggest gains come quickly, the increases on the bar should be the greatest at that time also. The guidelines to follow are: add ten pounds to the bench, power clean, and military press, and twenty pounds to the squat. For the leg hyperextensions add ten pounds and the leg biceps curls, make it but five. You will be in a position to cross-check these jumps just in case some fellows aren't able to handle this much of an increase. If, after the ensuing 10-pound increase on the bench, the player is **not** able to do a minimum of three repetitions, then the increase has been too great and should be cut back. He has to make three. If he is really zipping and makes all five with the increase, load 10 more on the next week.

A trained eye and close supervision will also allow the coach to correctly pick the right increase for each player. If you watch a certain player do five reps on the bench with 175

and it appears as if he could do five more, then move him up 15 or 20 pounds the next week rather than just ten. The jumps outlined are meant as guidelines, not hard and fast rules. You will have to be flexible throughout the program as individuals vary too much to set up a non-bending rule. Just keep in mind that the more the players progress, the more they are going to get totally involved in the program. Once they get into it 100%, you'll have to chain the weight room door to keep them out. Then the toughest job you will have will be to temper their enthusiasm. Otherwise, they'll be overtraining and this will defeat the purpose of the strength program. More on that later.

SMALLER JUMPS

When in doubt as to the proper poundage to jump to after a successful five sets of five on the heavy day, always select the lighter of the two choices. This will give the trainee a higher chance of success and the more times he is successful, the more enthusiastic he will be. The more enthusiastic he is the harder he works. The harder he works the more successful he will become. It's a continuous cycle of progress based on as many successes as possible. Success really does breed success when it comes to strength training and this success garnered in the weight room will spill over onto the gridiron.

Many coaches have reported to us that strength training has actually turned many player's mental attitude around completely. They trained, improved, and suddenly saw themselves on a par with their rivals. They got an entirely new picture of themselves. Their self esteem was heightened and they started carrying this new-found self assurance over onto the gridiron. It is a most satisfying experience for the coach to see this change occur and it happens quite frequently.

It happens even in the professional ranks. There is an omission of names in this true tale for obvious reasons. Two players from the Baltimore Colts were both involved in the same strength program the spring following their Super Bowl Victory over Dallas. They played the same position, were roughly the same size, and neither had prior strength training experience. They were both starting from the same point. The number two man always looked up to the starter and really assumed that he belonged in the number two slot. They usually came in and trained together during the off-season.

The fundamental difference between the two was that the back-up man applied himself much more diligently to the weights than did the starter. As a result, the number two player soon far excelled number one in the weight room and slowly he began to realize that he was stronger than his rival. It dawned on him one day, by his own confession, that he could move his friend around on the football field because of his superior strength. This fact prompted him to train even harder and by the time season officially opened, number two was elevated to number one and old number one never did figure out how all this came about.

INITIAL MUSCLE SORENESS

Some trainees will find a certain amount of muscle soreness following the first few workouts, especially the first heavy one. The degree of soreness depends on a number of factors, such as: prior physical condition of the trainee, diet, rest, and previous experience using weights. But even the best conditioned athlete will experience some amount of soreness since any new form of exercise acts differently on the body. This is especially true of weight training since deep muscle fibers are reached with resistance, in many cases for the first time ever.

The frontal deltoids usually are a bit sore from the bench pressing. The power cleans bring out soreness in the lumbars and trapezius and the squats make you aware of your leg biceps, quadriceps, and buttocks. This is typically the case and is nothing to be alarmed about. It merely means that you are attacking those muscles very directly. Actually, it is a good sign that you have worked the muscles sufficiently.

SECOND-DAY SORENESS

The term "second day soreness" refers to the fact that your muscles become more sore the second day after exercising them than they were the day immediately following a training session. This fact is often troublesome to the novice trainee as he feels that he may stay sore the rest of his life. The soreness only follows the heavy days and the light days, which come up next in the program, help to work the stiffness and tenderness right out of the body. Be sure to pay special attention to the stretching exercises on the days that you are sore.

A bit of muscle rub or other liniment may help to alleviate the soreness on workout days. Apply the liniment after you have done your sit-ups, leg raises, plus any other cardiovascular, respiratory work and stretching movements. Use only as much as is needed and do not let the liniment replace actual movements in your warm-up routine.

AVOID EXTRA TRAINING

The following bit of advice may seem rather strange in light of the fact that I have been praising weight training from the opening sentence of this book, but one of the things that a supervisor of the strength program has to watch closely is that his trainees do not slip in extra training. Once the players start making gains they naturally feel great. They enjoy the new-found physical strength and are more than eager to get stronger and stronger. They assume that more work is the answer, since it is generally true that more effort in any area of life produces more results than does less effort. This axiom does not always apply to strength training, however. More effort is often detrimental to progress.

The most common urge of players is for bigger upper bodies, with a special fascination with bigger arms. Arms can be seen by everyone. They signify a certain amount of masculinity. As the biceps and triceps begin to take on a new shape from the "Big Three" exercises, the trainees will become very eager to have them bulge even more. They begin slipping in a set of curls after the regular program. Then a couple of sets. Then a super-set of curls and triceps extensions. Perhaps a set of pullovers to fill out the chest. Before the coach notices, the player is doing a full scale body-building workout **after** he finishes with the "Big Three." It seems harmless enough, but soon his progress on the "Big Three" stops. Soreness does not go away as quickly. He becomes more and more entranced with dimensions rather than applicable strength. Flexibility exercises are seldom included in this pumping session, so flexibility soon wanes. The trainee's energy level begins to drop. He goes on the field in a state of fatigue — leaving himself wide open to injury.

Clinics and demonstrations are most valuable in teaching large groups the fundamentals of weight training.

A word to the wise. Unless a player has a special weakness in a certain muscle group, restrict him to the designated exercises. If corrective or therapeutic exercises are needed, add them in a constructive manner so that they do not interfere with the athlete's progress on the total strength program. I know, of course, that the coach cannot stand over the players every minute or watch them when they are away from school. Many players keep a set of weights at home and slip in extra training. But, the concerned coach can pass along this advice and keep an eye out for fatigue which is a result of the extra training. Those "extras" will have their place when the trainee becomes advanced.

GOING FOR LIMIT ATTEMPTS

Another "no-no" for the trainees is trying limit poundage too soon. There is a time and place for these, as will be pointed out directly, but not on regular training days. Novice trainees constantly want to see how much they can lift. Occasionally, after a work-out session, they will want to load up the barbell to see how much they can "pick up" (dead lift) or "put over their heads" (press or clean and jerk). The competitive spirit which makes them want to get stronger in the first place also pushes them to try to out-do their training mates. But more injuries have resulted from this practice of lifting limit poundages without proper education on the techniques of such lifts and performed while fatigued than from any other. It is to be prohibited completely in the early stages of weight training. No exceptions.

At the same time, the trainees are to be encouraged to reach for higher and higher goals in the weight room. They are to be urged to handle heavier and heavier weights and

the competitive atmosphere is most beneficial to overall progress. So how are these two seemingly diametrically-opposed factors rectified?

Every five or six weeks allow the players to go for a maximum single limit, but only for the "Big Three," and not for any exercise with which they are not familiar. Set a date a week or two in advance — always on the regularly scheduled heavy day — so that the trainees can plan for it. It serves a number of purposes. It is a terrific motivator and every player is in competition with every one else. One of the nice things about the weights is that they are absolute, constant, consistent. Two hundred pounds is always two hundred pounds today, tomorrow, the month after — whether it be wet, cold, sunny — in Moscow, Berlin, or Rock Run, Maryland. If a player does 200 pounds and another 195, the former is the strongest in that exercise — period. Strength in relation to bodyweight is another factor, most certainly, and is not to be shortchanged, but not where pure strength is the only consideration. The super heavyweight champion of the world is dubbed the "World's Strongest Man" because, in fact, he really is. The man who lifts the most in the workout room is the strongest man on the team and the players know this to be a fact.

The single, maximum repetition also helps to break down mental barriers on certain weights. A player can easily become stagnated at a certain poundage, especially those which round off nicely — like 200, 225, 250, 275, 300 and so forth. Some numbers, such as 300 and 400 set up rather tough walls to punch through and the coach should be aware that psychological factors do enter into the whole field of weightlifting. A trainee might be stuck at 225 for five in the bench press for two or three weeks and since this weight is the most he handles, it becomes an absolute limit. By going on past that weight, even though it be for less repetitions, it allows the trainee to break through the mental barrier that invariably builds up from staying on the same number. If the trainee can successfully do 260 or 265 for a single, which is about par for 225 x 5, then the next time around he can step into 230 or 235 with a renewed confidence. The generally applied guide to estimate a single maximum from repetitions is to figure ten pounds for every rep past the first. Hence, 225 x 5 could be fairly closely adjusted to 265 x 1. Ten pounds multiplied by the four extra reps past the first one, equals 40 pounds: $225 + 40 = 265$.

The warm-up to the lead-up sets and reps will be handled somewhat differently for limit days also. Start off with the same basic weight of 135 and do five repetitions. Take the standard jump to 155 and do five just as you would on a regular work-out day. Jump again to 185 and do a double. Now do 215 and a single; 235 for a single. If that single goes easy, jump 20 more to 255. If it was a bit sticky, just jump 10 or perhaps 15 pounds. Let each set thereafter be your guide. If the bar goes up nicely, take a sizeable jump as you only have so much energy and you want to hit your maximum poundage when you are completely warmed-up and have a surplus of energy. Chances are, you won't hit it on the button the first couple of times out, but you will soon learn just when your body and mind are in complete harmony to execute the maximum attempt.

Be sure to warm-up thoroughly. Most trainees are very eager to get to the big weights and don't want to be bothered with the dinky ones, like 135 and 155 for five. But these are extremely necessary. The Super Heavyweight Powerlifting Champion, Don Reinhoult warms up before each session, whether it be light workout, or the World Championships with the basic Olympic bar and two plates, 135 pounds, and then he goes on to elevate in excess of 800 pounds in the dead lift. So, if this man of strength takes the time to work up through the dinky weights then so should everyone interested in doing their best.

INFORMAL CONTESTS

On one of the scheduled test days, take the fellows out of the weight room into the gym or auditorium. Open it up to the entire student body and let it be an informal contest. Make sure that the players know this well in advance and inform them that the results will be published in the school paper. There isn't a player who doesn't want to be regarded as hard-nosed, tough, and strong. Its synonymous with manliness so each and every player will be primed and ready for the show.

Even if only a dozen or so interested spectators and girl friends show up to watch, the players will nonetheless put forth as never before. While this is to be an informal affair, still pay strict attention to the rules so that everyone has an equal chance. Besides, following proper procedure helps to make it something rather special. Weigh them in before the contest. Have judges and rules to follow. The coach's best bet in this regard is to go through the **AAU Weightlifting Handbook** or contact the local weightlifting club for assistance. Competitive weightlifters are usually willing to help out in these situations.

Have such contests perhaps twice during the year. Set the date as far in advance as possible so the players have time to train specifically for the contest. It adds a bit of incentive to the overall program and will help to stimulate the players to work harder on the regular training days.

Don Herrold, outstanding University of Hawaii linebacker, peaks out on strength program just prior to each spring and summer practice by competing in power-lifting contests. The "Hulk" set a state squat record with his 525 effort and is a ranked collegiate lifter. Quite a feat since he can only serious train six months out of the year.

THE RECORD BOARD

Make, or have made, a team record board. Break it up into a number of weight divisions so that more players have a realistic chance of seeing their name on the board. You can use the regular weight classes set up for competitive weightlifting or you can select some more suitable to your particular group. The ten weight classes for competitive lifting are: (fractions omitted) 114, 123, 132, 148, 165, 181, 198, 220, 242, and heavyweight. Since this is probably a few more than a high school football squad might need, I suggest: 145 and under, 165, 185, 205, and heavyweight. For colleges I would drop the 145 and add the 225 classification. Place the weight classes down the sides of the board, then list the lifts to be tested across the top of the board: military press, bench press, power clean, and squat. Leave a space under each lift. Line the board off so that there is a space large enough for a name, weight lifted, and the date. A large blackboard serves the purpose nicely. Paint the rule lines, weight classifications, and lifts to be contested in with permanent white paint and use chalk for the ever-changing records. Make it a rule that records can only be made on testing day so that this simple motivational device does not turn into a monster.

As the strength program becomes more and more established, the board should become a permanent part of the school records and should be displayed so that the entire student body can appreciate it. The records will become tangible goals and many erstwhile lethargic trainees will suddenly get very much involved when they see they have a realistic chance to hold a school record in one of the lifts.

UTILIZE LOCAL EXPERTISE

The local weightlifters can be of assistance in other ways other than helping the coach to conduct informal meets. The weightlifter can do much to explain points of form on all the exercises described. While I have attempted to explain each lift as clearly and as completely as possible, I still realize that it would be far better to be there in person to demonstrate and supervise each lift. The local competitive weightlifter can show the players how a power clean is done through actual demonstration. A knowledgeable weightlifter can quickly diagnose whether a player is squatting with his feet too closely together and he can explain just where the hands should be when gripping the barbell for the bench press. Some weightlifters are, obviously, better at presenting this technical advice than others, but all can be of some help to the coach. Periodical visits by the local "expert" can help a program immensely especially if the lifter is involved in this segment of strength training himself.

Brief demonstrations and exhibitions by accomplished weightlifters can also go a long way in helping motivate the players. The author and his York teammates gave hundreds of just such exhibitions while with the York Company and later for Fitness Consultants, Inc.

It helped the players to see that the lifting isn't done with mirrors, just through perfected technique and lots of hard work. Most players are astonished to discover that the state or national champions were not born strong men. The fact is that nearly every accomplished strength athlete started from scratch or even below scratch. This testimony gives the weaker trainees a glimmer of hope. It all helps the program and if the personnel is available, then it certainly should be utilized.

SPECIAL INCENTIVES

As a few of the trainees break certain numerical barriers, such as 300 in the bench press, 200 in the military press, 250 in the power clean or 400 in the squat, make a big thing of it. Organize a 300-Club and award T-shirts for those who can make the qualifying lift. Spread the news around when someone makes it into one of the select groups and award the shirts, or whatever, at a public or semi-public gathering. Getting them to train will stop being your chief worry. Your new problem just may be keeping them out of the weight room.

Strength is a fascinating quality, as anyone can testify who has increased this attribute to any degree. Strength spawns more self confidence, more self assurance, more of just about everything. But strength is a most greedy mistress. You can never get enough. The stronger you become, the stronger you want to be. When you reach the magic 300 mark in the bench you are elated, but before the bar gets cold from the lift you begin thinking of 325. After 325, there's 350 and the super-imposing 400. Since strength is so closely tied into the whole concept of maleness in our culture (for good or evil) it is quite easy for a young man to be seduced by its desires.

The coach must temper this thirst for strength with wisdom as he is wanting a stronger football team, not a group of weightlifters. It can be accomplished quite simply as so many high school and college coaches have shown in the past.

Close supervision is again the key to success. Be aware of what's going on in the weight room. Stick to the schedule and only use the motivational gimmicks occasionally. Make strength gains a big thing, but not the biggest thing. That has to be reserved for the playing field. There will be no real difficulty in this department if the coach is aware of the addictive characteristic of strength gains. Like so many other things in this world, the progress can be beneficial or it can be detrimental. All it takes is a bit of awareness and a pinch of horse sense.

ONLY TEST PERIODICALLY

Some trainees seem to be much better at single repetitions than are others. Perhaps it is the competitive urge or perhaps they have not built up a sufficient backlog of muscle endurance so as to handle the five heavy reps.

Keep a record of these maximum days. They can be most helpful to the coach for motivational purposes. After the first maximum day the athletes will be chomping at the bit for another one right away, but get them back on the fives as the maximum days are merely "testing" days and are not "building" days. As in many other areas of this activity, too much of a good thing is not better, but worse. Do not fall into the trap of testing too often. Remember that you can fairly accurately interpolate from the five reps just where the trainee stands for a heavy single, so it is not really necessary to test but every five or six weeks. The novelty — and therefore the motivation — of the activity wears off if it occurs too frequently.

The testing day will immediately bring out a competitive flavor in the workout room, if it is not already present. This is to be desired for through challenges and personal competition the players push and pull each other to greater levels of strength. Encourage this, while tempering their competitiveness with a dash of common sense. As was previously stated, do not go for limit attempts but every five or six weeks. Also, never let the trainees attempt a maximum effort in a lift other than the ones they use in their programs. Absolutely no dead lifts (advanced trainees are exceptions to this rule). They usually try to zip these in at the end of the workout. This is extremely dangerous as the muscles are most fatigued at this point and more susceptible to injury. The supervisor should stay in the weight room until everyone leaves. Allow two or three trainees with a competitive spirit to be left alone with a loaded barbell and you can be guaranteed that someone will try to "pick it up." I recommend that you do not test the military press because of the stress on the lower back, but if they must do it be sure they wear a belt and do not allow excessive layback.

OTHER MOTIVATIONAL IDEAS — KEEP RECORDS

The testing day is a great motivator. It stimulates harder work on the less exciting training days where only 80 or 90% of maximum are handled. It is often difficult for the beginning trainee to see a reason for handling such light weights. After a couple of test days, the coach can show him how the steady work on the training days has made the difference in his maximum strength level. Each trainee should have his own record of progress, so that his increases can be charted week by week. If the coach cannot do this himself, then he should assign someone to handle the record-keeping.

Record both maximum efforts for the five repetitions and the maximum single. The trainee who has made the most progress can be singled out for his achievement. This encourages those who start at the bottom of the strength ladder to work harder. There is a truism in weightlifting that states, "It doesn't matter where you start, only where you finish," but it is often difficult to impress this fact on a novice. Yet, if he sees himself gaining 10% a week, then the coach can graphically point out how he can realistically be lifting as much as anyone in the class in a projected four or five months.

If time allows or if you can handle the statistics, chart each trainee's progress on individual sheets and post them for all to see. The weight room should have a bulletin board. The progress sheets do help to encourage everyone. Those who are ahead want to stay there and those eagerly trying to catch up will work even harder.

IN-SEASON PROGRAM

One of the biggest problems I faced when I first set up this outlined strength program was determining how to keep the players strong during season — without tapping into their energy reserves so deeply that it adversely affected their playing ability. Coaches came to me confessing that they could get their players strong in the off-season, but mid-way through the year they had lost that newly achieved strength. Most coaches were dead-set against using a weight program during the season. The few that tried it met with disastrous results. It was just too taxing to the body to have four days of football practice, a game on Friday or Saturday, and three days of weight training. The players became fatigued, were left open to injury, and actually became weaker rather than stronger.

So what to do? My proposal, after viewing all of the elements involved, was a slight adaptation of the present off-season program (so that no new learning skills had to be learned). The idea utmost in my mind was to retain the strength and conserve energy. I felt it could be done and convinced a few high school and college coaches in the Pennsylvania area to try the plan. It worked very nicely. I had hoped, at the onset of the in-season program, that the players would be able to retain the strength that they had built up during the off-season through the 10-11-and some-times 12-game schedule. As it turned out, all the players not only held their strength levels, but actually made slight gains during the football season.

The in-season program is an adaptation of the "Big Three."

Here's how the in-season program works. Use the same basic exercises: power clean, bench press, and squat. If the overhead press is to be utilized, it has to totally replace the bench press. There is no provision for alternating them as you'll soon discover.

The players do but one exercise per day, training on Tuesday, Wednesday, and Thursday. Monday is a rest day since most high schools and colleges play their games on Saturday and it was felt the two days of rest were important. Friday, also, is a rest day so that the muscles will be fresh for competition. Tuesday will be bench pressing day, five sets of five working up to a maximum set, just as in the off-season program. Wednesday is a power clean day. Same five sets of five going heavy. Thursday is the squat day and the routine is identical. The order of lifts can be varied so that all the players are not stacked up waiting to bench on Tuesday. Break them into A, B, and C groups. While the "As" are benching, the "Bs" are power cleaning, and the "Cs" are squatting. Alternate them each day so that all these groups get in each exercise. The order during the week is not significant, just the fact that they do them at least once a week. Every player does a minimum of two sets of leg hyperextensions and leg biceps curls each day — not just once a week. These preventive movements are to be done three times a week. Do not slight these two important exercises.

The weight workout follows the practice session on the field so the players should be sufficiently warmed-up when they come to the weight room. Nevertheless, it is still most advisable to loosen all the major joints: wrist, elbows, shoulders, lower back, knee and ankle as described in Chapter Four before touching the barbell. Stretching is definitely advised at the conclusion of each workout also.

The logic behind this program is that it provides sufficient work to stimulate muscle growth, but does not overtax the body. Coaches who utilized it came back with stories of how their teams continued to manhandle opponents at the **end** of the season. That's when the true value of a strength program really comes to the forefront. The professional players were most pleased with this concept as it allowed them to hold their strength through the long season, which starts for them in August and ends for some in January. There simply is no way to hold the off-season strength gains for six long months without doing some work during the season.

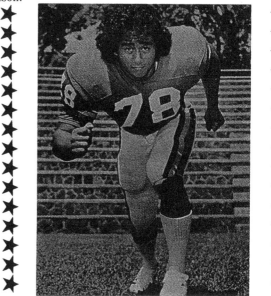

Charlie Aiu made the San Diego Chargers as a free agent, due primarily to his excellent strength training background.

WHEN TIME IS SHORT DURING SEASON

Time seems to be a most precious commodity and a very limiting factor at many schools. Coaches informed us that they just could not get all their players through five sets of five after football practice. Many players had to catch special buses or travel long distances and to keep them too long brought down the wrath of the parents. I suggested this variation and it seemed to work nicely.

Use just three total sets, instead of the regular five, and make the jumps bigger between sets. I know that the players are already warmed up sufficiently from their activity on the field so the risk of injury is negligible. For example, if a player is going for 250 x 5 in the bench he could go about it in one of two methods. One, he would warm up with a very light first set, 135 x 5, jump to a moderate weight, 205 x 5, and then to the top poundage, 250 x 5. Others prefer warming up with a slightly higher first weight, 175 x 5 then going to 225 x 5 and finally to 250 x 5. The latter group felt that by starting heavier the larger jumps weren't so noticeable, while the former group preferred feeling a very light poundages first set. It became a matter of preference as both arrived at the same top weight and that is the important set.

Stephanie Ciarelli was the first female to train with the men at U.H., thus becoming the original "Herculette." It fit. Herc went on to become an outstanding scholastic strength coach and has coached international Olympic lifting teams. Named High School Strength Coach of the year by American Football Monthly in 2004, she is currently the SC at Newport Harbor H.S. and is considered to be "pound for pound, the best strength coach in the country."

The same rule applies to power cleaning and squatting. If time is extremely precious after practice, have the players do the leg extensions and leg biceps curls **before practice.** Since these are high rep movements they actually serve as excellent warm-up exercises for the practice session and it does insure that they get in the program. The three sets of five is also a good program to be used during spring practice, summer two-a-days, and immediately following two-a-days. This is a time when energy level is at its lowest. A player will find enough time and energy to do three quick sets during these physically tiring days, but he may shy away from five sets.

WHEN THERE'S AN ABUNDANCE OF TIME

At the other end of the pole there are some instances when players, especially in the college and pro ranks, find that they have plenty of time in which to train. Should they continue to do the "Big Three" right through the season? My only answer may seem a bit evasive but it is the most honest one I have. It depends strictly on the individual. Some players thrive on the strength work. They seem to need it for both physical and psychological reasons. Some players have so much physical energy that they have to release it some way and the weights are certainly a constructive way to do so. The pros, especially, do not put heavy physical demands on their players during the season. Training camp

is something different, but during the season the practice sessions are really more tiring mentally than they are physically.

So many thrive on this strength work. Ray May, the outstanding linebacker for the Colts, and now with the Denver Broncos made significant gains right through the season and he did bench presses, squats, power cleans and overhead presses three times a week. Others, such as Bubba Smith, Mike Curtis, and Bill Curry specialized on the bench press during the season and felt that the increases which they made on that one lift helped them on the field.

I would merely state that the individual player or coach has to use his own judgement on this issue and perhaps a bit of trial-and-error is in order. If you find your players, or yourself if you are involved in a program, extremely fatigued the day after a full strength program, then you can bet it's a bit too much. Cut back and try less and examine your energy level the following day.

The individual body has to be the final barometer in this case. Be flexible and aware enough to adapt your schedule to the demands on the playing field. If you just had a tough scrimmage in full pads with lots of contact work, then you might be very wise to skip the weight room entirely. Understand the motive for strength training. It's to get stronger so that you can be a better football player. If going to the weight room too often is making you weaker, then step back and reevaluate the entire program. ★

7

CHAPTER SEVEN
ADVANCED TRAINING PROGRAMS

THERE ARE SEVERAL instances where the strength coach must be prepared to up-grade the programs of particular individuals. Some players reach plateaus in their schedules and are not able to progress with the regular five sets of five. Mental staleness is sometimes the culprit and a change of routine is definitely in order. Others become quite strong in all three of the lifts and because of this, they are not able to handle maximum poundages on all three of the lifts every single week as is outlined in the schedule. It just becomes too demanding to do super heavy bench presses, squats, and power cleans every week on the same day. It's like lifting in a contest weekly and it becomes much too fatiguing on both the mind and the body.

Similarly, a few players want to specialize on one of the lifts in the off-season to become extra strong in that lift. A 400-pound bench press, or 500-pound squat, or a 300-pound clean are frequent goals and most players, in order to realize these standards, must give some added attention to the specific lift.

Finally, the Strength Coach will be working with many of the same players for perhaps as many as four years. To attempt to motivate them year after year with the same programs and the exact same exercises is extremely difficult. Change is necessary for progress, even if it is but a temporary chance. The player in his second year on a strength program will be at an entirely different level than he was the year before. The third year will find him much more further along than in year two, so adjustments must be made in order to have a program that continually produces results.

This chapter, then, is for the advanced trainee who desires some change — for whatever reason. It must be strongly emphasized from the onset, however, that this is an advanced program and should not be slipped in prematurely on the beginning trainee. Without a firm strength foundation, these programs will bear no fruit. In fact, they will be a severe disappointment to the unprepared trainee. Without the background of hard work the body will not have a strength base on which to move on to the advanced exercises.

It should also be emphasized that these advanced programs are designed for individuals rather than for groups. It is not that they could not work for groups — for if they can work for one then they most certainly can work for 50 — but it is that they are so time consuming. It would be nearly impossible to have a 40-man squad do any of these advanced programs as a group. A half dozen players could, however,

be assigned advanced schedules and work their programs together as a smaller unit. It can all be coordinated into the total scheme of things, but the reader should not be misled in believing that he can incorporate these advanced methods wholesale on the entire squad. Some coaches have their advanced men train at a different hour than the rest of the team. Others schedule them right along with the remainder of the squad but segregate them. Your method depends to a great extent on your equipment and time resources.

The same program does not work for the same individual every time.

INDIVIDUAL DIFFERENCES

Since no two individuals respond to the same programs in exactly the same way I am presenting a selection of programs for each of the three basic lifts. Unfortunately, there is no sure-fire way of knowing exactly which program will suit which individual beforehand. Admittedly, it would be nice if we had some sort of pre-test that was accurate, but none exists. It boils down to trial-and-error. If, after you place a player on a special program, he still remains at the same plateau after giving it a fair test of 4-6 weeks, then another alternative is in order. If he starts making gains again — and generally this is the case after any change — then you know you're on the right track, at least temporarily.

One other note that you can store away somewhere for future reference. The same program does not always work on the same individual every time. This may seem like utter nonsense, but it's a fact. The program that brings a player to a 300-pound bench press, for example, may move him no further. He may need a change in order to attain 350 and perhaps another change to get to 400. For some exceptional trainees, the reverse is true. They merely have to plug in a given program and their lifts will go up. Bob Bednarski, World Champion and World Record holder, used only one routine for the five years I trained with him. All that changed were the weights he used and he made steady gains using that method. It's nice if you fit into the latter category as it makes setting up schedules much easier, but I must warn you that this type of individual is the exception rather than the rule.

I mentioned that I do not have a sure-fire method of determining whether a certain program will work for a player, but I can relate a few clues that may assist the Strength Coach when he is assigned advanced programs. Players who are long on stamina and energy and who thrive on lots of work do better on the programs that require more time and total energy expenditure. The reverse is also true. The low-energy individual may need a change that allows him to expend less total effort. Instead of him doing three days of squats per week, for example, the lower energy trainee may be better off doing squats but two times a week. His high energy counterpart may need to do heavy squats three times a week in order to realize any gains. Again, it is a trial-and-error method, but the aware strength coach will be able to differentiate between these two types of trainees quite quickly.

After a player has been on the five sets of five circuit for five or six months his poundage on the three lifts often becomes very considerable. On a given heavy day, for instance, a trainee may be handling 350 x 5 in the bench press, 250 x 5 in the power clean, and 400 x 5 in the squat. This becomes far too mentally and physically exhausting. The player has to gather so much energy to hit three limits which are often also personal limits. Putting three limit lifts back to back becomes much like lifting in a weightlifting contest weekly. Even competitive lifters know that they can't limit out too frequently in training or it will burn them out for the actual competition. Many only reach genuine strength peaks twice a year. The same holds true with the football player.

CHANGE IN HEAVY, LIGHT, MEDIUM

But a player can go heavy on a single lift every workout. This, in fact, is quite stimulating to most trainees as it gives him something to look forward to each and every session. It breaks the monotony of the light and medium days. So we break up the limit days and spread them through the week. The program might be constructed in this manner:

Monday:
    Power clean — heavy
    Bench press — medium
    Squat — light

Wednesday:
    Power clean — light
    Bench press — heavy
    Squat — medium

Friday:
    Power clean — medium
    Bench press — light
    Squat — heavy

As the reader can easily see, the order of heavy days followed by light days followed by medium days is kept intact. The order presented above may not be the order in which the trainee actually does the lifts. He may prefer to do the lift which he is going the heaviest at the first of the workout.

DROPPING THE CIRCUIT

At this point the trainee may want to drop the circuit. Some find that they can handle more weights if they do all the sets of an exercise in order, rather than in a circuit. Then they can concentrate on just one movement and put more mental and physical concentration into each lift. Dropping the circuit also becomes necessary sometimes because of a lack of equipment. It becomes quite impossible to set up three stations when a gym is full or when only a couple of Olympic bars are open. I also realize that most players train in the off-season at health clubs, YMCA's or school weight rooms and one person cannot dominate all the equipment in such facilities designed for a large, diverse and sometimes paying public.

It is permissible, then, to do one lift through its entirety in the advanced stages of training. Some like to do their heavy lift alone and then do the other two lifts in a circuit. This works nicely also. Others like to do each lift separately and if this fits your personal needs best, then by all means do it. But regardless of whether the trainee decides to keep the circuit, use it half and half, or drop it entirely, it is still quite imperative that he keep the same fast pace in his workout schedule. Dropping the circuit does not mean dropping the conditioning factor in strength training. On the contrary, now that you do not have to move from station to station with the inherent time hangups of that system, you should learn to move through each lift faster than before.

The trainee should go through the first three sets of an exercise, even the heavy ones, very quickly and then take a brief rest before the fourth and fifth sets. More explicitly, if he is going heavy on the bench and plans to go: 135 x 5, 175 x 5, 225 x 5, 275 x 5, 305 x 5 he should move quite rapidly through 135 to 175 to 225 and then pause for 3-4 minutes before going to 275. He may wait another 4 minutes before taking the limit set, but he definitely should not sit around for 8-10 minutes as it is not building the kind of strength needed for football. Many are pleasantly surprised to find they can lift more weight if they move quickly rather than doddering between sets. In weightlifting competition the athlete only has three minutes between attempts if no one else is taking that weight and I have seen lifters break their personal records three consecutive times with that brief rest in-between. To sit around and psyche up becomes an unnecessary habit. A well-conditioned athlete is able to handle heavy weights in rapid succession, especially if he has been conscientiously applying himself on the "Big Three" in the circuit. If he has not been doing so, then it is doubtful if he belongs in the more advanced training.

BENCH PRESS ROUTINES

There are always two distinct routes to take when progress comes to a halt on a particular lift: 1) to do more total work on that lift or 2) to do less. Seems most simple, but it is surprising how many miss this basic fact when altering programs. The latter applies most often in the bench press. Generally speaking, most people over train the bench press in early training and by easing off a little, the progress picks up again. Bench pressing is a relatively fun exercise. Compared to full squats, it's a delight. Trainees look forward to bench pressing. It builds those big chest and arm muscles and seems to be the standard by which the world tests its strength. "How much can you bench press" is asked a thousand more times than "how much can you squat" or "how much can you power clean."

OVERHEAD PRESS

People are familiar with this lift and it is understandable that the young trainee will get caught up in trying to do extra well in this one lift. As a result, most trainees keep their bench pressing muscles in a constant state of fatigue, hence the progress comes to a dead stop. As progress stops, most figure they are not doing enough and add a few more sets or few more reps. The result is predictable. When fatigue sets in, less, not more, is in order.

PERILS OF OVERTRAINING

Here's an example of what I mean by overtraining the bench press. Our trainee has achieved the lofty plateau of doing five reps with 325 pounds on his final set of five. His lead-up poundages go like this: 135 x 5, 225 x 5, 275 x 5, 305 x 5, and finally, 325 x 5. This gives him a total of 6,325 pounds. A lot of weight. The light day follows, 80% of 325 is 260 x 5. Lead-up: 135 x 5, 175 x 5, 215 x 5, 240 x 5. Total weight lifted, 5,115 pounds. Medium day, 90% or top weight of 295 pounds. Lead-up weights: 135 x 5, 185 x 5, 225 x 5, 255 x 5, 275 x 5. Total on medium day comes to 5,575. Even though the lifter handles considerably less on the light and medium days, it's still too much to allow the muscles to rest sufficiently. You have to remember that the bulk of the work in bench pressing is done by the arms and those muscles just aren't large enough to handle in excess of 5,000 pounds work load three times a week in the early stage of training. The arms are also involved in power cleans, so additional energy is tapped. What is needed at this stage of development is exercises to stimulate strength increases without producing fatigue. To do a lot less weight on the light and medium days would not serve this purpose as it would not increase overall strength.

It should be reiterated at this point that as long as the trainee is progressing do not alter his program. The best program is the one that works. If he levels off because of mental or physical fatigue, then that's the time to suggest some changes, but if he is steadily moving upward, just leave him alone.

INCORPORATING THE OVERHEAD PRESS

If you have read Chapter Five you already have a clue to my first recommendation. I mentioned incorporating the overhead press into the bench press program at that time for the purpose of variety. Now I suggest utilizing other pressing movements to increase the bench press itself.

In order that you not be required to flip back to Chapter Five to understand what I am referring to, I will once again explain how this program works. The exercises will be the bench press, behind-the-neck press, and the military press. The bench falls on Monday and serves as the heavy day of training. The behind-the-neck press comes on Wednesday and is light and the military press is the medium workout on Friday.

Although they have been designated as heavy, light, and medium, the trainee actually goes to maximum at each work-out. The reason that the behind-the-neck day is a light day is because relative to the weight handled in the bench press the trainee is handling a light weight. The military serves as a middle ground. More weight can be used in the military press than can in the behind-the-neck press, but not as much as in the bench press.

A slight modification in the sets and reps is also in order for the advanced trainee. The modificaiton is slight and enables the trainee to handle heavier weights on the final sets. Instead of performing five sets of five repetitions, the advanced trainee will do seven sets of the following repetitions: 5, 5, 5, 3, 3, 3, 6-10. The first three sets serve as warm-up sets and by dropping two reps on the next three sets allows the trainee to use more weight in the lift. The final back-off set insures the trainee of sufficient work as he will be doing a minimum of 25 reps per exercise. Any less is not going to be enough total work, regardless of the top weight handled. The 6-10 range is allowed because it is not always easy to pick a back-off set exactly on the money on any given day so it's sort of a ballpark figure.

Your program for total shoulder power might look like this:

Exercises modeled by Steve Dussia

Bench press (Monday) 135 x 5, 175 x 5, 225 x 5, 275 x 3, 305 x 3, 315 x 3, 255 x 6-10.

Behind-the-neck press (Wednesday) 135 x 5, 145 x 5, 155 x 5, 165 x 3, 174 x 3, 150 x 6-10.

Military press (Friday) 135 x 5, 155 x 5, 175 x 5, 195 x 3, 205 x 3, 215 x 3, 185 x 6-10.

The back-off set generally will fall somewhere between the third and fourth sets, depending on how tired you are after the first five sets and how strong you happen to be in that specific movement.

General speaking, most people overtrain the bench press in early training.

ONE OTHER VERSION

One final version of substituting the overhead pressing movements into the total program is to bench press on heavy days, behind-the-neck press on light days, and military press on medium days. The big difference in this type of program is that every day is really a heavy day for each of the three lifts. That is, the trainee goes to maximum on each day for five repetitions. The reason this program works is that the lift itself restricts the total amount of poundage handled. Let's take our 250 x 5 bench presser again and see how his weekly pressing program might appear in terms of total poundage used:

Monday, Bench press: 135 x 5, 175 x 5, 205 x 5, 225 x 5, 250 x 5, (total of 4,950 lifted)

Wednesday, Behind-the-neck presses: 105 x 5, 115 x 5, 125 x 5, 135 x 5, 145 x 5, (total 3,125 pounds)

Friday, Military presses: 115 x 5, 135 x 5, 150 x 5, 160 x 5, 170 x 5, (total 3,550)

In case the total amount lifted is confusing you, it is obtained by multiplying the weight on the bar times the repetitions, then adding the five sets together. The bench press total broke down like this: 135 x 5 = 675, 175 x 5 = 875, 205 x 5 = 1025, 225 x 5 = 1125, 250 x 5 = 1250. Add 675 + 875 + 1025 + 1125 + 1250 to get 4950, the total poundage lifted that day in the bench press. This tonnage system can be most useful in figuring up a day's work load or a week's total or even a month's accumulation. It is often helpful to see if you are actually doing more or if you might be doing too much.

By scanning the total poundage the reader can quickly see the heavy, light, and medium formula has been kept in tact. The behind-the-neck presses uses 1825 pounds less than the bench press workout and the military presses some 1400 pounds less than the bench, yet the military presses employed 425 pounds more than the behind-the-neck days. As the bench press becomes stronger this difference will become even greater as the total poundage will increase much greater on the bench than the other two. This is because the poundage used in the bench is greater and 300 multiplied by five adds up to a lot more than 200 times five, although the increase per individual may be exactly 20 or 30 pounds in each lift.

Each day finds the muscles of the shoulder girdle being stimulated in a slightly different manner, although all three exercises are quite similar. Some trainees like this program since they can go all out at each workout without limiting their progress. It affords variety and for many this is most important to stimulate constant motivation. It's, in essense, three different pressing programs incorporated into one. It is, in conclusion, a good program for one who is stuck in the bench press or for the individual who is fairly advanced and would like to try something different for a change.

THE
BENCH PRESS

BENCH PRESSING ALA DOUG HEPBURN

In 1951 a fine gentleman from Vancouver, Canada won the World Heavyweight Weightlifting Championship, upsetting a few more publicized strength athletes from the United States, Europe, and South America. Doug Hepburn had developed his superb strength through training methods which he developed himself. He passed this information along to the rest of the strength athletes of the world, but his routines get lost in the shuffle every so often. While the routine I present may not be the Simon-pure Hepburn, I still want to give him the credit since the idea was original with him. He is a very creative individual, one of the few who formulated strength developing theories, and he tested them successfully on himself.

This routine is for the person who wants to improve his bench press, is willing to put in lots of work, and who has plenty of time to train. It is a very prohibitive program for a large group and equally unwise for anyone to attempt who is not ready to spend a solid hour just doing bench presses.

Begin with 3-5 sets of warm-ups, working up to a fairly heavy weight. Now select a poundage that you can comfortably do five singles with and still have a bit of reserve left. This isn't always as easy as it sounds. If you can single, say 325, you should use around 290-300 initially for this program. Do five singles with the selected poundage and then drop back to a weight with which you can do five sets of five repetitions.

Sounds quite easy on paper, but most start to run out of gas on their third or fourth back-up set. Most choose too much weight for this back-off poundage. It's usually about 50 pounds less than the top single you worked across. If you are in doubt your first couple of workouts, take the lower poundage. Then if you find that you can handle the five singles and the five sets of five comfortably, add 5 pounds next time around. Just take five-pound jumps as the tonnage really adds up quickly when you are doing ten sets plus five sets of warm-ups.

A sample program for someone doing 300 x 5 or 340 for a single would look about like this:

Bench press: 135 x 5, 175 x 5, 205 x 5, 245 x 3, 275 x 3, 315 x 1 x5, 265 x 5 x 5.

You will be doing around 15 sets (make sure you warm-up thoroughly) of bench presses with a total of 45 reps with a moderately heavy to heavy weight. It is quite demanding and should initially be performed once a week. The time factor drags out more so than on most routines because you are doing so many heavy singles and then heavy fives. These cannot be hurried too much as you will not be able to handle enough weight to make the program effective. The other two work-out days should find you doing: behind-the-neck presses, military presses, incline presses, or even light bench presses. It is very easy to overtrain the bench press while doing the Hepburn routine so be very aware of your shoulder girdle during this time. If it gets in a state of fatigue, back off on some of the other pressing movements. Maybe even skip a day of pressing if you are overly tired. Sometimes, the wisest thing to do is to walk out of the gym or drop an exercise from your schedule for that day.

Set up a schedule of weights you plan to use, as I did for the sample trainee. If you successfully perform all of these, then add weight to both the singles and the fives the following week. Don't jump too much, however, as you are multiplying your work load a great deal because of the ten total sets. Five pounds is sufficient unless you started the program extra-cautiously and then ten may be more appropriate.

It is a smart idea to have a training partner for this type of program as someone standing over you lends a bit of needed motivation. It is as taxing mentally as it is physically to do ten sets with a heavy weight and this is why I caution you to keep this Hepburn routine to just once a week in your total program.

Some find it so exhausting that they only do shoulder work twice a week. One day of heavy bench pressing and another day using light weights in any of the other pressing exercises. As was mentioned earlier, you must be quite aware of your bodily responses to this particular type of program. If you feel very fatigued on Wednesday after doing the Hepburn routine on Monday, then it may be wise to skip all shoulder work entirely and wait until Friday. Keep atuned to your own body and learn to read how it responds to certain exercises and programs. In the final analysis, you are your own trainer.

THE INCLINE BENCH PRESS

If you have an incline bench available it is definitely an asset to your bench pressing progress. If not, the other pressing movements will have to do. The incline will replace the military press as the medium day workout and the behind-the-neck press will be used as the light day as usual. Monday still remains the bench pressing day. Some enjoy this variation because they are allowed to go limit each and every workout and the incline is a bit more resting to the lower back than the military. It really is three separate pressing programs amalgamated into one. Each of the three individual lifts helps the other two. As your bench pressing power increases, this helps the behind-the-neck presses. They, in turn, add to the incline. Pounds added to the incline carry over to the benches on Monday. Around and around the shoulder strength goes up and up.

The incline press works many of the same muscles as the bench press, but from a slightly different angle so it allows those bench pressing muscles some degree of rest.

Your shoulder girdle program might look like this:

Bench press (Monday) 135 x 5, 175 x 5, 225 x 5, 275 x 3, 295 x 3, 305 x 3, 255 x 6-10.

Behind-the-neck (Wednesday) 135 x 5, 145 x 5, 155 x 5, 165 x 3, 175 x 3, 185 x 3, 150 x 6-10.

Incline presses (Friday) 135 x 5, 155 x 5, 175 x 3, 185 x 3, 205 x 3, 215 x 3, 185 x 6-10.

You will notice that the poundages listed for the incline press are about the same as those for the military. This is generally the case and that is why they can be interchanged so easily. Some people do have better leverage in one or the other, however, but it usually doesn't vary much. The total weight lifted each day still allows you do to the heavy, light, and medium system as the tonnage is highest on Monday, lightest on Wednesday, and at a medium on Friday.

ADVANCED PULLING PROGRAMS

When I speak of pulling power, I am basically referring to strength of the back. While it is true that the legs do a good portion of the work in any pulling motion, it is the back that is most involved, so pulling exercises are considered back exercises.

My basic pulling lift, the power clean, will be the first to plateau in the program. Ironically, the gains also come the quickest in the power clean for a number of reasons. The muscles involved in the pull are generally not used in day-to-day activity, so once they become stimulated they develop rapidly. Then too, the power clean requires the most athletic ability. As soon as the trainee's technique develops, then the poundage goes up in direct proportion to his athletic ability. But when these two factors begin to level off, the gains come more begrudgingly.

INCLINE BENCH PRESS

IMPROPER RACKING IN THE POWER CLEAN

The Strength Coach has to be very aware of one factor in the power clean, this one dealing with safety. Many trainees, once they start handling quite heavy weights, have a tendency to hook the bar over in an arch at the top of the pull. As the weight strikes the chest it forces the upper body backward to stop the motion of the loaded barbell. The shock is taken up by the lower back and since the lower back is not constructed to bend backward resisting heavy weights, lower back trouble may result. A few changes are in order when this happens.

POWER PULLS

The power pull is a name given to an adaptation of the power clean. It is referred to as the hi-pull in the sport of

weightlifting. The power pull is an ideal movement for anyone who: 1) has leveled off on his progress on the power clean, 2) has wrist trouble when he racks the weight on his chest in the power clean, or 3) allows the weight to force his upper body backward when the bar racks at his chest.

The straps mentioned earlier in the book will now come in handy. The straps allow the trainee to hold more weight than he would be able to grip otherwise and since this movement is concluded with a snappy motion, it is rather critical to have a gripping aid. Keep the chalk handy and use it before each set. Gripping the bar becomes very important when you begin overloading the pulling muscles.

The power pull is done exactly the same as the power clean except you do not rack the barbell on your chest. Rather, you pull it to chest level and put it back to the platform. The advantages are obvious. Since you do not have to rack the bar at your chest, there is no stress placed on the wrists or lower back. More weight can be used so you can overload the pulling muscles more than in the power clean.

The disadvantages are more subtle. Since you do not rack the bar, the tendency is to move slower at the top part of the pull. If this happens you are defeating part of your purpose because it's that final snap that really involves the trapezius. A full, quick contraction will enable you to use more weight than if you merely pull slowly as in an upright row.

The Strength Coach has to constantly pound this fact into the trainee. The bar comes off the floor slowly, as in a dead lift. Then, as the bar passes the trainee's knees it begins to accelerate. The hips come towards the bar in a snappy motion, the traps contract and the arms bend. The bar should be at top speed at chest height. The trainee should be up on his toes with his head up, his body straight, and his elbows pointed upward — rather than backward. I teach a

THE POWER PULL

Using the Straps

Wrap the straps (in this case the straps are pieces of seat belts) around your wrist. Bring the straps up under and around the bar. They go the opposite direction from your fingers. Pull them around snuggly and grip your hands over the straps tightly.

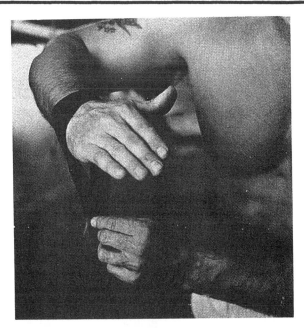

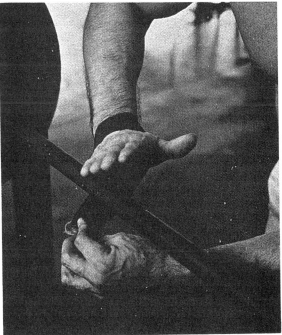

beginner to imagine that he is lifting the barbell to place it on a high shelf. He has to keep pulling up and up and up, fully extending his body. Lower the bar slowly, making certain that the same correct flat-back position is maintained. The aware coach must remember that there is just as much weight being lowered by the trainee as there is being lifted, so breaking the form while lowering the weight is just as hazardous as it is while elevating the barbell.

Let the weight come back to the platform. Reset your body to assure proper positioning with the hips low, the lower back flat, the shoulder back, and the head straight ahead or slightly upward. Now repeat the lift until you do the required five repetitions. Five sets of five are still in order. You should eventually be able to handle 50-100 more pounds in the power pull than you do in the power clean, that is if you have been doing power cleans regularly. This is assumed as the power pulls are a more advanced exercise and should not be done before you have spent sufficient time learning the power clean and developing the necessary muscles for the power pull to be effective.

Warm-up in the same manner as you do in the power clean. Most trainees find it very advantageous to power clean the first couple of sets so as to get the "feel" of pulling completely through at the top. I believe this is a good idea and definitely recommend it. Your third set should find you very close to your best power clean for five repetitions. Then add 10 or 20 pounds for your fourth set and, depending on the degree of difficulty of that fourth set, add 10 or 20 more for your final set. Assuming that you are doing 225 for five in the power clean, your beginning power pull routine might look like this:

Power pull: 135 x 5 (power clean), 175 x 5 (power clean), 225 x 5, 245 x 5, 265 x 5.

The power pull can fit into your program very nicely. Insert it on your heavy and medium days and continue to power clean on your light days. This way, you will be able to keep the power clean form which you have developed and still be able to overload the pulling muscles safely.

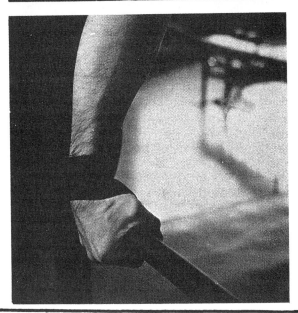

SHRUGS

BUILD A SOLID STRENGTH FOUNDATION

The shrugs are a step up from the power pulls, so don't involve shrugging in your program until you have been doing the power pulls for at least two months. Whenever you are doubtful as to when to move up to a more advanced exercise, check a few facts about yourself before making the move. Have you been making steady gains with the current exercise? If so, stay with them. Any program that is producing results is a good program. Have you been doing the less advanced exercises for a sufficient length of time to reap the full benefit from them? Four to six weeks is a minimum amount of time for any exercise. If you have been doing it less than this, stay with the less advanced exercises a bit longer. And finally, when in doubt it is usually better to stay with the lesser of the two. You'll find that long-range progress comes to the more patient trainee.

A firm foundation is critical for continued progress. While you might make an initial increase by incorporating an advanced exercise into your schedule prematurely, it will be short-lived because the strength reserve has not been filled sufficiently through lead-in exercises. Progressive weight training really has to be progressive in order to be effective.

SHRUGS

The very best exercise to overload the trapezius muscles is the shrug. It is a short-range motion and involves the strong upper back muscles so a great deal of weight can eventually be used. Some trainees work up to 500 pounds in this lift in just two or three months. This specific exercise for the trapezius carries over to the power cleans and power pulls since the trapezius is the primary muscle that brings the bar from belt height to chest level. As the traps become bigger and stronger, the trainee will be better able to violently snap the bar at the very top-most part of the pull. The shrug also involves the flexors of the upper arm to a high degree. The strong brachioradialis and brachialis come into play during this final snappy pull. These important muscles serve to stabilize the elbow joint.

Shrugs are only to be used by the advanced trainee. Without a proper strength base in the pulling muscles, shrugs will serve little purpose except to tire you. The overload has to come in a progressive sequence. To attempt to jump ahead without first building a proper foundation on any lift is a mistake. It's like trying to understand physics without first learning algebra. It's just too tough to pull off.

In performing the shrug, you will again use straps. If at all possible, set the loaded barbell at a level so that it strikes you just above your knees. This will enable you to do the shrug without lifting the weight off the floor. You will eventually be able to shrug much more than you can dead lift, so you do not want to limit the amount of weight that you will be using. Also, if you have to dead lift a heavy weight (I am talking about 400-500 pounds) you will drain so much energy that you will not be able to put your full effort into the shrug itself.

Set the loaded barbell on two blocks or boxes or at knee level on a power rack (old metal milk crates make ideal blocks). The power rack is ready-made for this exercise. Walk to the barbell, strap tightly to it and set your body in a very solid pulling position. Your pulling position should duplicate the position you would have as if the bar was passing that particular point on your body in the power clean or power pull. Do not attempt to jerk the bar from this starting position. Ease it off the blocks slowly, making sure that your body stays very tight, and accelerate it rapidly. As the bar leaves the blocks, the hips will drive quickly towards the bar and the traps will lift upward. The arms bend very slightly and then only at the last split second of the upward pull. The upward thrust is concentrated in the trapezius. Think of pulling the trapezius up towards the ears. At the very top of the pull, resist the bar and try to hold it high for a second. Lower it back to the blocks slowly, making sure that your back is still flat on the decent. Reset your body position and pull again.

The general tendency of most trainees is to jerk the weight from the blocks in hopes that this initial acceleration will carry over to the top. Alas, this is not true. Rather, the opposite happens. When the bar is jerked from the blocks the lower back and shoulders round. When this occurs, the body is no longer in a position to utilize its most favorable leverage and the pulling strength is greatly diminished. The bar must be kept very, very close to your body throughout the movement. I suggest that you do not wear a belt when shrugging as the bar will catch on it either going up or coming down and a nasty pinch on the tummy will result.

You can demonstrate to yourself the great importance of keeping the bar close to your body. Load a barbell to about 300 pounds and place it on your shrugging blocks or in the power rack at the desired knee height. Stand so that your legs are about four inches away from the bar. Attempt to lift it straight up, not towards you, but in a direct vertical line. Chances are, you will not be able to do it with any degree of success and you should feel a great strain in the middle and lower back. Now step in tight against the bar and lift it again so that it slides straight up your body. The second movement will be quite noticeably stronger. Even the most conditioned weightlifter has trouble moving 400 pounds if the bar is away from his body, but quite a few have shrugged in excess of 700 pounds because they have learned the importance of keeping the bar in close.

The purpose of the shrug is to overload the trapezius muscle, so heavy weights must be employed if you are to achieve your goal. If you are power cleaning 200 x 5 you will need to be eventually shrugging 400 x 5. If you power clean 250 x 5, then your goal will be 500 x 5, after a period of getting used to the exercise, of course. My rule of thumb is to double the weight used in the power clean to determine the shrugging poundage. This does not imply, once again, that you should use 400 pounds in the shrug in your very first workout on the exercise. You will work into the heavier weights progressively, but the standards are mentioned so as to give you a gauge to work towards.

Since the shrug is a short-range movement and since the weights are extra heavy, you are not expected to pull the bar as high as you did in the power clean or the power pull. I teach players to pull as high as they possibly can and if I see that they are getting a good trapezius contraction, then I am satisfied. The most important part of the shrug is the very last snappy motion. If this final tugging on the bar to elevate it to the ultimate height is not done with a snap, then the trapezius does not contract as fully and part of the effect is lost.

Assuming our trainee is using 200 x 5 in the power clean, here's what his shrugging routine might look like:

Shrugs: 135 x 5, 225 x 5, 305 x 5, 325 x 5, 355 x 5 — working towards a final set of 400 x 5 in three to four weeks.

WORKING SHRUGS INTO THE PROGRAM

The shrug can be inserted into your pulling program quite simply. Use shrugs for your heavy day, power cleans for your light day, and power pulls for your medium day. This is, quite obviously, a lot of pulling but it must be remembered that this section is only for an advanced trainee and should not be attempted by anyone who does not have at least six months to a year of hard training behind him. Remember that the muscles have to be coaxed, not pushed, into submission. Otherwise, they will rebel and you will be left with, at best, sore muscles, fatigue, and lack of progress or at worst, slip to the far end of the negative ladder, injury.

FATIGUE IN THE PULLING MUSCLES

One additional note concerning fatigue and the pulling muscles fits in this section nicely. It is very difficult to identify fatigue in the pulling muscles (primarily those of the back). When the legs are fatigued they generally exude some soreness and you can feel the tiredness when you walk or try to run or jump. Likewise, the muscles of the shoulder girdle give you plenty of clues as to when they are over trained. But the back muscles, after the first few weeks of hard training, feel very much the same all the time. As a result, it becomes quite difficult to determine when they are fatigued. The only way to do so is to observe the speed of movement of the pulling exercises. If the trainee is moving slower than usual on the power clean, for example, it is a fairly certain indication that his back muscles are fatigued and appropriate steps should be taken.

When the fatigue is evident, take a day off from pulling or go extremely light for that day. A bit of rest will often be the perfect prescription. It takes a certain amount of training for the Strength Coach to identify this fatigue, but the aware individual will make it his duty to be observant of all his charges in the weight room.

Don Herrold performing a shrug with 585. A great deal of weight can be handled in this short-range upper back movement, once the athlete has established a solid strength foundation. Don has used over 700 pounds in this lift.

OMIT THE DEAD LIFT

At this point some readers are going to ask why I have not mentioned the dead lift in my advanced section, or even in the entire book for that matter. It is an advanced exercise used to build a stronger back, is it not? It is, but it also has a high casualty rate, especially in trainees who are not adequately prepared for the great stress placed on the lower back. Very few people, and this includes the top competitive weightlifters, keep a good back position on a heavy dead lift. The football player can build the same power in the lower back through the other suggested exercises without the risk of injury. It's just not worth the risk because the trainee can accomplish the same goal by other means.

The author knows of several instances where Olympic weightlifters did power cleans, power pulls, shrugs along with their cleans and snatches. These quicker movements made many of them stronger in the dead lift than their fellow powerlifters who practiced the dead lift two or three times a week. As I have said before, there's more than one way to skin a cat. I'll pass dead lifts for football players for safety is my primary consideration when I recommend any exercise. If the danger is higher than the benefits, I discourage the exercise. So it is with the dead lift.

ADVANCED LEG AND HIP PROGRAMS

Squats

Squats are a most integral part of total body strength. Without strong legs and hips, the rest of the body is built on a shaky foundation. As the squat poundage increases, so does the bench press and the power clean, or any other exercise which has been included in your program. Almost universally, squats thrive on hard work. This is why few trainees succeed in this particular lift. Everyone seems to enjoy bench pressing, but few look forward to squats. The reason is simple. Squats are about 10 times more taxing than bench presses.

A thorough squat program will leave you with wobbly legs and panting for air. It feels as if all your energy has drained into your socks. Few realize, also, how important it is to handle heavy, heavy weights in this important lift. I have had trainees swear that they can only handle 200 pounds for five. I put 20 more pounds on the barbell and they do five. After a certain poundage, all squats feel just about the same — heavy. Then it's merely a matter of convincing your mind to do one more repetition, and then one more yet. This is where a training partner comes in handy. Having someone standing near-by prodding you on certainly helps in squats.

A great deal of weight has to be handled to produce significant results for the simple reason that the muscles of the legs are just so large. While a big arm measures 15, 16, or 17 inches on a 200-pound individual, the upper thigh on the same person will register 26, 27, or 28 inches (assuming that he has been doing plenty of leg work). Yet it is not unusual to discover some trainees using the exact same weight in both squats and the bench press. There should be a minimum of 100 pounds difference between the two lifts.

Assuming that you have invested sufficient time into a serious leg program and have leveled off in your progress, I am offering a few suggestions to help you break out of that rut. I should reiterate the statement I made at the start of this chapter concerning individual variances in work load. Most trainees, when their squatting progress comes to a halt, need more work since the tendency is to slacken off on this tedious exercise.

But this is not usually the case. Other individuals tend to progress if the total weekly work load is lightened somewhat. My training partner for 4 years, Tommy Suggs, makes progress by squatting just twice a week, heavy once and medium the other. I could only improve my squat by going heavy three times a week. Two very different approaches to the same goal, based entirely on individual differences.

HIGH AND LOW ENERGY TRAINEES

In adapting your program to suit your individual needs you will have to decide, once again, into which category you belong. My basic rule of thumb still holds true 99% of the time. That is, high energy individuals tend to thrive on more work while their lower energy counterparts make better progress with less total work. This does not mean, however, that the latter group does not put out 100% while doing squats. On the contrary, they expend maximum effort on their heavy days and use very heavy weights. They just do not do as much total weekly work, but their top effort is just as high or higher than their higher energy peers.

I should mention that if you are not certain as to which category you belong, then join the group which does more rather than less in the case of squats. It's always simpler to drop an exercise than it is to add one, so experiment with yourself first by training more. If, after a four or five-week testing period, you find yourself overly tired, then try the other routine. Please read the section on nutrition before deciding finally whether you are a high or low energy person. A change in your dietary habits might just reverse your energy potential.

Also, when you first upgrade your squatting program it is only natural to experience a bit of extra tiredness as heavy squat work is extremely demanding. Do not jump off the bandwagon too soon and figure that you are just a low energy sort. Give the program a fair chance to have an effect on your total strength before changing.

It should also be recorded that some individuals are just better constructed for squatting than others. This holds true for any exercise and not just for squats, by the way. Because of bone formation, ligament and tendon attachments, length of bones plus various other factors certain people just naturally have an edge in the leverage department. This usually balances out overall so it is nothing to be concerned about. If you have poor pressing leverage, chances are you have an advantage in the pulling movements or the squatting movements. Very rarely does one come equipped with exceptional leverage in all departments and equally rare is the individual lacking leverage in all lifts. They balance each other out so that total strength comes out the same assuming the same amount of work is applied.

TENS, FIVES, AND THREES

Tens, Fives, and Threes

A squat program that has proven itself on football players throughout the years is a program I developed that combines one day of high reps, one of low reps, and one of moderate reps. The higher the repetitions, the lower the intensity and vice versa. The ten repetitions build a tremendous reservoir of power, the threes attack the ligament and tendons more deeply since greater weight is utilized and the fives are the basic power formula which I have been using throughout.

QUARTER SQUATS

The success of this program depends almost entirely on the trainee's ability to work hard at every workout, since he will be going "all-out" each time he trains. There are no easy days, although the threes are a welcome relief after the tens. The program is essentially three separate squatting programs rolled into one. You will be improving each of the three every week — you only do each of them once a week. Most trainees enjoy this variety of programming as it allows them to put full mental effort into a different type of squatting each workout. If they were just doing tens three times a week they would have a tendency to get stale.

It is difficult for most trainees to gear up for heavy tens or triples more than once a week. The fives seem to be the most palatable compromise between the two. This variety of programming helps to stimulate motivation. Sometimes, only the tens will improve for a week or two. This is encouragement enough. If the trainee were only doing 3s or 5s, he would be much less excited about squatting since they are difficult enough when gains are being made. What usually happens is that each of the three different routines help the others. As the tens climb higher and higher, the threes come easier. The threes help break mental barriers of heavier weights and allows more poundage to be used in the fives. The fives, being the basic strength builders, enable the trainee to attack the tens with more total hip and leg strength.

Here's how you go about setting up your program. Do the five sets of tens on Monday, counting the warm-ups, as usual. Stagger the sets so that your final set will be the most you can do for ten repetitions. For the first few weeks some trainees find that they can do the highest set of tens on the fourth, rather than the fifth set. This is permissible, just so long as you back off and do a final set of ten with a moderate heavy weight. It's rather like skipping the fourth set and then backing off to it, but make sure you get the work in. Until you get used to doing ten reps you may under-shoot or over-shoot the proper poundage rather easily, but after a couple of workouts you should be right on target.

The Wednesday workout will find you doing five sets of three reps, again working to maximum. The threes take a slightly different toll on the muscles, tendons, and ligaments. This basically, is the purpose of doing threes. The heavier poundage allows you to overload the legs and hips to a much greater degree than the lighter poundages for higher reps. Not as much total work is performed on the three days, but the deep muscles and important attachments are thoroughly stimulated and strengthened.

Friday is the day for the familiar five sets of fives. This is the least taxing, speaking from both a mental and physical standpoint. The tens are the buggers physically and the threes zap the mind, but the fives are cool. They seem to keep a healthy balance to the overall program and fully complement the high rep and low rep days. You will be going all-out on this day too for your best five repetitions.

Your squat program might look like this:

Monday: 135 x 10, 155 x 10, 175 x 10, 205 x 10, 225 x 10, total 8950 pounds

Wednesday: 135 x 3, 185 x 3, 245 x 3, 275 x 3, 305 x 3, total 3435 pounds

Friday: 135 x 5, 175 x 5, 225 x 5, 250 x 5, 275 x 5, total 5300 pounds

As the reader might notice, the program still follows the heavy, light, and medium system, based on total tonnage lifted. Even though the tens utilize the lightest weight, they also produce the most total work load, due to the fact that the reps are high. In our sample program the total poundage for the ten days was 8950 pounds. The three work the body the least because of the low reps so this day is the light day, tonnage-wise, although it takes perhaps the most mental concentration. The threes used a total of 3435 pounds. The fives are the mid-point, both physically and mentally, so they rightfully belong to the medium day, Friday. They used 5300 pounds.

As you meet your schedule on any of the three separate programs, then you will increase the poundage on that particular segment of the squats the following week. That is, if you are scheduled to try a final set of ten with 235 and succeed, then add ten pounds to that final effort next week. It does not mean, however, that you add weight to the threes or fives. You only increase those after you have accomplished your goal for that week. Should you only do a double with 315 on your three day, then you will have to use 315 the following week once again.

No hedging. If you do not achieve your designed poundage for the required number of reps, then use that same weight the following week. You may find one of the three programs taking a rather abrupt jump for two or three weeks while the others remain dormant. This is not unusual and is merely a breaking-in-period. It's sort of like water finding its own

level. Once this point is obtained, however, typically all three of the programs begin improving simultaneously.

As the tens go up, the threes become stronger. As the threes increase, more power is available for the fives. The fives, in turn, help the tens. Your progress chart, after the initial breaking-in period of soreness and finding the correct poundages to use in each of the three segments, should improve steadily for quite some time.

QUARTER SQUATS

One of the best ways to overload the muscles of the legs and hips is by doing heavy half or quarter squats. What most people call a half squat is in actuality a quarter squat so I will use that latter term.

The quarter squat allows you to overload the squatting muscles. Whereas you might only be able to full squat with 250 x 10, or 300 x 5, or 325 x 3, you will be able to use in excess of 400+ in the quarter squat. This builds a great deal of strength in the hip area which is the center of power for any athlete.

Quarter squats are only to be performed by the more advanced trainee. To start a player on this movement too soon is merely inviting problems. Most players will be able to handle the weight, but until the muscles that support the lower back, knees and hips are strong enough to withstand the added stress of the overload it is not a safe lift. One move that puts the body out of perfect alignment may cause muscle damage without the proper supporting strength. This strength comes from the lead-in high sets and reps or regular full squats.

Some like to do the quarter squats in the power rack and I believe this is a good idea because it is the safest way to do the exercise. If a power rack is not available, be sure the spotters are capable and close at hand. I do not feel that it is wise to use a bench for this lift. The bench hits everyone at a different height. I also find that the trainee will "reach" for the bench and relax his lower back momentarily. If he sets and relaxes, all the pressure is placed on his lower back and this is not good.

It is far better to squat down until the bar touches the pins on the power rack or have your training partner signal when you have gone low enough.

As you take the loaded barbell off the squat rack you have to be very careful that your body is straight and tight from tip to toes. Move out slowly — unless you are in a power rack — making short baby steps so that the heavy weight stays evenly distributed on your back.

Go down as low as desired, usually about 8-10 inches and come back erect quickly. Go as low as you can without sticking with each weight. As the bar gets heavier, don't go quite so low, but always go to a point where you can just barely recover.

The quarter squat can work into your program very simply. It can either replace the 10s, 5s, or 3s (one of these, not all three) if you are using that system, or it can be dovetailed behind any of those days. For example, some trainees like to work up heavy in fives and then continue on for five more sets of five in the quarter squat. After such a strenuous workout it is usually wise to bypass squatting the next session or to cut back on the total work as ten sets of squats are very demanding. Yet, some can carry the work load while others need to rest more inbetween heavy days.

Still another routine is to do two or three sets of full squats and then continue on with five sets of quarter squats. This only makes eight sets and since quarter squats are a short-range movement, they are not nearly as taxing as are squats. The full squats serve as a warm-up for the overloading which is a wise idea.

Assuming that you can squat with 300 x 5 and select the latter program, it might look like this:
Squats: 135 x 5, 185 x 5, 250 x 5
Followed by Quarter Squats: 300 x 5, 325 x 5, 350 x 5, 375 x 5, 400 x 5

It is a good idea to keep the reps up to five in the quarter squat so that you are getting sufficient total work. Anything less does not build the reserve that you are after as readily.

MORE REST IS OFTEN NECESSARY

As you get into heavier and heavier poundages, you might find it necessary to give your hips and legs a bit longer rest, especially after the ten-day. One of my University of Hawaii players, under this system, increased so rapidly that he was handling 15,000 pounds in one work-out. Don Herrold's final set of ten was with 400 pounds. When you get up around a weight equal to 1½-2 times your bodyweight in the tens, then an extra day of rest is definitely in order.

Then you might start flip-flopping the squat days so that they do not necessarily fall on any specific training day. For example, you might do the tens on Monday, wait until Friday to do the threes, the fives on the following Monday and the tens again on Wednesday and tens on Friday, and so on and so forth. Or you might just skip one day a month and fill in the others. These are merely suggestions for you to keep in mind when you find your progress coming to a halt. Staleness is generally attributable to mental or physical overwork, so some change is in order. In this case, merely skipping a day is usually sufficient.

It's a demanding test, but one which will produce results. The legs, generally, need lots of work to jar them into strength gains. After you have obtained a satisfactory goal for yourself, you can switch back to the five sets of five system for three days a week with an occasional ten day and still maintain your strength level. The toughest chore is getting the leg and hip strength up initially. After that, it's not so difficult.

At the beginning of the section on the bench press I mentioned that some trainees respond better with more work while others improve with less work. Most trainees need to do more, rather than less in the squat, but this is not universally true. Some individuals do better by squatting very heavy once a week and medium one other time. Again, it is the duty of the Strength Coach to be aware of these individual differences. If the trainee is consistently tired in the legs and hips and his squat plateaus or regresses, then a change is in order.

FRONT SQUATS

The front squat is a variation of the more familiar back squat. The front squat involves the muscles of the front of the leg (quadriceps) more thoroughly than does the back squat. It also has the advantage that it eliminates much of the pressure on the lower back. They are most useful for variety as back squats month after month do become monotonous to most trainees.

Since the movement is slightly different it does bring into play a few different muscles and this is desirable for overall development. Many authorities believe that the front squats puts less stress on the knee joint and recommend it over the more traditional back squat.

The front squat can easily be inserted into your program on your light day as less weight is used in this exercise. Keep your repetitions at five until you begin handling 300+ and then reduce your over-300 sets to but three reps.

A sample program for a 305 x 5 back squatter would be set up in this manner:
Front Squat: 135 x 5, 175 x 5, 215 x 5, 235 x 5, 255 x 5.

A fifty-pound difference is allowed between a maximum back and front squat. There is a bit of new flexibility needed in order to correctly perform front squats, especially in the shoulders and elbows so it is best not to overdo this exercise until the positioning feel secure.

In performing a front squat, place the loaded barbell across your frontal deltoids with your elbows held high. Your triceps should be parallel with the floor throughout the movement. Be certain to go into the bottom position slowly and keep your elbows up at all times. The initial move out of the bottom-most position in with the elbows. You cannot allow them to drop or the bar will go foward and you will not be able to put a full effort into the lift. The weight must be kept back so that your hips and legs are able to do the bulk of the work.

Some trainees find that when the bar lies across their high chest that it restricts their breathing. If the elbows dip, then the weight is being supported on the clavicles and breathing is difficult. Keep the elbows high so that the frontal deltoids do the supporting rather than the clavicles.

After you move the weight to 300 x 5 alter your program in this manner: 135 x 5, 205 x 5, 255 x 5, 275 x 3, 325 x 3.

The threes are necessary for most trainees since it becomes extremely difficult to breath properly with a heavy weight lying across the throat.

THE FRONT SQUAT

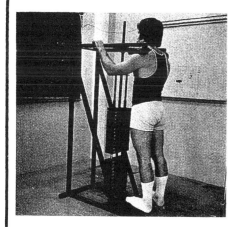
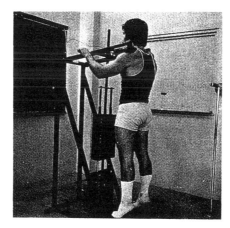

TOE RAISES

The toe raise, also referred to as the calf raise, is a most useful exercise for the football player as it involves the gastrocnemius directly. As was pointed out earlier, this muscle extends across the back of the knee and helps to stabilize it.

The gastrconemius is most useful to football players as it is one of the primary muscles used in running and jumping. It is possible to add as much as six inches to one's jumping ability in a four-month period with this exercise.

The one draw-back to the toe raise is that it requires a special piece of equipment for good results. Calf raises can be done in a squat or power rack, but then the factor of balance limits the total amount of work that can be performed. In a calf raise machine, all the effort can be centered into the muscle group.

The gastrconemius muscle is a difficult one to stimulate. It is tough to make it grow or to become stronger because it is a weight-bearing muscle and is worked constantly. In order to make it respond, it has to be worked very hard.

High reps are in order. Initially, do three sets of 30 reps with enough resistance so that the last 8-10 reps create a "burning" sensation in the muscle. Change the angle of your feet on each set of the three sets. Point your toes straight ahead on the first set, pigeontoed on the second, and pointed outward on the third. This will give you a more thorough, well-rounded development. After three or four weeks on this program, begin doing a total of six sets of thirty reps, again changing your foot angle on each of the sets.

It is critical to stretch the calf muscles immediately after each and every set. Step out of the machine and stretch each leg. If this stretching is not done, tightness will invariably result and the risk of pulling this muscle goes up.

Select a weight that forces you to work very hard on the last 8-10 reps. Be sure that you do full-range movements so as to get a complete development. If you are doing the exercise on a rack, use a 2 x 4 under your toes so that a full-range is performed.

TIMED SQUATS

Timed Squats

During the summer of 1967, Tommy Suggs and I decided to experiment on ourselves with a squat program designed to increase cardiovascular, respiratory fitness. This may seem to be a strange goal for a pair of aspiring competitive weightlifters, but actually cardiovascular, respiratory fitness is an important variable in our sport. Total conditioning counts for a great deal as some contests drag on for as long as twelve hours and the more fit athlete has a definite advantage over his opponents. Those who are in better shape can train harder and longer and, if they are practicing the right kinds of things, should improve more than those who do not do so. All serious weightlifters generally spend time in the off-season doing some type of endurance work such as jogging, playing paddleball, handball, or basketball.

We wanted to see if we could accomplish the same goal via the weights, something most authorities felt was not really possible. But most authorities, which include the majority of the pure researchers, do not utilize a heavy training movement like the squat. They test their subjects on hand gripping, or leg extensions. We wanted a test that would relate to the strength athlete. If it worked for him, then it could have applications for everyone.

We immediately selected squats for our testing lift as we already knew that this lift placed the greatest demand on the heart and lungs, save perhaps repetition clean and jerks which required a too high level of learning.

We wanted something that could be used by everyone interested in obtaining a higher level of cardiovascular, respiratory fitness and everyone can learn to do squats in one or two workouts.

We set up the following schedule: five sets of ten repetitions were to be performed, starting with a light weight and working towards a heavier set. The major difference in this routine from any other squatting program would be that we would time our squatting sessions. We carefully calculated how long we would be allowed to rest in between each set and projected the time it would take to actually perform the ten repetitions. Our goal was to do the five sets in 12 minutes or less the first day.

We warmed up thoroughly before going to the squat rack, but made the squat our first exercise for the day. We did this program just twice a week, allowing three days rest between sessions to the exclusion of all other squatting movements. We felt it would be too demanding to attempt to do more and we didn't want to entirely neglect our other Olympic lifts during the experiment.

Since we were just about equal in our squatting ability we would both be taking the exact same weights so that there would not be any time wasted in changing the plates twice As soon as one finished his set the other would jump right in and do his. One squatter was allowed 15 seconds rest after the first set, which was almost exactly the time it took the other to do his reps. We tried to get the bar on our shoulders, step out of the rack, place our feet properly and begin just as rapidly as possible. There was very little genuine resting time since as the weight got heavier it took longer to perform the reps and, of course, we were getting more and more fatigued as the sets added up. We marked down the exact time we commenced each set, elapsed time it took to do the reps, resting time between sets, and poundage used for each set.

The first session we did: 135 x 10, 175 x 10, 205 x 10, 255 x 10 275 x 10 in a total of ten minutes from the time the first lifter did his first rep until his final rep on the last set. We were, to greatly understand a fact, breathing heavily at the conclusion of the five sets. More like asthmatic rhinos really. We checked our pulse rates just as soon as we were able (within 15 seconds after the completion of the final set) and found them to be 180+.

We wanted a squat program that would increase cardiovascular, respiratory fitness.

It should be noted that this was not the first cardiovascular respiratory type of training that we had engaged in that summer. If it had been we never would have gotten through the five sets at all. We were able to play paddleball at a good clip for 1½ hours without a break and both could run a couple of miles without any great stress. We were also in strong shape as far as squatting power goes. Both could do over 500 for a single and we were handling 425 x 5 regularly in training. Nevertheless, the timed squats put us down. No amount of running could get us that tired because we would stop running first. But when you are standing in one spot and merely going up and down, it's surprising what you can trick your mind into doing.

This was to be but the first step, however. We knew that we could get a terrific fitness workout from the program but we wanted to see if we could get stronger at the same time. Our idea was to increase the top poundage used each time while decreasing the time factor. Seemed a bit insane after that first workout but we were determined to stick it out. We were, quite honestly, tired of hearing pseudo-experts say that weights cannot build cardiovascular, respiratory fitness. We stayed with the program for a total of four weeks and increased the top weight by ten pounds each workout. This amounted to eight individual workouts. At the conclusion of the experiment, eight workouts, we did 355 x 10 as our top weight and did all five sets in seven minutes. An increase of eighty pounds and a shaving of three full minutes. The increase in weight wasn't nearly as difficult as the time factor. There is only so much time that can be clipped away as it takes time to load the bar, get set, and finally to do the repetitions, regardless of the weight.

We learned that the body can be pushed to ridiculous limits. We would walk to the bar, feeling dizzy and seeing those funny little spots popping in front of our eyes. It felt as if we had just run ten 440s in a row. Yet we discovered that the body would still respond. We would go down and come back up, regardless of how winded we were. It helped us a great deal to realize that we seldom genuinely tap the deep reservoir of strength. Previously, we had become so accustomed to taking a 5 to 10 minute break between sets that we felt that it was essential. We discovered it was only essential if you trained that way.

We only stayed on this program for a month because we just became too exhausted mentally. There's only so much masochism in each of us and we had used ours up in four weeks. It took a great deal of mental preparation for each squat workout as we realized after that first time that we were walking (voluntarily yet) into a torture chamber. The program never had a break in it because we kept increasing the weight and squeezing the time.

The experiment is recorded here because I feel that it does have a place in the Strength Coach's log book. The timed squats can help a player who has been stuck on this lift for a prolonged period of time. It is also a worthwhile routine to know in case other cardiovascular, respiratory fitness exercises are not available, because of lack of facilities, inclimate weather, or whatever.

It is also handy to have around just in case some "Doubting Thomas" wanders into an argument concerning the cardiovascular potential of weights. Just put the skeptic on this program and watch him change his opinion. I have done this on several occasions. Few get through three sets of a ten-minute schedule. This is the ace up your strength coaching sleeve.

Since this was an informal test I did not present any hard statistics, but I do know that anyone who wants to duplicate this experiment will discover a tremendous cardiovascular exercise exists in the weight room.

THE "OTHER" EXERCISES

At this point, I am certain that a majority of the readers are wondering why I didn't include the many other exercises that can be utilized in weight training for football. What about the: bent-over rows, up-right rows, close-grip bench presses, pullovers, leg presses, lat pulldowns, good mornings, triceps extensions, dips, and the wide variety of curls?

There is no end to the number of exercises that could be recommended or explained. What I have presented is a series of exercises and sample programs that are the **most** useful. The question is in priorities. There is only so much time to be spent on strength training in any football program, so it should be spent on the most useful movements as they relate to football.

In actuality, the "Big Three" would serve any football team extremely well. The others have been mentioned primarily for variety. Variety to break up the monotony and to move through the sticking points.

There are plenty of exercises outlined in this book to occupy any football player for his entire career. Too many changes are not recommended. Do not change merely for the sake of change. Use the selection presented in this chapter only to further motivate and assist the players to obtain higher strength levels.

SEEK PROPORTIONATE DEVELOPMENT

Earlier I mentioned the principle of priority training, but a bit of clarification of that concept is now in order. As the trainee starts progressing on to higher and higher strength levels it is important for the Strength Coach to observe and make certain suggestions so that the trainee does not let certain body parts get further developed than others, at least not by a wide margin.

I realize that some fellows will become more powerful in the shoulder muscles more quickly than they do in the back. Or their legs blossom, but their arms and shoulders lag behind. This is fine, just so long as one lift does not dominate the total workout to the exclusion of the rest. The biggest

The giant Tongan, John Phillip, prepares himself for a limit squat. A former All-American Rugby player, John began training with Bill Starr soon after the author moved to the islands. In less than 18 months of training on the powerlifts, John progressed to the point that he placed second at the 1975 World Powerlifting Championships held in Birmingham, England. Many of the methods in this book are a result of working with "super specimens" like Big John.

problem arises in the bench press as this is, by far, the most popular lift and, as a result, the trainee often becomes fixated on it to the total exclusion of serious work on the other portions of his body. Lopsided or top-heavy development is not desirable for the athlete. The bodybuilder is on a different trip. For him a 50-inch chest and 19-inch arms are goals within themselves. Not so for an athlete. His goal is total body strength and any area that is noticeably weaker than the rest is hindering his chances of becoming completely strong and a functional performer.

WEAKEST LINK

A cliche' is unfortunately best suited for this occasion. A chain is no stronger than its weakest link. It is often difficult for the Strength Coach to convey this truism that stronger legs actually benefit the bench press. Stronger shoulders assist in more pulling strength. A strong back brings the leg strength up and so on and so forth. But, they have to be kept in proportion to each other. If one area of your total body strength, i.e., legs, back, or shoulders, drops way behind, it adversely affects the other two. So, it is imperative that the Srength Coach does not allow his players to get so infatuated with the bench press that they neglect their pulling or squatting routines.

It is always rewarding to see a trainee break through the 300-bench press barrier, but if this same trainee is only squatting with 300, then just how totally strong is he really?

This is why they test all three lifts in powerlifting competition: bench press, squat, and dead lift and the winner is determined by the total lifted on the three separate lifts, rather than by individual performances.

The player should work just as hard on his leg biceps as he does his shoulders because a weak leg biceps will put him out of action fast. The Strength Coach must instill pride in a 400-pound squat just as readily as he does for a 300-pound bench press. The trainee is quite aware of the Strength Coach's attitude. If the coach is talking it up around school about Beryl Fleming doing a 300-pound bench press, but avoids mentioning Herb Davis' 400-pound squat or Talmadge Cheek's 250-power clean, then which lift do you suppose the boys will work on the hardest in the future?

If the Srength Coach sees a certain player getting too involved in one lift, like 90% of the time on the bench press, then he should step in immediately. He should not, however, discourage progress on any lift, including the bench press, but merely get the other lifts up to par. This can be done rather simply.

THE "BACK-OFF SET

As the trainee becomes more advanced in his program, he will be able to handle more and more work load. An ideal and time-saving method of adding extra work without severly tapping the energy level of the trainee in to use a "back-off" set.

After the usual sets allocated for a specific exercise, you may have the trainee drop to a lighter poundage on that exercise and do a final set of relative high repetitions, usually 8-10.

This "back-off" is especially useful in leg and shoulder exercises, but has not been as useful in back exercises. I only use it for squats and pressing movements. It helps to build a terrific strength reserve.

It is only to be used, however, after a trainee has worked for a sufficient time on any of the exercises. My guidelines are: if the trainee can bench press 225 x 5 or squat 300 x 5, then he is ready for a "back-off" set. Otherwise, I keep them on the "Big Three" until they reach that strength level.

A "back-off" for the squat would be set up in this manner: Back squat: 135 x 5, 175 x 5, 225 x 5, 275 x 5, 305 x 5, back-off 225 x 10.

The basic guideline in selecting the "back-off" poundage is to choose a weight 50-pounds less than the trainee can use for five repetitions.

PRIORITY TRAINING

Priority training was mentioned earlier and simply means that the trainee is to put the lift which is most important first in his program. In this case, I am talking about the weakest lift. So, if a trainee is falling off on the squats, drop the circuit and put squats right up front in the workout. Put the next weakest lift second in the program and continue right on down the line to the strongest. The rule in any athletic endeavor is "work the weak points." It is especially true in strength training as the weak points will be the ones to hold you back in the end.

Keep pulling those weaker lifts up and while you may not out-bench press everyone else, you will be the strongest overall and this is exactly how progress should be graded by the Strength Coach. Not by one lift, but by total progress on all the designated exercises.

An athlete must work for total and functional strength.

ADDING A DAY

As some players become more and more advanced the Strength Coach may find that they are doing far too much during their three workouts a week. The time spent in the workout room becomes fatiguing in itself and the exercises that come up last in the program receive little emphasis. This may necessitate adding another day of training to your program. Players who have trained for three to four years often build up a great capacity for weight training and are able to work for 1½-2 hours in the weight room without becoming overly fatigued. Those that adhere to the concepts of sound nutrition are able to handle terrific training loads after a few years. But, since most are handling quite heavy weights in all the exercises, they find that they simply cannot do justice towards the end of their programs.

By dropping a few of the Monday-Wednesday-Friday exercises and putting them in on an extra day they find that they have plenty of energy for a full week of training. Caution is in order at this juncture however. Only experienced, seasoned trainees with a couple of years backlog should even consider adding on an extra day. Again, that firm foundation has to be laid and it should be remembered that football players, unlike competitive weightlifters, are not able to go full blast on the weights year round. At best, high school players can squeeze in six months and college and professional players around four. So it takes a football player about two or three years to accumulate the weight training experience necessary to be classified as an advanced trainee.

When that time arrives, however, try a Monday-Tuesday-Thursday-Friday schedule. Some like to skip Friday and train on Saturday. Setting up two separate programs, an "A" and a "B" program is often desirable. Do the "A" routine on Monday and Thursday and the "B" on Tuesday and Friday. This allows three days of rest between specific workouts and seems to work out fine for some. Others like to mix and match, using the three regular days for the basic exercises and the extra day for the specialized movements they have added in over the years.

DANGERS OF OVERTRAINING

When a player becomes an advanced weight trainee, he has to be prepared to adjust his thinking on ideas of training and also on those of rest and recovery. Some players are quite seasoned in strength training. A few I know started in junior high school. Others were exposed on the high school or college level. A couple of professionals, like Ray Schoneke of the Redskins and Bob Grant, who was with the Colts, had over 10-years of weight training behind them. These experienced men have spent four or five months a year working as diligently as an Olympic weightlifter in order to become stronger. Most players, after a three or four-year backlog of hard training start to add exercises to their schedule each year. Soon they are doing a 1½-2 hour routine, three to four times a week.

The mere fact that the veteran trainees are engaged in 6-8 hours of strenuous weight training per week is not necessarily harmful. On the contrary, if they can build up to this level of total work, then they will become stronger than their peers who are not able to work quite so hard. The fly in the ointment is overtraining. This must be avoided as it deters progress and invites injury.

The total workout can most certainly be increased month by month and year by year. Seasoned competitive weightlifters have been able to build up their training load to the point where they can train twice a day for six days a week and continue to improve. It cannot be done haphazardly, however, as certain rules must be adhered to or the trainee will completely defeat his purpose.

The rules concerning nutrition and rest are very important and will be covered in later chapters. The rule dealing with periodical lay-offs will be presented now.

PERIODICAL LAYOFFS

It is a wise idea to set up advanced programs on a 6 to 8 week basis. Competitive weightlifters, the practical researchers in the strength field, generally set up a 6-8 week schedule which culminates in a contest. So, if they have a contest scheduled for the end of March, they begin their heavy training schedules the first week in February. Each week they build up the tonnage so that they are at the peak of their strength for the competition.

After the contest they take a week off. This is a most necessary week of rest. It allows the mind and body to recover. Then they set up another 6-8 week schedule, often changing one or two exercises to attack their weaker lifts and work towards another peak. Then another week of regeneration.

The same rules apply for the football player in off-season. He may have two such eight-week schedules during his off-season strength program. He can set up a program designed so that he increases his poundage on each of the lifts every week for eight weeks. At the end of those two months he might want to have a "test day." It would be similar to the contest for the weightlifter. Something to aim towards. He would go for limit on one, two, or maybe all of his exercises either in the form of limit repetitions or a heavy single lift.

I set up the University of Hawaii programs so that the players would peak the week prior to spring practice and again immediately before summer camp. Some of the athletes entered powerlifting contests at this peaking-out time.

Then he should lay off. This is the message I want to convey here. This one week lay-off is most critical for long-range progress. It may seem to some as if you are breaking your momentum. Not so. The recovery period is most necessary. It gives the physical plant a chance to recuperate. The mind also gathers new energy.

REBUILD ENTHUSIASM

After about five days of laying off you start getting very eager to go to the weight room again. At the end of the week you are really hungry to lift some weights. This rebuilding of enthusiasm is very important as long stretches of handling heavy weights can become most tiring to the mental attitude.

The rest allows time for the much-needed enthusiasm to rebuild. At the end of eight hard weeks of training you may find it a chore to go to the weight room. You may have a few sore spots, some muscles that feel fatigued, and you begin forcing yourself to dress out and train. After a week's rest you are anxious to go to the weight room once again and this renewed eagerness is most important for continued progress.

Some like to do absolutely nothing for a full week while others insist on doing a bit of something. That something should be restricted to cardiovascular exercises and movements that do not attack the major muscle groups. The big muscle groups need to be rested. Running in any form, toe raises, and abdominal work is most sufficient. Do not start

slipping in shoulder, back, or leg exercises (with the exception of the toe raises mentioned, as they work a minor, or I should say smaller, muscle group in the legs). The objective of the rest week is just what the name implies. Rest. The more the better.

When you start back you will be much stronger and much more eager to train. The one week of rest will carry you for another two months and, most likely, that will be time to terminate heavy training as summer camp will be coming up. It's a wise idea to lay off heavy training the week before going to camp. You will need to be well rested when you enter that portion of your training. To go to camp over trained is a mistake, so arrange your off-season schedule so that you have a full week's rest just prior to camp. Get in some extra running that final week but lay off the weights.

Regardless of how you work a rest period into your schedule, just be sure that you make allowances for it. If you feel unduly tired and fatigued, skip a workout or maybe even two. Training while fatigued only invites problems. This doesn't imply, by any means, that you should skip training whenever you feel a bit tired. Hardly anyone would train in that case. I said unduly tired. Learn to perceive the difference in your own body. Don't be lazy, but likewise don't be foolish. Sometimes it's a mighty thin line between the two, but the aware athlete can tell the difference.

BE INTUITIVE

The most difficult task for the Strength Coach is directing his very advanced trainees. Their needs change almost weekly. Variables such as diet, rest, work, school, and other physical activities come into play very dramatically. In short, the trainee cannot always stick to a hard and fast schedule. The Strength Coach must be able to adjust his program to meet the trainee's daily needs.

The trainee may be scheduled to do heavy triples on the squats, but he feels extra tired since he stayed up half the night studying for finals. The tens would serve his needs better, and he may even drop one set of the tens. Should he have a slight lower back problem, he may slip around heavy pulls and add another pressing movement just for that day.

In short, the Strength Coach must be aware of his trainee's total need and be flexible enough to change the program to satisfy these needs. The majority of the Strength Coach's time will be spent adapting and adjusting the advanced trainee's weekly program. The Strength Coach will be a tremendous asset to the football team if he is aware enough to make these adaptations in the program. ★

A SAMPLE ADVANCED PROGRAM

Monday

Bench press: 135x5, 175x5, 205x5, 225x3, 245x3, 265x3, 188x10

Power clean: 135x5, 155x5, 175x5, 195x5, 215x5

Back Squats: 135x10, 175x10, 205x10, 225x10, 245x10

Leg extensions: 80x20, 90x20, 100x20

Leg biceps curls: 40x20, 50x20, 60x20

Tuesday

Overhead press: 135x5, 145x5, 155x5, 165x3, 175x3, 185x3, 135x10

Power pulls: 135x5, 155x5, 175x5, 215x5, 235x5, 255x5

Toe raises: 80x30, for three sets

Wednesday

Incline press: 135x5, 155x5, 175x5, 195x3, 215x3, 235x3, 185x10

Power cleans: 135x5, 145x5, 155x5, 165x5, 175x5

Back squats: 135x3, 205x3, 255x3, 295x3, 325x3, 255x10

Leg extensions: same as Monday

Leg biceps curls: same as Monday

Friday

Bench press: 135x5, 155x5, 175x5, 195x5, 215x5, 185x10

Shrugs: 135x5, 205x5, 275x5, 325x5, 375x5

Back squats: 135x5, 185x5, 255x5, 295x5, 245x10

Toe raises: same as Tuesday

• •

WEIGHT TRAINING INFORMATION SHEET

Name _____ Sport _____

Height _____ Weight _____

Neck _____ Waist _____

Chest _____ Hips _____

Upper Arm _____ Thigh _____

Forearm _____ Calf _____

Power Clean

Bench Press

Squat

Leg Extension

Leg Bicep Curls

Other

WEIGHT TRAINING SCHEDULE FOR THE BIG THREE

Name: _____   **Date:** _____

MONDAY (heavy)
Cardiovascular Work, Stretching, Sit-ups

Power Cleans:

B/P:

Squats:

Leg Extensions:

Leg Biceps Curls:

Leg Raises, Stretching

WEDNESDAY (light)
Cardiovascular Work, Stretching, Sit-ups

Power Cleans:

B/P:

Squats:

Leg Extensions:

Leg Biceps Curls:

Leg Raises, Stretching

FRIDAY (medium)
Cardiovascular Work, Stretching, Sit-ups

Power Cleans:

B/P:

Squats:

Leg Extensions:

Leg Biceps Curls:

Leg Raises, Stretching:

REFERENCE LIST —
WEIGHT TRAINING SECTION

REFERENCE LIST

Adams, A. "Effect of exercises upon ligament strength," **Research Quarterly**, 37: 2: 163, 1966.

Basmajian, J.V. **Muscles Alive**. Baltimore: Williams and Wilkins Co., 1962.

Berger, Richard. "Effect of varied weight training programs on strength," **Research Quarterly**, 33: 2: 168, 1962.

ibid. "Comparisons between static training and various dynamic training programs," **Research Quarterly**, 34: 2: 131, 1963.

ibid. "Optimum repetitions for the development of strength," **Research Quarterly**, 33: 3: 334, 1962.

Best, C.H. and Taylor, N.B. **The Living Body**. New York: Henry Holt and Co., 1959.

Burnham, S. "The value of combined isometric and isotonic exercises: the overload," **Physical Power**, 4: 14: 16, May-June, 1963.

Caldwell, S.F. "Weight training," **The Physical Educator**, 14: 1-17, March, 1957.

Calvin, Sidney. "Effects of progressive resistive exercises on the motor coordination of boys," **Research Quarterly**, 30: 4: 387, 1959.

Capen, E.K. "The effect of systematic weight training on power, strength, and endurance," **Research Quarterly**, 21: 83: May, 1950.

Clark, D.H. and Henry, F.M. "Neuromotor specificity and increase speed from strength and development," **Research Quarterly**, 35: 264-57, 1964.

Cooper, Kenneth. **Aerobics**. New York: M. Evans and Co., 1968.

Cureton, Thomas K. **Physical Fitness and Dynamic Health**. New York: The Dial Press, 1965.

D'Armi, T. "Stretch to Win," **Coach and Athlete**, 28: 8: 34, 1966.

Darcus, H.D. and Salter, N. "The effect of repeated muscular exertion on muscle strength," **Journal of Physiology**, 129: 325-326, August, 1955.

Davis, Elwood and Logan, Gene. **Biophysical Values of Muscular Activity**. Dubuque, Iowa: William C. Brown Co., 1961.

DeLorme, T.L. and Watkins, A.L. **Progressive Resistive Exercises**. New York: Appleton-Century-Crofts, 1951.

Fallon, M. **Weight Training for Sports and Fitness**. London: Nicholas Kaye, Ltd., 1957.

Foti, J. "Keeping fit in the off-season," **Athletic Journal**, 43: 8-12, April, 1963.

Gilletter, H.E., et al. "Heavy resistive exercise," **Journal Association for Physical and Mental Rehabilitation**, January, 1948.

Gray, R.K., et al. "Relationship between leg speed and leg power," **Research Quarterly**, 33: 3: 393, October, 1962.

Guyton, A.C. **Textbook of Medical Physiology**. Philadelphia: W.B. Saunders Co., 1966.

Hixon, Chris. "The back squat," unpublished term paper for Kinesiology, HPE 463, University of Hawaii, Fall, 1975.

Karpovich, Peter. **Physiology of Muscular Activity**. Philadelphia: W.B. Saunders Co., 1965.

ibid, and Hale, C.L. "The effect of warming up upon athletic performance," **Journal American Medical Association**, 162: 1117-1119, 1956.

Klein, K.K. "Acceptable weight training squat exercises," **Texas Coach**, 6: 3: 16, October, 1967.

ibid, and Allman, F. **The Knee in Sports**. New York: The Pemberton Press, 1969.

Layman, R.G. "The case for deep knee bends," **Scholastic Coach**, 35: 5: 38, January, 1966.

Leighton, Jack. **Progressive Weight Training**, New York: The Ronald Press, 1961.

Lewin, P.E. **The Knee and Related Structure**. Philadelphia: Lea and Febiger, 1952.

McClements, L.E. "Power relative to strength of leg and thigh muscles," **Research Quarterly**, 37: 1: 71, March, 1966.

Masley, J., Hariabedian, A., and Donaldson, D. "Weight training in relation to strength, speed, and coordination," **Research Quarterly**, 24: 3: 308, 1953.

Metheny, Eleanor. **Body Dynamics**. New York: McGraw-Hill Book Co., 1952.

Morehouse, L.E. and Miller, A.T. **Physiology of Exercise**. St. Louis: C.V. Mosby Co., 1963.

Morgan, R.E. and Adamson, G.T. **Circuit Training**. New Rochelle, N.Y.: Sportshelf and Soccer Associates, 1958.

Morris, Carrie. "The measurement of muscle relative to the cross section," **Research Quarterly**, 19: 295-303, 1948.

Murray, J. **Weight Lifting and Progressive Resistive Exercises**. New York: A.S. Barnes and Co., 1954.

O'Shea, Pat. "Effects of selected weight training programs and the development of strength and muscle hypertrophy," **Research Quarterly**, 37: 1: 95, March, 1966.

ibid. **Scientific Principles and Methods of Strength Fitness**. Reading, Mass.: Addison-Wesley Publishing Co., 1969.

Rarick, Lawrence. **Physical Activity, Human Growth and Development**. New York: Academic Press, 1973.

Rasch, Philip J. "Relationship of arm strength, weight, and length to speed of arm movement," **Research Quarterly**, 25: 328-332, 1954.

ibid, and Burke, Roger. **Kinesiology and Applied Anatomy**. Philadelphia: Lea and Febiger, 1963.

Scott, Gladys. **Analysis of Human Motion**. New York: Appleton-Century-Crofts, 1963.

Sheldon, W.H. **Atlas of Men**. New York: Gramercy Publishing Co., 1954.

Sills, Frank (ed.). **Weight Training in Sports and Physical Education**. Washington, D.C.: American Association for Health, Physical Education, and Recreation, 1962.

Smith, L.W. and Whitley, L.D. "Influence of strengthening exercises on speed of limb movement," **Archives of Physical Medicine and Rehabilitation**, 46: 772-777, 1965.

Souder, Marjorie and Hill, Phyllis. **Basic Movements: Foundations for Physical Education**. New York: The Ronald Press, 1963.

Starr, Bill. "Organizing a high school weight program," **Weightlifting Journal**, July, 1971.

Steinhaus, Arthur H. "Strength from Morpurgo to Muller — a half century of research," **Journal of Association of Physical and Mental Rehabilitation**, 9: 147-150, 1955.

Stepanov. A.S. "Electromyogram changes produced by training in weight lifting," **Sechenov Physiological Journal** (USSR), 45: 115-121, 1959.

Thompson, H. "Weight training versus isometric training," **Scholastic Coach**, 32: 2: 42, October, 1967.

Vorobyev, A. "Russian training methods," **Strength and Health**, York, Pa., January, 1968.

Wallis, Earl and Logan, Gene. **Figure Improvement and Body Conditioning through Exercise**. Englewood Cliffs, N.J.: Prentice-Hall, 1964.

Walters, E.C. "Scientific foundations of the overload principle," **Scholastic Coach**, 27: 8: 20, April, 1958.

Wilkins, Bruce. "The effect of weight training on speed of movement," **Research Quarterly**, 23: 361-369, October, 1952.

Willgoose, Carl. "The relationship of muscular strength to muscular coordination in the adolescent period," **Journal of Educational Research**, 44: 138-142, October, 1950.

Wolfe, J.B. "The heart of the athlete," **Journal of Sports Medicine and Physical Fitness**, 2: 20, 1962.

Wright, Wilhelmine. **Muscle Function**. New York: Hafner Publishing Co., 1962.

Zorbas, W.S. and Karpovich, P. "Effect of weight training upon the speed of muscular contraction," **Research Quarterly**, 22: 2: 45, May, 1951.

THE STRONGEST SHALL SURVIVE...

STRENGTH TRAINING FOR FOOTBALL

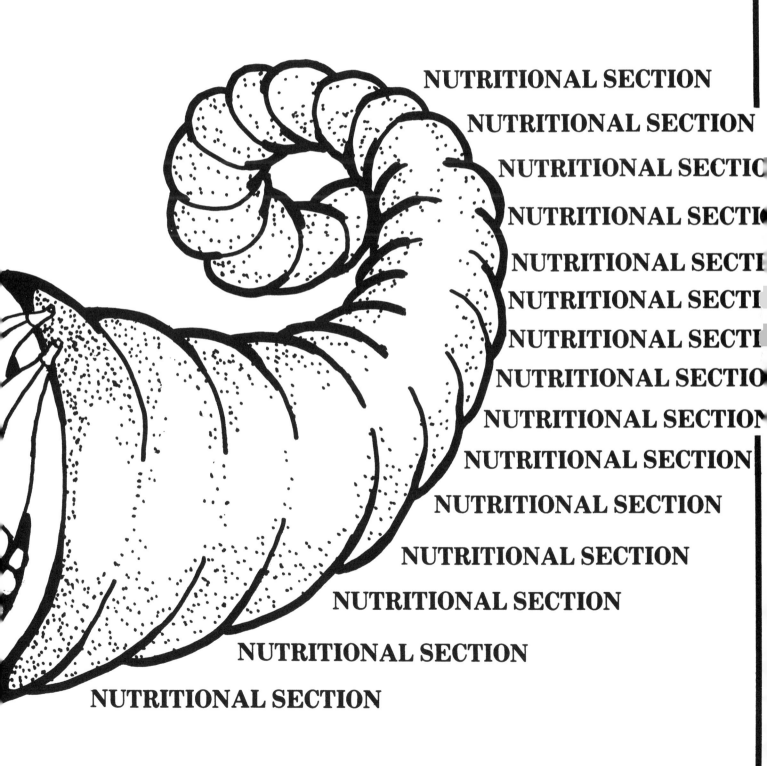

NUTRITIONAL SECTION

NUTRITIONAL SECTION

NUTRITIONAL SECTIO

NUTRITIONAL SECTI

NUTRITIONAL SECTI

NUTRITIONAL SECTI

NUTRITIONAL SECTI

NUTRITIONAL SECTIO

NUTRITIONAL SECTION

NUTRITIONAL SECTION

NUTRITIONAL SECTION

NUTRITIONAL SECTION

NUTRITIONAL SECTION

NUTRITIONAL SECTION

NUTRITIONAL SECTION

8

CHAPTER EIGHT
THAT EXTRA EDGE — PROPER NUTRITION

NUTRITION AND THE ATHLETE

Until very recently, the application of nutritional research was only utilized by a small handful of individuals. Those who reached advanced ages or who succumbed to various illnesses learned, out of necessity, the value of eating properly. Others, generally regarded as health freaks, dove into the field with vigor for reasons of health, fitness, and mental vitality. Then came the athletes who, through a bit of personal trial-and-error testing and researching, discovered that the nutritional knowledge they gathered improved their performance.

INDIVIDUAL SPORTS LEAD THE WAY

Competitive weightlifters and bodybuilders have really been the pioneers in the field of applying nutritional research to sports. Other individual sports such as wrestling and track and field came into the arena some ten years later. Most other sports take the data which has been utilized by the weight men and use it for their particular activity.

Team sports have been very laggard in learning and applying sound nutrition to their activities. The reason behind this fact is really rather simple. Team athletes become accustomed to being told how to train. They very rarely check things out for themselves. They depend on their team trainer and team doctor. Individual athletes, on the other hand, have to be their own coach, trainer, doctor, and advisor. Competitive weightlifters, typically, train alone without any supervision other than that derived from articles in periodicals and from talking to other lifters. They learn all they can about their own bodies; what makes them perform better and what deters progress. If there's a thin chance anything will help make them stronger, then they will try it. As a result, they get taken on lots of gimmicks, but by the same process they learn over the long haul how to build muscle and strength. They make themselves the guinea pigs and, as a result, find out lots of interesting things about their own bodies.

One of the more important pieces of information has been available since the early forties. Nutritional supplements became available to the weightlifters at that time. Since the national champion weightlifting team, the York Club, used these supplements, the rest of the weightlifters in the country followed suit. What worked for the winners might have application for everyone, was the logical assumption. It was worth a try anyway and, delightfully, it seemed to work. Lifters who utilized a complete nutritional program received a new surge of energy. They found that they could train longer, recover faster, sustain fewer injuries, and become considerably stronger if they provided their bodies with all the needed nutrients.

For some twenty years, competitive weightlifters have been using nutritional supplements to improve their muscle size and strength. Yet, as a general rule, their experiences did not attract any attention from the other sports. It wasn't until the middle sixties that a few progressive coaches (I use the term progressive, but actually wonder why they have avoided available evidence for so long) began incorporating **some** nutritional ideas into their training programs. But very few.

PROPER NUTRITION IS A NECESSITY

Even at present, nearly every coach will agree that some sort of strength training is desirable for his team, but he is not at all convinced of the value of extra nutrition for his team. Yet, to state it quite simply, the two programs are inseparable. To organize a strength program without administering nutritional advice is performing just half the necessary task. The athlete can only become as strong as his physical plant allows. But by adding nutrients to that plant he can literally elevate his physical potential. Through proper nutrition an individual can change the chemistry of his body. He can add nutrients which allow the heart and lungs to perform better — an important asset to an athlete. He can supplement his diet so that he builds muscle faster, recovers from injuries quicker, and is able to train longer and harder. By regulating nutrition he can assure himself of utilizing all the foods he takes in more efficiently. If an athlete, for example, can assimilate 100% of the protein he eats in a day, then he is a jump ahead of his competitor who only utilizes 80%. This can be done through the application of sound nutritional principles.

LACK OF MEDICAL GUIDANCE

Part of the reason that football players and coaches have drug their heels on the nutrition question is that they rely on the advice of the team physician and unfortunately, most medical people are grossly ignorant on the subject of nutrition — especially nutrition as applied to athletes. Those of us who have read the research (and there is an abundance of it available) tried the recommended supplements, and realized the results have been aware of the benefits of proper nutrition for some time. Yet everyone who advocated a nutritious program still has to contend with the medical profession's backward attitude on the subject.

This attitude has deterred progress in the field of athletic training. Ironically enough, the major pieces of research have been done by medical men, but for some strange reason physicians look upon this data as if it was whipped together by some retarded organic farmer.

There are quite a few medical men, thankfully, doing more than counting their weekly receipts or trying to figure out which golf course is easier to play. Outspoken men like the Drs. Shutes in Canada, Dr. Miles Robinson, Professor Linus Pauling, Dr. Abram Hoffer, and Sir Julian Huxley are just a few who have dedicated their lives to the scientific study of nutrition. They are too few by any count. Strangely enough, these research pioneers who only want to improve the health and well-being of the public are often shunned by others in the medical fraternity. Their findings are skimmed over or completely ignored. Those familiar with medical history realize that this is not a new phenomenon in the profession. Anyone with a new idea has always had to fight through the politics and mumbo jumbo associated with the medical fraternity. Dr. Ignaz Semmelweis fought for almost twenty years merely trying to persuade his brothers of the scapel merely to wash their hands before operating. Pride was above death and most refused to change for two decades. Dr. William Harvey also faced years of a personal hardship because he revealed how the blood circulated in the body. It took years and years before doctors would use Rene Laennec's simple but effective device, the stethoscope. The medical profession is a rather conservative group and they detest change. Why shouldn't they resist change. They have things going their way so why stir the soup?

DOCTOR'S RESIST EVIDENCE

The author decided that a physician may be in a better position to examine the strange situation of why doctors are so against accepting the findings of the nutritional researchers. Dr. Miles Robinson in **Your Key To A Healthy Heart** states his views on the medical profession in regards to their position on the usefulness of Vitamin E: "The author of this book has some severe criticisms of those presently in control of official medical groups, such as the American Medical Association, and governmental agencies, such as the Food and Drug Administration, for their indifference to Vitamin E. On behalf of individual doctors, it must be said that they are usually too busy extinguishing the acute fires of disease to have time to study or work for major reforms in the field of health. Most have to rely solely on AMA reports for their information. This should not be.

"With regard to the official position of the American Medical Association, however, little can be said in the way of extenuation. The AMA has plenty of time and facilities for scholarly investigations, but we have learned that the leaders of this organization in the last twenty years have become much more interested in expediency than in basic principles. Probably the chief and insidious reason for this is that the AMA has been much more corrupt as a result of receiving in recent years over half its income from drug companies which advertise in its many journals. This serious conflict of interest tends to stifle broad and scholarly views on health, and to permeate all through the ramifications of the AMA influence — in its journals, in industry, and in the governmental agencies which participate in the twenty-six billion dollars spent annually on health in this country.

"By the time humanity wakes up to its danger, the men involved are not only the victims of long habit, but also find that it is expensive or individually ruinous to change their ways. For self-preservation, they may mislead themselves and others and oppose reform as long as possible."

The medical people still continue to tell athletes in hard training merely to eat a normal diet. This medical fallacy has not only limited progress in the field of athletics, but has contributed to the poor physical and mental health of all Americans who follow such outdated advice. From **Mental Health Through Nutrition**, Tom Blaine says: "The expression 'average American diet' is merely a figment of the imagination. It is ridiculous to assume that any political authority or any medical specialist can set up a mathematical formula of food values that will apply to all. When we ignore the relationships between the condition of the various soils in which our foods are grown, the losses in nutritional value due to marketing, processing, storing, cooking, menu balancing, and, most important of all, the problems of food absorption by human bodies, either healthy or diseased, we see how foolish is the generally accepted view of physicians that we get a balanced food intake, containing all the vitamins and minerals necessary for health, in an 'average American Diet'."

Dr. Frederick Kilander, of New York, after 28 years of study on the subject, declared that two out of three Americans cannot select a well-balanced meal in a cafeteria, even when cost is not involved.

Medical people are seldom nutritionists and when we turn to them for advice we are merely inviting unfounded opinion. Dr. Willard Krehl, President of the American Society for Clinical Nutrition, recently said, "It is unfortunate that we have in our medical schools few, if any, professors of clinical nutrition." Dr. Donald Watkin wrote in the April 1965 issue of the **American Journal of Public Health** that "despite nutrition's impact on medicine, it does not have a place in the curricula of more than a handful of medical schools."

Why am I spending so much time knocking the good doctors? Because it is necessary for you to realize that if you are sincerely interested in learning about nutrition then you must turn away from your family physician or team doctor for nutritional advice. I do not intend to condemn all. Some doctors have taken the time to learn about this important subject and are well versed on nutrition as it applies to the athlete. But, generally speaking, they are not a good source of information.

LEARN ABOUT NUTRITION

Books are your most valuable resource on the subject of nutrition, and there are scores of good books available. I recommend the reference list at the end of this section.

If you only feel that you have time to read one of these, I suggest starting with **Let's Eat Right To Keep Fit** by Adelle Davis. She has compiled a huge amount of nutritional research and the book is literally crammed with useful data. Since it is research it cannot be read and absorbed like a novel. Read a chapter at a time, go over it, reread it, and then start applying it. Those who try to grasp the science of nutrition at one sitting are certain to be frustrated. Learn a little at a time and your storehouse of information will grow quite rapidly.

It needs to be recalled that not everything in print is always 100% correct so make it a point to follow up on any specific subject in which you have some questions or doubts. The research library can be an enjoyable place to spend an evening if you are learning something that you are particularly interested in.

I also suggest that if the opportunity arises for you to learn some biochemistry or take a course in nutrition at a local college, take the time to do so. Talk to athletes who are using nutritional programs and obtain their opinions. And, if possible, read what the European athletes are doing in this field because they are far ahead of us. Lastly, read over what I have to say. My advice is backed by some 20 years of study. During these years when strength was my advocation, I read every piece of data that I could find on the subject of nutrition. Some applied to strength training, but a great deal did not. I put a great deal of weight on the information obtained from my fellow weightlifters. I have personally visited with well over a thousand competitive weightlifters and learned something from every one. But perhaps the most important thing that I have done which does give me a bit of an advantage when advising athletes on nutritional matters is that I have obtained vast amounts of research done by the European Weightlifters. The Europeans, especially the communist countries, use their heavy training athletes like Americans use race cars. They test them under stress and what they learn nutritionally helps them to better understand just how the body functions in its ultimate physical state.

FOREIGN SOURCES OF DATA

Through foreign friends whom I have met at international contests or through correspondence, I obtained much valuable information as to what the Europeans are doing in their training. I found, for the most part, that they trained much the same way as we did. Most had supervision and most were able to train harder for many reasons. But they did not supply their bodies with the same fuel that we did. Some of the top European teams now have a team nutritionist assigned to them. After each training session the nutritionist checks the athlete to see just what he is lacking (a simple finger puncture test is now available) nutritionally. If he is low in, perhaps potassium, after his workout then this mineral is supplied on the spot. No deficit, hence no lag. Should he be below the desired level in calcium, Vitamin C, or niacin, then this too is immediately given to him. Very effective. The machine is never under supplied, even when placed under stress.

OUR FOOD IS RAPED

Unfortunately, this type of up-to-date service is not available to any athletic group in this country — not even our professional athlete. Our heavy training athletes must use some other method of supplying their bodies with the needed nutrients. "But," you must be asking, "if I eat a balanced diet won't I be supplying my body with all that it needs?" I wish that this were possible but it's not simply because the food manufacturers and processors have raped the food that goes on our tables. Add to this the fact that heavy training athletes just need so much more than the average person and you soon realize that its almost impossible to eat enough food to supply the body with what it needs.

Take our fruits for openers. Our grandparents could be fairly sure that every orange they purchased contained 75 mgs. of Vitamin C. We can't. The grower picks the fruit green before it has had time to fully mature and develop its full potential of Vitamin C. It is then artificially ripened, sprayed, colored, and shipped. It dries out on the super-market's shelf until you come along and buy it. You're lucky if there is any Vitamin C in the orange by the time you eat it.

Or take the staple food of our Western culture, bread. From **Your Key To A Healthy Heart** we find the following:

"Only a few people appreciate that the 'staff of life' had been emasculated by the use of the high speed roller mill which removed the bran and germ, containing practically all the minerals and vitamins, from grain used in bread and other foods. The new white flour made fluffy bread, and through advertising, convinced the public that white was synonymous with good. Almost no insect could live on it, so the flour could be milled in a few places by powerful monopolies and shipped all over the world with almost no spoilage. The alteration of bread has now proceeded to the point where some seventy different chemicals are used in it and practically all flour, white or whole, is devitalized by strong bleaching agents. Over twenty known vitamins or other beneficial substances are removed from flour; only about six or seven are replaced in today's so-called 'enriched' bread. Significantly, Vitamin E is not among them. The entire process is a splendid commercial success. In the light of what we now know, it was also an unparalleled mistake in health which will probably take generations to overcome."

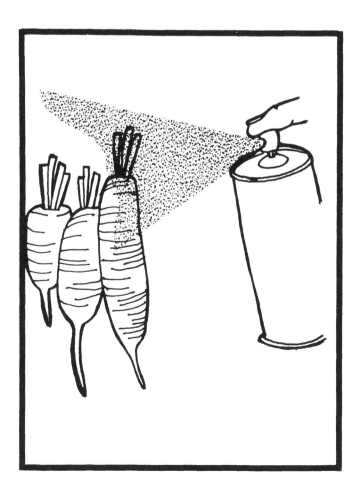

MILK TAMPERING

How about our most stable nutrient, milk? Pasteurization destroys its Vitamin C, enzymes, and l-lysine, an essential amino acid. Homogenization destroys its cellular structure. Contamination is not at all unusual. Such things as formalde-hyde, insecticide residue, and penicillin from cows treated with mastitis is often found in milk.

Linda Clark devotes an entire chapter in **Stay Younger Longer** to the abuses of our so-called "natural" foods. Here's what she has to say about a few of our products we find on our daily menu.

"Butter is salted to give it a long shelf life. It is hardened with water, and colored with artificial colors which are subject to question. Cheese, when processed, may contain artificial coloring and flavoring, texturizers, modifiers, and a number of chemical additives of questionable value to the consumer. Our fruits and vegetables are subjected to any number of practices which should come under close scrutiny. Weedicides are used to reduce weeding, labor, and costs. Giberellin, a hormone, is used to make fruit larger. Remember, this practice does not improve the nutritional quality of the food, only the appearance and weight. Sweet potatoes are dyed red. White potatoes get anti-sprouting additives. Citrus fruit may be waxed, gassed, dyed, and fumigated. Cucumbers and turnips may be dipped in paraffin for long shelf life, yet wax is listed as a carcinogen. Lemons are washed in a chemical dip to reduce tip-end decay. Grapes are gassed by the carload before shipping to prevent mold. Many canned fruits are put through a chemical dip to remove the skins. Asparagus and other vegetables are washed with a mold inhibitor. Nuts are bleached for uniformity of color. Peanuts are salted chemically in the shell."

Vegetables? Much the same story. Again, in the name of economics, the end product is almost useless to the con-sumer. Vegetables are sprayed with powerful insecticides in the field. They are picked before maturity, thus cutting down on their vitamin and mineral content. They are arti-ficially colored, sprayed again to preserve them as they travel to the market, and finally they end up in your kitchen.

Cereals, which many people start each day with feeling content that they are fulfilling their nutritional needs for breakfast, are a waste of money. Researchers at the Uni-versity of Georgia studied a group of different breakfast cereals. Then reported: "The cereal boxes, if taken with milk and raisins, are as nutritious as all but the most sophisti-cated of the cereals."

Eggs are injected with preservatives. Meat is sabotaged with growth hormones. Poultry is dipped in an antibiotic bath to prevent spoilage. Even honey is watered down by the greedy manufacturer so that he can suck another few cents profit from the unsuspecting buyer. Nearly everything that passes through the hands of food processors is tampered with for the simple reason that these people are economically motivated; they could care less about the nutritious value of the end product. Nothing escapes them. Examine your refrigerator and pantry shelves and you'll see what I mean.

DECEIT IN ADVERTISING

The food manufacturer is a master at the subtle white lie. Skimmed milk is sold as a diet food, yet it has more carbohydrates in it than regular milk. They advertise cereal as a protein food, yet even the best is less than 10% protein and most are about 1 or 2%. Uncreamed cottage cheese has a higher nutritional value than creamed cottage cheese but just try to find the uncreamed variety at the store. It doesn't exist because the creamed is cheaper to make and additional weight can be added to the carton making the total profit just that much better. If the honey you buy does not specifically state that it has not been diluted or cooked or blended, then you can bet they have added sugar (seems silly but it's true), water, and cooked the contents so that it blends together.

"But the FDA will nab these people," you may be thinking. Don't count on it. The FDA is understaffed and overworked. They only have the power to make the manufacturers and producers change their ways, they do not hand out punishments. So a large distributor will take a gamble. If he is caught, which usually takes at least a year, he's that much richer and the American public is that much sicker. Seldom does the FDA attack the large organizations. Their history discloses that most of their suits are against the smaller companies. They seem to spend a great deal of their valuable time trying to keep Americans from taking vitamins rather than investigating the bogus food industry.

THE NEED FOR SUPPLEMENTS

The hard training athlete is faced with a super problem. If he cannot even get his basic requirement off the table, then how can he expect to obtain sufficient nutrients to supply his body's extra needs? By using supplements. It's the only sure way for the athlete. I should state that it is possible to obtain sufficient nutrition from the table if you know what foods to eat, how much to eat, when to eat them, and don't mind eating lots of food. I should add that you have to buy this food and that it becomes very expensive to eat properly if you are an athlete in serious training.

Supplements are easier to obtain and much less expensive in the long haul. The athlete must take what he needs nutritionally from supplements and add to it from the table, rather than the other way around. I said that it was possible to obtain the necessary nutrients from the table because theoretically it is, but let me point out just how difficult it is to put the theory into actual practice. I'll use Vitamin C as an example.

While the minimum daily requirement (MDR) for everyone in America, according to the wisdom of the FDA, is 30 mgs. (this includes children, adolescents, women, white collar workers, farmers, stevedors, telephone operators, secretaries, people who weigh 100 pounds and people who weigh 300 pounds). The European nutritionists by contrast insist that heavy training athletes use 5,000 mgs. or 5 grams of Vitamin C daily. I go along with the Europeans since all sorts of research has shown that — physical exercise, mental stress, smoking, and individual metabolism all influence the amount of Vitamin C needed by the individual each day.

EATING YOUR C REQUIREMENT

To obtain 5,000 mgs. of Vitamin C for just one day would be a sizable task if you decided to do it by way of your grocery foods. You would have to force-feed foods of high Vitamin C content nearly all day long. One medium-sized orange contains 75 mgs. of C and an eight ounce glass of fresh orange juice has 130 mgs. of Vitamin C. So you would need to munch some 66 oranges in a day or drink almost 40 glasses of orange juice to obtain just this one nutritional

requirement. Even if this were your choice you would have to be aware of the fact that as you were pursuing your Vitamin C requirement you also ingested 1,056 grams of carbohydrates or 10,880 calories in the oranges or, if you selected the juice, 1,000 carbohydrate grams and 10,000 calories. In short, you would be as round and plump as a watermelon in just a few weeks in pursuing your Vitamin C requirement.

It's much easier to take a couple of tablets once or twice a day. Simpler and much less expensive. It's really just a matter of changing your total concept of taking pills and tablets. The American public has been oriented into thinking that all pills are medicine or drugs and they are usually associated with ill health because as we grew up the only time we took pills was when we were sick. Most people find it difficult to swallow pills because they still associate them with nasty tasting medicine and days when they felt miserable. "Swallow this, it'll make you feel better." Often the cure seemed worse than the disease.

SUPPLEMENTS ARE FOODS

Vitamins and minerals are not drugs. They are valuable nutritional substances extracted from natural sources and condensed into pill form. And there is absolutely no reason why they can't be swallowed as simply as an M&M candy. Think of Vitamin C tablets as concentrated oranges or grapefruits. Once you reorient your thinking on taking pills, then the rationale behind taking supplements becomes much more clear.

Dessicated liver, as another example, is raw liver that has been condensed into either powder or tablet form. The tablets really are just small, pill-sized pieces of liver, usually containing about ½ gram of good protein each. So in order to obtain an added protein supply, which is the primary reason most athletes take them, they have to be eaten in large quantities, 50-75 per day. This affords the athletes 25-35 extra grams of high quality protein which is exactly like eating a small portion of liver. Yet some shudder at the thought of taking this many tablets. It's certainly a lot simpler to swallow 50 tablets in 2-3 minutes than it is to prepare liver to be eaten. But again, that's how people generally feel about pills and tablets. That it isn't natural to take pills. In short, the athlete has had to alter his thinking on the subject.

READ THE LABELS

One final caution before moving into the specific nutrients. I mentioned how the processed food companies rip off the public. Well, unfortunately, some nutritional companies are equally as devious. You must learn to read labels, compare quantities and prices to insure yourself of receiving quality merchandise for your money. A favorite trick is to list the ingredients of the supplement and then mention that two tablets have to be taken three times per day. This is fine just so long as you don't compare the first tablet with a second that only has to be taken once a day. Likewise, do not assume all vitamins and minerals are natural. The manufacturer has a million and one ways to mislead your thinking. They might call the product "Nature's Own" or "Natural Base," anything to slip in the word "natural" or "nature" so as to throw you off. Most hurridly look over a label and if it has what they want and is reasonably priced then they take it home. If it does not say explicity that the product is derived from natural sources, then you can be assured that it is synthetic.

Vitamins and minerals from natural sources are universally better for you than those which are made synthetically. This is not 100% true, but the exceptions are too small to worry with in this case. It's better to set your thinking towards natural products. Synthetic Vitamin E, just to cite one example, which goes under the code E2 or dl-alpha tocopherols, possesses only one fifth the potency of the Vitamin E derived from natural sources. Natural Vitamin C is more effective than synthetic ascorbic acid although some doctors still contend that Vitamin C is Vitamin C regardless of whether it is natural or synthetic. For the athlete the difference is significant. Natural Vitamin C contains a group of substances known as bioflavonoids. When given to athletes, the bioflavonoids speed the healing of muscle strains, skin abrasions, and joint injuries. So check the label for the word natural.

It's always a good idea to check quantity against price. Nationally-advertised brands will cost you more because someone has to pay for the advertising. Most vitamins and minerals are packaged by a few pharmaceutical companies and the label is merely changed for different distributors. If it's Plus Products, Thompsons, or Fibertone and they all have 100 capsules of 400 I.U. of d-alpha tocopherols, then buy the least expensive. Checking the multiple vitamins or multiple anything tablets or capsules is a bit tougher problem as frequently they have a high dosage of one vitamin, like Vitamin A, and a lower dosage of another, such as B6. A little time spent investigating, however, will insure you of receiving your money's worth. It's best to check the more costly ingredients as another gimmick is to load up a multiple vitamin with 2-300% the MDR of an inexpensive nutrient and keep the more costly ones very low. Remember, just so it contains some of a particular vitamin, it allows them to advertise it on the label. It's another thing to put in enough of the substance to make it worthwhile.

KNOWLEDGE IS YOUR BEST DEFENSE

Once again, knowledge of the subject you are dealing with is your best defense against being cheated. Spend a little of your free time reading the various recommended books on nutrition. It's best to read nutritional information in bits and pieces. Taken in large chunks it becomes rather difficult to assimilate. Read a portion on protein. Study it and try to apply what you read in your meal selection. When you feel fairly confident that you know at least something about protein, then move on to the B-complex vitamins or minerals. Slowly, but surely you will begin to accumulate a considerable storehouse of information that will prove to be most useful to you not only in your training but for the remainder of your lifetime.

The next chapters in this section on nutrition deal with those various aspects of nutrition which are so important to the athlete. I have attempted to present the research so that it applies to the weight trained individual. Some of my nutritional recommendations may seem quite high, when compared to others that you have read, but my resources are from Europe rather than the U.S. You must be reminded that we are dealing with a machine that requires a top grade of fuel and lots of it. This, then, is nutrition as it applies to the super species — the heavy duty machines of humanity, homo sapiens in his highest physical stage of evolution — the athlete.   ★

TABLE I

MEASUREMENTS USED IN NUTRITION
CONVERSION FACTORS

1 gram (gm.)	1000 milligrams
	1/28th of an ounce
	15.432 grains
	1/5th of a teaspoonful
	weight of one cubic centimeter of water
1 ounce (oz.)	28.35 grams
	437.5 grains
1 fluid ounce	29.573 cc
1 milligram (mg.)	1000 micrograms
1 microgram (mcg.)	1 millionth of a gram
	1 gamma
1 minim	1 drop
	0.003759 cubic inches
1 teaspoon	60 drops
60 minims	1 dram
	1 teaspoonful
480 minims	1 ounce
	8 teaspoonfuls
1 pound	453.6 grams
453.6 grams	
1 pint	16 ounces
1 quart	32 ounces
1 grain	0.065 grams
	65 milligrams
1 gamma	1 microgram
	.001 milligrams

CALORIC VALUES

1 gram carbohydrate	4 calories
1 gram protein	4 calories
1 gram fat	9 calories

VITAMIN UNITS

1000 I.U. of Vitamin A	.6 milligrams
1000 I.U. of Vitamin C	50 milligrams
1000 I.U. of Vitamin D	.025 milligrams

VITAMIN E

The National Formulary presents tocopherol products in international units.
The equivalents are as follows:

1 mg. dl-Alpha Tocopherol Acetate	1 I.U.
1 mg. dl-Alpha Tocopherol Unit	1.1 I.U.
1 mg. d-Alpha Tocopherol Acetate	1.36 I.U.
1 mg. d-Alpha Tocopherol	1.49 I.U.

When vitamins are analyzed, they are measured in "units".
A unit is the amount of that particular vitamin which is needed to produce the identifying action of the vitamin.

CHAPTER NINE
UNDERSTANDING PROTEINS, CARBOHYDRATES, AND FATS

The foods we eat include proteins, fats, carbohydrates, mineral salts, vitamins, water, and oxygen. For convenience and ease of understanding I am separating the first three from the vitamins and minerals.

PROTEINS, THE BUILDING BLOCKS OF LIFE

Proteins are extremely important to the weight-trained athlete as proteins are the building blocks of the human body. Your bodies are composed largely of protein. Some 15% by weight of the total animal body is made up of protein. Your muscles, skin, nails, hair, brain, internal organs, and portions of your bones are made of protein. Since the muscles contain a greater amount of protein than do other body structures, it is extremely important for the hard training athlete to supply his body with this essential nutrient.

Proteins do more, however, than just maintain and rebuild muscle tissue. The amount of energy you have is a direct result of your protein consumption, although not in the manner usually expected. Proteins supply less direct caloric energy than either carbohydrates or fats, only four calories per gram of protein. Yet all energy is produced by means of enzymes, organic substances which principle component is protein. When protein is inadequate, however, none of the enzymes can be formed in adequate quantities. Fatigue is the end result.

Suffice me to add that without an adequate supply of protein the athlete cannot build his muscles, tendons, and ligaments stronger and he will not recover sufficiently from a heavy workout. They are, by all counts, critical and it's important to know something about them. I'll discuss the amino acids, complete and incomplete proteins, the athlete's requirements, sources in foods and supplements.

AMINO ACIDS

The amino acids are the building blocks of protein. Adelle Davis compares them to the alphabet, "Just as thousands of words are made from the 26 letters of our alphabet, so are thousands of proteins made from different combinations of amino acids." The complexity of the protein is illustrated by their molecular weights: whereas the molecular weight of glucose, a typical carbohydrate, is 180, that of a protein may vary anywhere from 10,000 to 10,000,000.

There are twenty-two different amino acids known presently. Most of the 22 are needed in forming tissues. All but eight can be manufactured within the human body. The eight are referred to as "essential" and the remaining 14 as "nonessential." The terms are not strictly accurate, however, as all 22 are really quite essential. What the terms really mean is that the essential eight must be supplied in our food whereas it is not necessary for the other 14.

I am presenting a listing of the amino acids, not because I expect any reader to remember them by the time he reaches the bottom of the page, but they are placed here as a reference source. When you go to select a protein supplement you might check back and be certain that it contains the essential amino acids.

The essential amino acids are: tryptophane, lysine, methionine, phenylalanine, treonine, valine, leucine, and isoleucine. The others, which the body can manufacture are: glycine, alanine, glutamic acid, proline, hydroxproline, aspartic acid, serine, tyrosine, cystine, hydroxglutamic acid, norleucine, and di-iodo-tyrosine. You might find it useful to become more familiar with the essential ones, but as I mentioned, they are here as a reference if you should ever need to check on them.

COMPLETE VS. INCOMPLETE PROTEIN

A complete protein is one which contains the eight essential amino acids in adequate amounts. Some authorities refer to them as "adequate," rather than complete. A protein lacking an essential amino acid or one which has too little of an essential amino acid to support health is classified as incomplete or inadequate.

Milk, as an example, is a complete protein. Gelatine is not. Animal proteins are more complete than vegetable sources. Glandular meats such as liver and kidneys contain more of some essential amino acids than do the muscle meats. The muscle meats would include: steaks, chops, ham, and roasts. Egg yolk, fresh milk, liver, and kidneys rank highest in essential amino acid content.

Soybeans, cottonseed, brewer's yeast, and wheat germ contain protein which is complete. Most of the other vegetable sources are lacking in one or more of the essential amino acids and should not be eaten alone.

If an incomplete protein is eaten along with a complete protein or even with another incomplete protein, then they often complement each other. It is important, therefore, to eat some complete protein at each meal for the liver only stores complete protein and if, as Dr. Paul Cannon in **Recent Advances in Nutrition** has pointed out, "If there is so much as an hour time lag between eating incomplete proteins and complete protein, the value of the incomplete is lost. So, in order to insure yourself that you are utilizing all the protein, even if it be an incomplete source, a bit of complete protein, such as milk, with each meal is in order.

The problems encountered through eating incomplete protein became quite vivid a few years ago when many women started on an all-gelatin diet. Gelatin is lacking two essential amino acids and is almost lacking three others, yet the dieters were not informed that they should supplement the gelatin with even a small portion of complete protein. They merely mixed the gelatin with water, as directed. After some length of time the proponents of this fad diet came down with specific symptoms of ill health associated with protein deficiency. A tough way to lose weight.

ATHLETES' PROTEIN NEEDS

The protein requirement for heavy training athletes is much higher than it is for less active individuals. The National Research Council suggests that boys between 16-20 years of age have 100 grams of protein daily, whereas adults need only 70 grams per day. There are nutritionists who feel that 100 is safer for a margin of safety and 150 grams may be necessary for the recovery from illness or from a prolonged protein deficiency. Americans have done very little research on the special nutritional needs of athletes so I turn to the Russian research for my guidelines.

The Russian heavy training athlete ingests no less than 200 grams of protein daily and for those who weigh between 220 and 300 pounds, it reaches 300 grams per day. I believe that the rule of one gram of protein per day for each pound of

bodyweight is adequate for the athlete. Some people, because of individual differences in metabolic rate, energy requirement, and total work load may need more. But this is a good starting point.

Since most football players hover near the 200-pound mark, I will use this figure as our standard. You **can** obtain your protein needs from the table — if you know what to eat and if you have enough control over the eating situation to eat what you need. Most high school players live at home and since protein foods are more expensive than carbo-hydrate foods, it is often a burden on the family to afford the luxury for the athlete. Similarly, athletes eating in the school cafeteria are faced with a daily barrage of high carbo-hydrate foods with very little protein available.

PROTEIN SUPPLEMENTS

For the people who cannot obtain their protein needs from the table, I recommend a high protein supplement.

There are a few good protein supplements on the market. The powders are better than the pills, as a binder must be added to the pills, so in effect you end up paying a high price for roughage. The protein powders made of milk and egg sources are superior to those derived from soybeans or other vegetable sources. Soybeans are, true enough, complete protein but the human organism is not fully able to assimilate soybean protein as readily as protein from animal sources or from dairy products.

The milk and egg proteins mix much better in milk than vegetable proteins. Some protein supplements are so diffi-cult to mix that an outboard motor is recommended. Many taste like chalk or even worse. A blender is a handy piece of equipment to have around the house when you are dealing with protein supplements. You can quickly whip up a nutritious meal with milk, eggs, wheat germ, and protein supplement. It will, in all likelihood, supply you with more nutrition than a meal which takes hours to prepare.

There are a few fine protein supplements made from glandular sources. These can be mixed with vegetable juices such as tomato or V-8 juice or added to gravies, meat loafs, and such. They are quite difficult for most people to take straight, but they are as high as 98% protein.

Another fine method of obtaining a high quality protein in a convenient form is by taking dessicated liver tablets. Most contain ½ gram of high quality protein so it's a simple matter of taking 50-75 tablets a day in order to run up your protein count to the desired level. I mentioned that powders are always superior to tablets and that rule still holds true with liver products. Liver powder, however, comes under the heading of protein from glandular sources and needs to

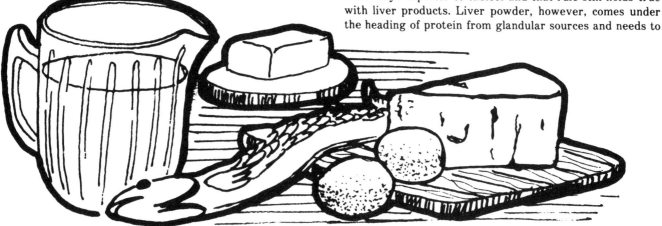

be mixed with something to camouflage its taste. The tablets are easier to take and just a bit less potent. They are merely compressed desiccated liver so there is little binder present. Most people find them quite simple to take.

Let's assume that our 200-pound athlete eats the following protein foods in a given day: two eggs (12 grams), large wedge of cheese (20 grams), cup of cottage cheese (30 grams), one 7-ounce can of tuna fish (58 grams), two pieces of fried chicken (50 grams), and a quart of milk (32 grams). Granted, this is an exceptional diet but it is, quite realistically, one which all could follow. Our fine-eating friend has taken in a total of 202 grams of high quality protein and has, therefore, satisfied his protein requirement for the day.

Should he have missed lunch, where he planned to eat the tuna and cottage cheese, he would be deficient by some 90 grams. This is where a supplement would be handy. Or perhaps our athlete is traveling and doesn't have the opportunity to regulate his protein intake. Again, supplements in the form of a high protein milkshake or liver tablets would be most useful. Take 100 tablets (it's just like eating a few pieces of liver but in tablet form) and a couple of glasses of milk and you're home free, nutritionally speaking.

PROTEIN FOLLOWING EXERCISE

The Russians have also pointed out that it is quite useful to eat protein soon after heavy exercise. It seems that the sooner the body is supplied with a deficient nutrient the sooner it can recover. When we trained at the York Club, we used to go to the in-house snack bar immediately after a training session and drink a high protein milkshake. It contained yogurt, protein powder, ice cream, and milk. It gave us about 35 grams of protein quickly. In less than two hours we would feel fully recovered and many times we would train again that same day. I should note that the lifters also took a full range of vitamins and minerals at that time because protein was not the only nutrient depleted. I'll mention those as I proceed.

TOO MUCH PROTEIN?

A question very frequently asked by the athlete who is engaged in a high protein diet is whether he can eat too much protein? Is it harmful to overdo a good thing? It is highly unlikely that you will do so but even if you do eat more protein than your body needs, there will be no harm to your health. Adelle Davis summarized this point in **Let's Eat Right To Keep Fit:**

"When you eat more protein than your body can use immediately, your liver withdraws amino acids from your blood and changes them temporarily into storage protein. As your cells use amino acids, the supply is replenished from the breakdown of stored protein. As long as your diet is adequate, the amount of amino acids in your blood is thereby kept relatively constant. If you ignore your health to the extent of eating insufficient protein, the stored protein is quickly exhausted. On the other hand, it is possible, although not probable, that you may eat more protein than your body needs. After the storage depots are filled, the leftover protein is changed by the liver into glucose and fat, the nitrogen portion being excreted in the urine; the sugar and fat may be used immediately to produce energy or may be stored as fat. Proteins are also used to produce energy whenever too few other foods are eaten to meet the calorie requirements, a situation which rarely occurs for the simple reason that protein foods are too expensive to be eaten exclusively."

Generally speaking, your problem will be to obtain enough high quality protein to meet your daily needs, rather than being concerned about overdosing protein foods. Obtaining sufficient protein day in and day out is not quite as easy as it may at first appear. When you are in heavy training it is most critical that you take in the required number of grams every day. Otherwise, your body taps into the less important body tissues so as to release the amino acids to rebuild the more vital structures.

PROTEIN SOURCES

The following chart lists a number of complete protein sources and the grams of protein they contain per ounce.

eggs	6 grams per egg
whole milk	1 gram per ounce
cottage cheese	4 grams per ounce
yogurt	1 gram per ounce
cheddar cheese	3 grams per ounce
tuna fish	8 grams per ounce
chicken	8 grams per ounce
steak	8 grams per ounce
hamburger	7 grams per ounce
liver	8 grams per ounce
pork chops	5 grams per ounce
ham	5 grams per ounce
brewer's yeast	12 grams per ounce
wheat germ	8 grams per ounce
cottonseed flour	7½ grams per ounce
soybean flour	7½ grams per ounce
nuts*	3-5 grams per ounce

*the protein in some nuts is not complete.

The protein content of meat is dependent on the amount of fat and bone it contains. Meats with little bone or fat — 5 grams per ounce; meats with moderate fat and bone — 4 grams per ounce; and meats with much bone or fat — 3 grams per ounce.

Measurements
1 cup = 8 ounces
½ pint
16 tablespoons
1 quart = 4 cups
16 ounces = 1 pound

CARBOHYDRATES

It is important for the weight training athlete and Strength Coach to know about carbohydrates primarily so that he may avoid eating them. Carbohydrates are the most unnecessary nutrients in the spectrum of foods. Some nutritionists feel that we could exist in excellent health without them and have studies to back up their beliefs. Others, however, feel that a certain amount is useful, but that amount should be kept extremely low.

Americans are carbohydrate piggies. All sugars and starches are carbohydrates and these foods make up the bulk of the average diet in this country. Breads, potatoes, rice, cereals, pastries, soft drinks, fruits, candies, and vegetables are largely carbohydrates.

SUGAR

Carbohydrates, in the form of sugar, have only been an important part of our diet for the last hundred years. Sugar was first introduced to Europe by the Crusaders. Only the rich could indulge in the expensive additive and it was handled by the forerunner of the pharmacy, the apothecary. It was dispensed by the teaspoon and used at state affairs.

Americans use lots and lots of sugar in their diets today. Some call it the biggest dietary change in fifty million years. It is estimated that the average Englishman ate some four pounds of sugar in 1750. By 1850 Americans were using 10 pounds per person annually. Today that amount is calculated at 175 pounds per person. Three doctors doing research at Iowa State University: Mohamed Antar, Margaret Ohlson, and Robert Hodges, estimate that we take in as much as 110 pounds of sugar and syrup per person per year, in everything from soups and salad dressings to soft drinks. We also eat another 65 pounds of simple carbohydrates in honey, fruit, and milk bringing our consumption of various kinds of sugar to a grand total of 175 pounds a year.

GLUCOSE

Carbohydrates, once ingested, break down quickly into glucose (a simple sugar). Glucose is immediately used as an energy supply. Unfortunately, the majority of Americans do very little physical activity so they do not need a great deal of energy food. The extra sugar is not passed off, but stored as fat. The combination of low activity and a high carbohydrate diet results in a nation of fat, overweight people. The athlete has enough trouble getting into shape without adding fat to his body.

Whereas protein foods are expensive, foods containing a large amount of carbohydrates are cheap. This is the reason nearly all institutions offer meals burdened with carbohydrates and severely lacking in proteins. School cafeterias are notoriously poor places to gain adequate nutrition. A typical meal will be centered around a starchy food such as spaghetti with plenty of bread, some high carbohydrate, overcooked vegetable, perhaps a piece of fruit (more carbohydrate) and topped off with a piece of cake or pudding. Upon examination it is often discovered that the only protein available in such a meal is in the milk and milk itself contains more carbohydrates than proteins.

WE EAT LOTS OF CARBOHYDRATES

Since most of us were raised on a high carbohydrate diet, we have become quite accustomed to eating these foods. Many start each day off with cereal, perhaps some fruit, toast, and coffee with sugar and cream. Commercial cereal is really sugar in disguise, some as high as 90% carbohydrates which is converted immediately to sugar. Toast, especially toast made from rolled white flour, is nutritionally suspect. Again, it is sugar in a mask. If the wise (?) eater decided to add some kind of fruit to his cereal he usually figures that he has increased the nutritional value considerably. Perhaps, but really very little since fruit is sugar in solid form — almost 80% carbohydrates. A couple of teaspoons of granulated sugar added to the morning coffee adds to the increasing volume. Our example has taken in well over 100 grams of energy-driving carbohydrates but eleven grams of protein (two of which were found in the cereal, one in the banana, and the other eight in the milk).

Lunch involves a sandwich, dinner features a noodle casserole. T.V. snacks of pretzels and chips washed down by some soda or beer are the order for late evening munching. A typical day might find the average American eating over 1,000 grams of carbohydrates. When this is converted to calories (4 calories per gram) it is discovered that he has ingested a staggering 4,000 calories, and I have not even bothered to count the protein or fat calories.

It is quite doubtful if even the athlete in heavy training uses this large amount of calories and even if he did he would want the energy to be derived from foods which can give him some nutritional benefit. Carbohydrate foods typically only provide energy, they do not contain vitamins and minerals or other vital elements for the body.

The athlete needs energy, but it is to his advantage to obtain this through fat primarily and protein secondarily. That is unless he is trying to gain weight. I will expound on gaining and losing weight in chapter fifteen. At this time, however, I will deal with the athlete who desires to maintain his present bodyweight while attempting to become stronger.

CARBOHYDRATE REQUIREMENT

The athlete needs only ½ gram of carbohydrates for each pound of bodyweight if he is trying to maintain his bodyweight. A two-hundred-pounder can get along nicely on 100 grams of carbohydrates per day. It is also very advisable to obtain these carbohydrates from food sources which can supply a bonus of vitamins, minerals, and perhaps even protein as well. For example, one cup (8 ounces) of cottage cheese contains 36 grams of carbohydrates. So does one medium-sized plate of spaghetti or four slices of bread. But the cottage cheese also has 32 grams of protein plus an ample supply of potassium, phosphorus, and Vitamin A.

VALUABLE SOURCES OF CARBOHYDRATES

Fruits and vegetables were mentioned as foods which are high in carbohydrates, and most certainly are, but it is much better to obtain your carbohydrate requirement from fruits and vegetables than it is from starchy foods like rice, potatoes, gravy, or the wide variety of desserts available. The vitamins and minerals found in fruits and vegetables are a valuable addition to your daily food intake, just as long as you don't overdo a good thing. The starchy foods only provide empty calories and this is what you want to avoid.

Actually, if you are attempting to eat 200 grams of protein each day you will, in all likelihood, meet your 100 gram carbohydrate requirement in the process. Most dairy products are high in both protein and carbohydrates. Yogurt, cottage cheese, and whole or skimmed milk all contain 1 gram of protein per ounce but they also have just over 1 gram of carbohydrate per ounce. This is why it's so easy to gain weight by drinking milk. It's also, ironically enough, why so many dieters never lose weight. They eat plenty of yogurt, cottage cheese, and drink only skimmed milk but find that their weight stays the same. In order to lose, carbohydrates have to be eliminated from the diet.

As you put together your diet, select a food which offers some extra nutrition ingredients over the one with empty calories. Be careful not to overindulge in carbohydrates. You don't want to spend time in the weight room or running track burning off excess, useless fat. One hundred grams of carbohydrates is very easy to get, as you will very quickly discover, so be careful as carbohydrates are sneaky. They lurk everywhere.

AVOID SUGARS AND STARCHES

Try to avoid all sugars and starches. If you must have bread, select one which is made from unmilled wheat flour and has not been abused by the processor. Use fresh fruit and vegetables rather than canned ones. Canned fruit is usually weighted down with heavy syrup and that syrup is pure sugar. Canned vegetables have been overcooked and the goodie has been discarded. Most fruits and vegetables are better for you raw than when cooked so learn to prepare and eat them this way.

Finally, learn to cut back on foods high in carbohydrates even if they are ok-type foods. One or two strips of carrot adds to your nutritional requirement. Five or six pushes the carbohydrate count up too high in relationship to carrot's other nutritional benefits. It's better to save room for more protein foods or at least carbohydrate foods which give more of a bonus.

DANGERS OF HIGH CARBOHYDRATE DIET

Unfortunately, eating too many starches and sugars has graver consequences than just holding back progress in weight training or football. Hypoglycemia often results when the diet is too richly laden with carbohydrates and athletes are not above this rather new malady. Hypoglycemia is a low blood sugar condition and is the result of too much insulin being produced by the body. In **Mental Health Through Nutrition** we find: "An abnormal craving for sugar is a common characteristic of low blood sugar. Chronic fatigue is the usual complaint. Doctors estimate there may be three to six times as many sufferers from low blood sugar as there are known diabetics, yet low blood sugar continues to be largely ignored by the men and women of medical science. Although many excellent articles have appeared in recent years in the medical journals explaining why hypoglycemia sufferers cannot eat quickly absorbed carbohydrate foods, many doctors still prescribe sugar for hypoglycemia. This is the worst thing they could do, since sugar primes the pancreas to secrete more insulin and make the hypoglycemia worse. The well-informed physician will treat hypoglycemia with a low carbohydrate and high protein diet. He knows that unless the patients are willing to change their eating habits — get off sugar and other quickly absorbed carbohydrates — they will continue to complain of a fatigue, anxiety, nervousness, headaches, and to have mental confusion."

Anyone who continues a high carbohydrate diet over a long period of time is faced with the unhappy possibility of becoming hypoglycemic, whether he is an athlete or not. The high protein, low carbohydrate diet which I recommend through this book should be your guideline for eating even after you have retired from active athletics. Your revised eating habits will reward you with a longer, healthier, and happier life.

Another important point to know concerning a diet which is high in carbohydrates is that the essential B vitamins are destroyed when carbohydrates are eaten. The B vitamins are most critical to the athlete engaged in heavy training as you will discover as you read that particular section on vitamins. Without them, an athlete is already nutritionally deficient.

SUGAR IS AN ANTINUTRIENT

Read what Dr. Atkins has to say on this subject in his book **Diet Revolution:** "In order to assimilate carbohydrates, large quantities of Vitamin B are required. Sugar, of course, contains no vitamins or nutrients of any kind, except sucrose. So the body is forced to draw on its own Vitamin B reserves. The more sugar you take in, the greater the Vitamin B deficit imposed on your body. It is important then, to understand that sugar has **antinutrient** properties. This is true to a lesser extent of all carbohydrates that you take in. Starch is the major source of hidden sugar, because your body turns starch into sugar while it is in the stomach. In order to know the truth about your sugar intake, you must visualize **all starch food** as servings of sugar."

FATS AND OILS

Fats may be the most thoroughly misunderstood of all the nutrients. Fats, to most people, is still a four-letter word. They are shunned, avoided, ridiculed, discarded, and generally held in high contempt. Yet they are valuable and most necessary for the maintenance of good health. It is ironic that we set the true villain of health, carbohydrates, in a place of honor in our diet while we relegate fats, an essential addition, to our nutritional black sheep's position.

Fats differ from oils in that fats are solids or semi-solids at room temperatures. Oils are liquids. Fats and oils are comprised of unsaturated fatty acids as well as saturated fatty acids. Some fats and oils are very unsaturated, others are highly saturated, and while yet others lie somewhere in between.

Fats and oils yield more than twice as much energy as carbohydrates or proteins. Fats undergo slow digestion by enzyme influence during digestion. The complex fat molecules are split into molecules of glycerin and fatty acids.

VERY ESSENTIAL TO GOOD HEALTH

Fats are quite essential to the maintenance of good health. Every body cell has to be supplied with certain fats. The nerves, brain, hormones of the adrenal cortex and the sex glands require particular kinds of fat. Bacteria in the digestive tract needs fat in order to multiply. The unsaturated fatty acids contain a growth promoting factor which is necessary for healthy skin, hair, and glands. They also promote the availability of calcium to the cells.

Many health problems occur when important fatty acids are eliminated from the diet. Burr and Burr, reporting in the **Journal of Biological Chemistry**, found that: "rats fed a fat-free diet soon developed scaly feet, swollen tails, dandruff on the back of the body, hemorrhagic spots and sores on the skin, and other symptoms of a diet-deficiency disease." They found that the disease could be prevented or cured by the inclusion of linoleic or linolenic acids (essential fatty acids) or fats containing them. They also discovered that the disease could not be prevented or cured by saturated fatty acids or fats."

UNSATURATED FATTY ACIDS

The unsaturated fats and oils (sometimes called polyunsaturated) are found in vegetable oils such as: soybean, corn, peanut, cottonseed, sunflower, and safflower; in fish oils like cod liver, halibut, liver, and salmon; nut oils, spreads, dressings such as mayonnaise, French dressing, whole grain products, dairy products such as raw cream and natural cheese, and egg yokes.

The unsaturated fatty acids are the ones to be sought after as they contain the essential fatty acids. Fats are classified as essential fatty acids and those which are not essential to good health. The unessential ones can be manufactured by the body from sugar but the essential ones (like the essential amino acids in protein) have to be taken in from the foods you eat.

ESSENTIAL FATTY ACIDS

The three essential fatty acids are well worth remembering. They are: linoleic acid, arachidonic acid, and linolenic acid. Linoleic acid is the most important of the three and is absolutely critical to life itself. Adelle Davis writes: "The bodies of persons and well-fed animals contain large amounts of linoleic acid. If animals are put on a diet lacking it, this fatty acid cannot be withdrawn from the tissues even when the supply in the blood falls far below normal and the deficiency becomes so severe that it causes death." There are two more unsaturated fatty acids, oleic and arucic, but they are not classified as essential.

SATURATED FATTY ACIDS

There are thirteen saturated fatty acids which are listed here for your convenience as a reference point. It's easier to check back here than it is to chase down a biochemistry text. The saturated fatty acids, along with their source are: acetic (vinegar), bytyric (butter), caproic (butter), caprylic (butter), capric (coconut oil), lauric (coconut oil), myristic (coconut oil), palmitic (animal fats), stearic (animal fats), lignoceric (arachis oil), arachidie (peanut oil), carnaubic (carnaaba wax), and cerotic (wool fat). These are not essential, nor even desirable and should be avoided.

It is highly recommended that the weight trained athlete assure himself of obtaining the essential fatty acids on a regular basis. Many athletes, in order to insure themselves of an adequate supply take three tablespoons of a good vegetable oil each day. Again, you will have to check the label to be sure that the product has not been abused by the processor. If the product does not mention that it has **not** been processed or refined then you can rest assured that it has been. Processing means that the manufacturer changes his original dark colored oil to a lighter oil for commercial reasons. People like the lighter color better. Refining requires the removal of linolenic acid and Vitamin C.

Cold pressed, unrefined oils are the best. They contain as much as twice the valuable ingredients as their refined counterparts. Since they may turn cloudy after they are opened, they should be kept in the refrigerator, away from light and should be used promptly.

RANCID OIL

If the oil should become rancid, promptly discard it. Eating rancid fats has been shown to induce serious vitamin deficiencies. Vitamin E, A and K and several B vitamins, can be destroyed. It's easy to slip a little of this in the diet, almost unnoticed, so you have to be careful not to use old bacon drippings for frying, or eat old packaged foods like chips or popcorn. Adelle Davis makes the statement that, "The nut and popcorn dispensers in public places, kept heated to give the illusion of freshness, are potentially so dangerous that they should be removed from the market."

Some nutritional companies handle a capsule containing unsaturated fatty acids and most people find this a simple and more palatable way of securing these fatty acids. The Fibertone Company, located in Los Angeles, has an excellent one, Lino F, which contains 500 mgs. of linolenic and 167 mgs. of linoleic acid at a cost of about 3c each.

Another excellent product which I recommend highly in Fearn's liquid lecithin. I will say more of the value of lecithin later, but this product contains a great deal of linolenic acid, linoleic acid, and oleic acid. Two tablespoons provides the following generous allowances: linolenic acid, 800 mgs; linoleic acid, 5,500 mgs; and oleic acid, 1,400 mgs. It comes from crude soybean oil and has been mechanically separated. In short, it's really a fine product and it's difficult to obtain this quantity of essential fatty acids.

The saturated fats are not necessary for maintenance of health and should be avoided. These include all solid fats which have been hydrogenated (the process of adding hydrogen to make the fat more solid), coconut oils and processed lard. There is a group generally termed inter-mediate fats. These contain some unsaturated and some saturated fatty acids. This group includes products such as: butter, pasteurized whole milk, pasteurized cream, meat, and poultry fats.

Your diet should emphasize the totally unsaturated fats, then go light on the intermediate group and completely avoid the saturated ones.

PASTEURIZATION AND HYDROGENATION

I have mentioned two processing terms, pasteurization and hydrogenation. Both of which destroy some important portion of the fatty acids. Pasteurization, under the guise of protecting your health, destroys the lecithin in the product and hydrogenation destroys the essential fatty acids themselves. Hydrogenation is merely another in the long line of commercial tampering of natural foods and, as in the case of white sugar and white flour, it has resulted in nutritional disorders. Many authorities, Dr. Philip Chen, among them, believe that the increased use of hydrogenated fats has contributed directly to the steady rise in arteriosclerosis.

CHOLESTEROL

The essential fatty acids are extremely critical to the bodies' cholesterol level. The medical profession has done the American public a great injustice with their campaign against cholesterol. Not that I advocate raising everyone's cholesterol level. On the contrary, my recommendations can assure you of a much lower cholesterol level. My complaint with the general medical fraternity is that they went about their campaign in such an uninformed manner. They misled the public and, as a result, ended up changing many people's diets for the worse.

The average doctor will tell you to avoid eggs as they raise the cholesterol level. Correct? Very incorrect. Cholesterol is a fatty substance found in foods. If cholesterol is not eaten then it is manufactured by the body. The body, in essence, needs cholesterol. It is necessary for the manufacture of sex hormones, bile, and Vitamin D.

EGGS AND CHOLESTEROL

Eggs are high in cholesterol and the medical men continue to tell patients to avoid a diet which is high in eggs. Some insist on dropping eggs from the menu altogether. Non-sense. Eggs also contain lecithin. In natural foods containing fat, there exists a naturally-balanced combination of choles-terol and lecithin. Lecithin is a homogenizing agent, capable of breaking fat and cholesterol into tiny particles which can pass readily into the tissue. When the oil is hydrogenated or refined, lecithin is discarded, and the cholesterol is left alone to pile up in the arteries and cause difficulty.

Linda Clark points out that, "People who are afraid to eat eggs because of the cholesterol are hurting rather than helping themselves. Eggs contain, in addition to cholesterol, important unsaturated fatty acids: lecithin, Vitamins A, B, and D; and all the necessary amino acids. Eggs are considered such a valuable source of protein that scientists use egg protein as the standard of protein measure in other foods."

The fat-free diets often advocated are not at all advisable. An experiment done by Doctor H.M. Sinclair showed that a fat-free diet on rats produced more rather than less cholesterol deposits in their arteries. The longer the diet continued, the more cholesterol accumulated. Since no cholesterol was eaten, the body began manufacturing it.

SUMMARY

Fat is, then, an important nutrient for the weight trained athlete. It is a rich energy source and will supply your body with valuable nutrients. The problem lies in the constant hide-and-seek game with the processor. Which fats are use-ful? Briefly, those which have not been tampered with by the processor. Avoid hydrogenated fats such as hydrogenated peanut butter, processed cheeses, solid cooking fats, and French fried foods cooked in these solid fats. Limit the solid (saturated) animal fats such as beef, lamb, and pork. Switch to fish or foul more often. Coconut and palm oils are highly saturated and have no place in your diet.

Use unrefined, cold pressed oils and keep them refriger-ated. No one has yet set a standard for the amount of fat needed by any individual. It varies with the amount of activity, your bodyweight, the climate you live in, plus other individual factors.

I would recommend that all athletes take three teaspoons of high quality vegetable oil daily, preferably after each meal. Again, there are some fine products to be found, although you may have to go to a natural food store to secure them. The oils are available as are the capsules. Whichever you select, be sure to add them to your list of important nutrients.   ★

10

CHAPTER TEN
THOSE VALUABLE VITAMINS

VITAMINS: SURELY ONE of the most debated subjects in the field of athletics today centers around the importance of vitamins. Many team doctors and trainers voice the strong opinion that vitamins serve no useful purpose whatsoever. Others pass them off as harmless, but mention in passing that they are probably not very helpful either. And some even go so far as to recommend them to the players. The athlete who is genuinely interested in obtaining the greatest progress in the shortest possible time wants to know the facts. Are vitamins really useful to athletic performance or are they merely gimmicks to milk yet another few dollars from the uninformed athlete?

THEY DO HELP

The evidence is very clear from where I sit — they definitely do help the athlete. The athlete is in a rather unique position in our culture. He pushes his body to the extreme limits of physical conditioning day in and day out in his quest for physical superiority. His body stores of vital nutrients are depleted through sheer physical exertion. Those elements which are drained must be resupplied or the human machine is at a deficit. When there is a nutritional deficiency, the body is handicapped and cannot perform at its full potential. Vitamins do many things for your body, as you will soon learn as you read further, and they must be made available to your depleted cells if you are to continue to compete and train at a high level.

Vitamins are not really new, although you might be inclined to think so because of all the attention that they have received in recent years. Doctor Roger Williams, the gentleman who discovered pantothenic acid (one of the B vitamins) wrote: "Some poorly informed people may think of vitamins as a recent fad. It is true that we have known about them for only a few decades, but there is abundant evidence that they may have been part of nature's equipment since long before man appeared on earth."

USEFUL TO ATHLETES

More and more research is being conducted which shows the close relationship between good health and the conscientious use of vitamins. No longer are they being used exclusively by the "health freaks." Everyone from well-read grandmothers to supervised children are receiving the benefit of nutritional research. Now, the research periodicals are jammed with data that directly affect the athlete.

One brief example. The vast amount of research done with Vitamin E should merit special attention from all athletes. Vitamin E is, among other things, a vasodilator. That is, it opens arteries and veins so that more blood can flow through the circulatory system. What does this mean to the athlete? Instant endurance. Tests have been conducted with rats, guinea pigs, race horses, and humans. It has been found that they all developed much more endurance when given large amounts of Vitamin E. For instance, it was found that Vitamin E-treated rats could swim nearly twice as long as non-treated animals. More on the merits of Vitamin E later.

The athlete who can utilize the nutritional research available has a definite advantage over his opponents. "But," you may be thinking, "I have made a 20% strength increase and have not bothered with any extra vitamins." Well and good, but I can assure you that if you had been following a nutritional program that you would have made a 40-50% strength increase over the same span of training time. It may sound a bit presumptious, but it has been demonstrated over and over by those athletes willing to follow the guidelines set forth by the researchers.

AN EXPERIMENT

During my tenure at the hub of competitive weightlifting in York, Pennsylvania, I had the opportunity to consul and advise many aspiring weightlifters on the advantages of proper training and nutrition. Very often, I would test a few training or nutritional ideas on agreeable subjects and my findings, while not within the framework of legitimate research, did give me many worthwhile clues as to how nutrition could affect the factor of strength.

One such experiment happened during the summer of 1968. Two lifters came to York from Virginia to spend the off-season there so as to train with the national champion team. Since both the lifters had been stymied in their progress for over a twelve-month period, they were most eager to learn and willing to try anything which might help them in the future.

They agreed to be test subjects for a nutritional experiment. Both lifters were to begin training on a revised schedule which was the same except for the difference in weight each could handle on certain exercises. Both were to eat the same foods, primarily foods high in protein content. The only difference between the two programs was that lifter A was to take a full range of vitamins and minerals while lifter B was to depend entirely on his diet for these specific nutrients.

The arrangement was as follows: Lifter A and B were to train for a total of six weeks on this program as I felt that it would take 7-10 days for the full effects of a complete nutritional program to take effect and I wanted my test subject (lifter A) to have at least four full weeks of heavy training after the vitamin supplements started taking effect.

Lifter A took the following supplements: Vitamin A (25,000 units), Vitamin E (1200 I.U.), Vitamin C (5000 mgs.) plus a compounded multiple vitamin, multiple mineral, and B-Complex vitamin. All the necessary nutrients were provided in these vitamin and mineral supplements and mega-doses were used as recommended later in this book.

Lifter B ate well, but he did not supplement his diet in any manner. He made sure that he obtained 200 grams of protein each day, primarily by eating lots of meat and dairy products. At the end of six weeks, lifter A had improved as much as 30% in some lifts and 25% overall. Lifter B had also improved, due to the enthusiasm at the training center and the revised training schedule, but his overall gains were but 9%.

Now the procedure was reversed. Lifter A stopped using supplements, but continued to eat high-quality protein foods, and lifter B began on the nutritional schedule. From this point, lifter A did not progress at all during the next six weeks, but in fact regressed 5% overall. His energy level dropped and he reported being much more sore and tired the day following a heavy training session. He mentioned that the weights began to feel heavy again and he seemed more lethargic throughout the day. He also sustained a small injury during this period, a slight muscle tear in the trapezius.

Lifter B, after he began the vitamin-mineral program, improved another 15%. Both lifters reported a terrific feeling of well being while taking the supplements. They, like most, said they noticed the change slowly after about a week. It takes this period of time to saturate the body with some of the necessary nutrients. While on the supplements, they reported that they could train longer, harder, and recover much faster. This physical uplift gave them a tremendous mental boost so that they went into each workout with high expectations and a very positive attitude.

Both lifters felt that the additional vitamins and minerals served their purpose and incorporated them into their total program immediately. After a time, both were able to train six days a week and three days a week they worked out for one hour at mid-day and another 1½ hours later that same evening. This afforded them nine total training sessions each week, yet they were fully recovered after each session and never sustained even a minor injury during this period of time.

Again, this was not meant to be a controlled study and is not presented as such. But the fact remains that results are produced when megavitamins are included in a training program. I have conducted similar experiments literally hundreds of times since this first experiment and the results have always been very positive for the supplement users.

A NOTE FROM THE BULGARIAN'S SUCCESS

It may be of interest to the reader to know something of the giant strides some of the foreign athletic powers are making in the field of vitamin supplementation. Bulgaria, a relatively small European nation, has recently emerged as the world champion in the sport of competition weightlifting, ousting the much larger Russian nation from this prestigious spot in international sports.

The Bulgarians have moved to the top in the strength sport primarily through their application of nutritional research for their weightlifters. Among other things they do for the athlete, they test each lifter immediately following each workout to discover exactly which nutrients he has depleted and how much is necessary for a quick and full recovery. These deficient nutrients are quickly restored so the body is only deficient for a short time. Hence, recovery is rapid.

As a result, these strength athletes are able to handle unthought-of training loads. Some of the more advanced are training twice a day for six days a week in two-hour training sessions. This enabled them to get a sizable jump on their rivals and they continue to hold this edge in world competition. They do, of course, many other progressive programs for their athletes, but the key to their recent success is their systematic nutritional regime. It should be noted that the medical people lend full support to this program in Bulgaria, whereas in our country the AMA and its many representatives, under a wide variety of names, severely limits progress in application of these progressive ideas.

THE MYSTERIOUS VITAMINS

To many people, vitamins are clouded in mystery and confusion. They seem like a montage of letters signifying, at best, chaos. How can you be expected to remember how much A, D, C, E, and so forth you must take each day? Which should be taken with which? How about amounts? Aren't some dangerous if overdosed? What authority should be believed?

I hope in these next few pages to take a bit of the confusion and mystery out of nutrition. I will explain briefly what each does in your body and then recommend a daily dosage for each vitamin and mineral. There are two things to remember as you read along. I am not able to explain all that each nutrient does in your body because of the limitations of

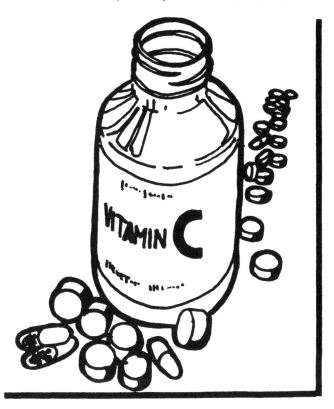

space. To do so would require much more space than I have
in the entire book. I have merely hit the high spots, but
those high spots should give you a clear insight on each
nutrient. Secondly, my program utilized the European research for my recommended allowances. These are, in
almost all cases, much higher than any recommended
dosages in this country. I never, however, recommend a
toxic dosage. I can validate my recommendations through
actual research out of Europe and also from findings conducted in our own country, so the reader need not be
alarmed that I am risking his health with my megadoses.

My recommendations are considered megadoses, but it
needs to be reiterated that athletes are megahumans. To
suppose that a football player who spends six to ten hours
per week in strenuous physical activity requires the same
amount of any nutrient as the sedentary secretary or
insurance salesman is pure foolishness, but that is often
what we are asked to believe by those who set the daily
amounts for the various nutrients.

THE "SHOVEL" METHOD

I believe in the "shovel method," at least until there is a
scientific and relatively inexpensive method of determining
exact individual needs. By the "shovel method" I mean
taking the top end of all the nutrients, including those about
which we know very little. So much is still being discovered
about the value of certain vitamins and trace elements that
it is quite conceivable that the researchers will find that
some so-called "trace elements" are indispensible to health.
For example, there is presently no minimum daily requirement for bioflavonoids and most medical men wouldn't
recommend any at all. But I do. I know that the bioflavonoids
are most valuable to the athlete. Why? Research has shown
that it is a nutrient that helps to strengthen fragile
capillaries. The circulatory system is only as strong as the
capillaries, as this is where the vital exchange takes place.
This nutrient is often used in the treatment of high blood
pressure. Anything that helps circulation is good for the
athlete because so much of his performance depends on a
strong circulatory system.

Vitamins, then, are very critical for optimum athletic
performance. And since every athlete is surely interested in
the highest achievement level for himself, then let's move on
to the various vitamins.   ★

11

CHAPTER ELEVEN
THE A, D, C, AND E OF IT

VITAMIN A CAN BEST be remembered as the eye and skin vitamin. It is a colorless substance formed in the animal or human body from a yellow pigment, carotene, found in all green vegetables, carrots, apricots and yams. The more yellow in the vegetable, the more carotene available. Liver, fish liver oils, egg yolks, butter, and cream are rich sources of both Vitamin A and carotene.

VISION

Vitamin A is vital to vision, especially night vision. People who use their eyes a great deal, such as typists and students, use much more Vitamin A than those who do not. Many who experience sensitivity to light are lacking adequate Vitamin A. Eye fatigue resulting from night driving or watching TV is not uncommon. Severe deficiencies bring on a stinging sensation in the eyes, nervousness, headaches, and visual fatigue. Dark glasses prevent light from reaching the eyes and thus reduce the amount of Vitamin A destroyed.

SKIN

Vitamin A is also closely associated with skin disorders. Adelle Davis in **Let's Eat Right To Keep Fit**, describes how a Vitamin A deficiency affects the skin. "Cells in the lower layers of skin die and slough off. They plug the oil sacs and pores, thus preventing oil from reaching the surface; the skin may become so dry and rough that the entire body sometimes itches. The pores plugged with dead cells cause the skin to have the appearance of 'goose pimples' although they are unaffected by temperature changes. Pores enlarge by an accumulation of dead cells and oil are spoken of as whiteheads or blackheads. If these cells become infected, pimples may result. The skin is likewise susceptible to such infections as impetigo, boils, and carbuncles. These abnormalities can usually be corrected by increased amounts of Vitamin A, provided the diet is adequate in other respects."

INFECTIONS

Vitamin A is valuable in that it helps to resist infections in the body. Bacteria grows only when it is provided with sufficient warmth, food, and moisture. When there is a lack of Vitamin A, the cells of the mucous membranes die more rapidly and begin piling up. The dead cells cannot excrete anti-enzymes and provide all the conditions necessary for bacterial growth. Since bacteria is ever present, infections generally follow.

Vitamin A is also essential to bone and tooth enamel development. It aids in digestion, reproduction, and the formation of both red and white corpuscles.

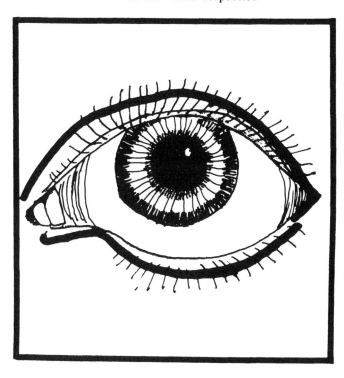

SOURCES OF A

Green leaf vegetables are rich in Vitamin A. Kale, spinach, and chard are all excellent sources. Also high in Vitamin A are: broccoli, string beans, carrots, yellow squash, sweet potatoes, tomatoes, celery, lettuce, and asparagus. Eggs, whole milk, butterfat, fish-liver oils, and liver are also rich sources.

You cannot, however, count on your diet to supply you with an adequate amount of Vitamin A. I recommend 25,000 units daily and this is most difficult to obtain from the foods purchased in a grocery store. Carrots have been analyzed which contain absolutely no Vitamin A whatsoever. Losses occur during cooking, canning, freezing, storage, and shipping.

By taking Vitamin A along with Vitamins E and C you greatly increase the curative effect of the A. Vitamin A is more effective if taken in small amounts two or three times daily, rather than all at once.

REQUIREMENTS OF A

Individuals differ in their need for this all-important vitamin. Requirements vary with how much you use your eyes, light intensity, amount absorbed Vitamin E and C taken, but even the Council of Pharmacy and Chemistry of the AMA has approved the following therapeutic doses: 25,000 units three times a day for prolonged deficiency. It is also recommended that you take 200 units of Vitamin E and 500 mgs. of Vitamin C at the same time you ingest your Vitamin A tablet. Capsules of fish-liver oils are considered the best source of Vitamin A.

VITAMIN D

The "sunshine vitamin" may just be the most misunderstood of all the vitamins. Since Vitamin D is an oil-soluble vitamin and stores on the body, most feel that you need very little of it for the maintenance of health. In fact, more has been written concerning the dangers of taking too much Vitamin D than has been written concerning the value of it for the body.

Vitamin D can be obtained from sunshine, under conditions. These conditions are rarely available, as Adelle Davis tells in **Let's Eat Right To Keep Fit:** "Vitamin D is formed by ultraviolet light from sunshine in the oils **on** the skin, provided you have oils on your skin and the shortest rays from the sun reach the earth. In winter, these rays do not penetrate our atmospheric blanket; during the summer they reach the top of the Empire State Building but usually not the street below it. Sunshine would be an excellent source of this vitamin if it were not for the facts that people are surrounded by smog, wear clothes, live in houses, and have bathtubs and hot-water heaters."

BODY OILS MUST BE PRESENT

Vitamin D is only formed on the skin, rather than in the skin, only if that oil is first present there. The oil is exposed to ultraviolet light, then absorbed back into the body. If you take a bath before going into the sunshine, the oils are removed and no Vitamin D can be formed. Likewise, if you shower or wash the skin immediately after being exposed to the sunshine the oils are thereby removed before they can be reabsorbed into the body and, hence, no Vitamin D makes it into your system.

Vitamin D aids in the absorption of calcium and phosphorus. Without an adequate supply of both these nutrients, your bones become porous and honeycombed. Individuals with Vitamin D deficiency experience more fractures and a higher rate of tooth decay. According to a study reported in Volume XI of **Nutritional Reviews**, an increased amount of evidence indicated that both the enamel and dentin of mature teeth can be built up provided the nutrition is adequate, especially in calcium and Vitamin D.

The presence of fat is necessary in order for Vitamin D to be absorbed into the blood. Individuals who only drink skimmed milk and who do not assure themselves of an adequate supply of fat are inviting problems.

REQUIREMENTS

Since the toxicity of Vitamin D is frequently mentioned, just how much is necessary and how much is too much? The National Research Council sets the lid at 400 units daily, but other studies indicate the toxic level is much, much higher than this figure. Dr. Johnston of the Henry Ford Hospital in Detroit gave adolescent girls as much as 3900 units daily and found the quantity of calcium absorbed was increased tenfold. A group of nurses who worked indoors throughout the summer were given 5000 units daily over an extended period with only positive results.

Doctor Roger Williams states, "The minimum of Vitamin D needed by any normal human being is not known, but the maximum is certainly twenty times what is considered average."

Adelle Davis recommends 4000-5000 units for all adults. From my review of research I concur, I feel the athlete has an extra high requirement for all nutrients and if "average" folks can handle 5000 units, then certainly heavy training athletes can also utilize this amount. I should also note that Vitamin D toxicity can be prevented by generous amounts of Vitamins C, E, or cholin. Since I am also recommending high dosages of C, E, and cholin I feel that I am providing a safe margin.

SOURCES

The best natural sources of Vitamin D is cod-liver oil. There is some Vitamin D in egg yolks and fortified milk. It is wisest to obtain your requirement of Vitamin D through a supplement as it is very difficult, perhaps even impossible, to obtain necessary amounts through the diet. Cod-liver oil capsules are inexpensive and very easy to take. They should always be taken just after a meal and with your other vitamins, especially with Vitamin E.

VITAMIN C

Until Professor Linus Pauling authored **Vitamin C and the Common Cold,** very few people outside health circles knew much about Vitamin C, although the vitamin has been known for over 200 years. It was discovered at the middle of the nineteenth century that scurvy could be prevented if citrus fruits were added to the sailor's diet and in 1795 the British Navy received a daily ration of lime juice to prevent the disease. Hence the nickname "limey" appeared. Vitamin C is also known as ascorbic acid as well as cevitamic acid. The name "ascorbic acid" is derived from its ability to cure scurvy — the "a" meaning against and "acorb" coming from scorbutus, the medical name for the disease.

Today, Vitamin C is called by many other names. One medical authority calls it "the antibiotic par excellence" because of its ability to cure so many infectious diseases. Vitamin C has been shown to be most helpful in counteracting infections such as: pneumonia, colds, meningitis, rheumatic fever, diptheria, and those involving ears, eyes, sinuses, and tonsils. It has also been used to prevent allergies.

PREVENTS FATIGUE

One of the most important discoveries concerning Vitamin C from an athlete's standpoint is its ability to help prevent fatigue. Since Vitamin C does not play a major role in actually producing energy, an example of a study might be in order to help explain how this phenomenon occurs. Adelle Davis writes: "A group of soldiers was given Vitamin C until the tissues were saturated. Their performance was compared with that of a similar group not given the vitamin. After maneuvers involving carrying heavy equipment, walking miles, and climbing mountains, the soldiers given Vitamin C experienced little fatigue, recovered quickly, and had no leg cramps, whereas the other soldiers suffered severely from cramps and fatigue and did not completely recover for days."

BRUISES

Athletes have found Vitamin C to be most useful in alleviating bruises, muscle strains, skin abraisons, and minor joint injuries. Small muscle tears rebuild much more rapidly when high quantities of Vitamin C are administered. The author has witnessed many episodes where sore muscles literally disappeared overnight as a result of high dosages of Vitamin C. It has also been found to help heal broken bones. The presence of Vitamin C enables the broken ends to knit properly; without Vitamin C, plus the necessary quantities of proteins, calcium, and Vitamin D, the process does not take place.

COLLAGEN

One of the more amazing properties of Vitamin C is its ability to form a substance called collagen. Collagen, very basically, binds the cells of your body together like a strong adhesive. Collagen is very much involved in building strong connective tissue found in all cartilage, ligaments, blood vessels, and is the base of bones and teeth. Vitamin C and calcium work together to build this strong connective tissue. Having strong connective tissue is most essential to good health and even more critical to the hard-training athlete. The cell walls are very thin, so it is up to the connective tissue to protect the cells from foreign agents. Vitamin C keeps this barrier strong; an undersupply of the nutrient leaves the cells vulnerable.

Bruises which do not dissappear are a sure sign that you are lacking Vitamin C. Bruises indicate a weakness in the capillaries, the tiny single-cells which make up the end of the circulatory system. When the capillary walls are weak, blood seeps through into adjoining tissue and is not reabsorbed readily. This locked-in blood discolors the skin and produces a bruise. When Vitamin C is added to the diet the capillary walls become stronger and the bruise subsides.

BIOFLAVONOIDS

Many nutritionists believe that substances called bioflavonoids also have a hand in this important process of strengthening capillary walls and recommend that some bioflavonoids be included in the Vitamin C. Bioflavonoids are found naturally in the pulp of citrus fruits. Its the white portion on the inside of the skin. Most people religiously peel this part off and discard it. Obviously it's a good idea to eat a bit of it in order to obtain those valuable hidden nutrients.

WATER SOLUBLE

Vitamin C is water soluble and thus, cannot be stored in the body. So it must be taken at regular intervals during each and every day. I feel that it is much better for athletes to break their dosages up into three or four equal parts and take them at regular intervals during the day. If, for example, you play to take 4 grams or 4000 milligrams of Vitamin C during the day, take 1 gram after each of your three meals and 1 gram at bedtime. If you were to take all 4 grams at one crack in the morning then you would merely pass off the unused vitamin in your urine and therefore be deficient for the remainder of the day.

REQUIREMENTS

The recommended dosage for Vitamin C in this country varies from 30 mgs. to 70 mgs. per day. Since it is known that exertion, heat, smoking, alcohol, and any form of drug quickly destroys Vitamin C at an alarming rate, I consider this minimum requirement asinine for "Mister Average," and totally ridiculous for the athlete. One cigarette, for example, destroys anywhere from 25-30 milligrams of Vitamin C immediately and even if you do not smoke yourself, merely being in the presence of other smokers still taps into your supply. Industrial or automobile smog will have a similar effect.

The European athletes take a minimum of 4 grams (4000 mgs.) of Vitamin C daily and some take twice this amount. If you have not taken Vitamin C for a long period of time you may need to take more at first in order to thoroughly saturate the tissues.

You can obtain a large amount of your Vitamin C requirement from natural sources. Fresh orange juice is not as dependable since the Vitamin C content is greatly influenced by the type of oranges it came from, how it was prepared, and how long it was stored. Fresh grapefruit and lemon juice yields approximately 100 mgs. per eight ounce glass. Tomatoes, strawberries, spinach, brussel sprouts, cabbage, lettuce, apples, bananas, and potatoes also contain generous amounts of Vitamin C.

It is known that 80-85% of this important vitamin is lost in the course of food preparation. Over 90% of the Vitamin C may be lost within an hour after frozen food is thawed. Vegetables lose 50-90% when cooked in water. Since Vitamin C is water soluble, even washing or soaking takes away from the overall supply.

For this reason I recommend that all athletes utilize a supplement to obtain adequate Vitamin C. They are simple to take and can be transported much easier than a similar quantity of natural foods.

Since Vitamin C is water soluble, it must be taken at regular intervals. Relatively large concentrations of Vitamin C are located in such areas as the adrenal cortex and the liver; but these organs are not storage centers. From **The Science of Nutrition** it is noted that, "Apparently all body sources are called upon when the dietary intake is inadequate. In the absence of a reservoir it is possible to explain the fact that the ingestion of excessive amounts of the vitamin (amounts over and above that needed to saturate the cells) is accompanied by prompt urinary excretion. This means that, unlike the fat soluble vitamins, which can be stored in the liver, ascorbic acid must be supplied to the body regularly."

NATURAL VS. SYNTHETIC

There has been an ongoing debate concerning the benefits of natural versus synthetic Vitamin C for quite some time. It is known that synthetic C does not contain the valuable bioflavonoics and it does not contain enzymes found in the natural form of C, so most authorities feel that it is inferior to the natural line. Since natural Vitamin C costs a great deal more than synthetic and since cost is important to anyone following a complete nutritional program, I recommend the following plan. Buy a small quantity of natural Vitamin C which does contain the valuable bioflavonoids and a larger quantity of synthetic Vitamin C, ascorbic acid. Take one tablet of the natural, maybe 100-200 mgs., and an additional 1000 mgs. of synthetic C four times daily. This way you get the best of both forms of this vitamin.

Regardless of how you obtain your Vitamin C, do be sure to get it in ample quantities. Vitamin C is most useful to athletes in many ways which will directly affect their performance.

VITAMIN E

Vitamin E, like Vitamin C, does so many things for the athlete that it could be considered essential to total conditioning. Research studies are being done constantly concerning the value of Vitamin E and many of these findings relate directly to the athlete in heavy training.

OXYGEN CONSERVATOR AND ANTI-OXIDANT

It has been found that Vitamin E is an oxygen conservator and an anti-oxidant. As an anti-oxidant, it delays the oxidative process which turns cells rancid and it prevents oxygen from combining with other substances to form hydrogen peroxide — which hastens the cells to die.

The anti-oxidant and oxygen conservator factors are very important for the athlete as it gives him quite an advantage over the individual who does not supply his body with adequate Vitamin E. In **Vitamin E, Your Key To A Healthy Heart,** author Herbert Bailey tells why this is so. "When richly supplied with Vitamin E, the cells of the body are able to perform more efficiently — not demanding as much oxygen for metabolic processes, thereby freeing more oxygen for those cells and organs needing it. The heart does not have to work as hard to convey blood to the cells. Also, the heart muscle itself is more richly nourished with oxygen through its main source of blood supply, the coronary arteries."

VASODILATOR

Another interesting attribute of Vitamin E is that it is a vasodilator. Literally, it opens arteries, so that more blood can flow through the circulatory system. This factor explains why athletes can train longer, harder, and recover faster when they are taking an adequate amount of this vitamin. Numerous studies have been conducted showing that rats, guinea pigs, race horses, and humans have much more endurance when Vitamin E is included in the diet. Rats given large doses of Vitamin E, for example, have been able to swim twice as long as non-treated animals.

The author saw many instances of Vitamin E boosting weight training progress. Individuals, after including Vitamin E in their diets, told me that they could train much more rapidly without experiencing fatigue. They also said that they recovered much faster after they finished training. Many expressed the feeling that they could, if necessary, train again later that same day. All felt that they had been energized to some degree and definitely did not care to train in the future without the benefit of Vitamin E.

I noted in the section on Vitamin C the importance of maintaining the permeability of cellular membranes, especially the capillaries. Vitamin E plays a role in this process also, along with Vitamin C and the bioflavonoids. It is very critical to have the capillary walls maintain a certain level of permeability. The capillaries are essential to proper circulation as they supply the nourishment to the individual cells. If the walls of the capillaries become too impermeable, that is, too tough and solid, their function of feeding the cells is seriously impared. If, on the other end of the pole, they become too thin and weak then they allow the nutrients to leak out into the extra-cellular spaces where it does no good for the body. An adequate and constant supply of the necessary substances are needed in order to keep this process operating on a healthy level.

Exposure to air destroys a goodly portion of the vitamin and heating, freezing, storage, and cooking also destroy a large percentage of Vitamin E. No Vitamin E is left in oils extracted chemically or in refined flour or packaged cereals, so it becomes very difficult to obtain sufficient amount of the vitamin directly from your diet.

So once again, supplements are in order. Vitamin E derived from natural sources is far superior to that obtained from synthetic sources. Synthetic Vitamin E is designated in testing procedures as E2. A commercial Vitamin E product will have (or more properly, should have) the letters d- or dl-preceding the types of tocopherols which make up the ingredient. The prefix dl- signifies the synthetic Vitamin E and the d- indicates that it comes from natural sources. The synthetic form has only one-fifth the potency of the natural vitamin.

HEALS SCAR TISSUE

Vitamin E has been shown to heal scar tissue almost miraculously. It is used both externally and internally on people suffering from severe burns, disfiguring scars, and painful sunburn. Pain, too, is quickly reduced with the addition of Vitamin E to the body and some more progressive medical men are now substituting this safe nutrient for aspirin and stronger pain killers. Some progressive hospitals give injections of Vitamin E to burn patients immediately to remove the suffering. Applied externally to any break in the skin, it literally keeps the tissue from forming scar tissue.

There is evidence that Vitamin E tends to normalize blood pressure in some people. While this fact should not concern the heavy training athlete, it is rather surprising just how many football players have either high or low blood pressure.

AIDS LIVER

One of the more interesting qualities of Vitamin E is its ability to help the liver detoxify substances such as food preservatives, bleaches which have been added to flour, residues from pesticides, nitrites, and nitrates from chemical fertilizers, industrial poisons, and toxic drugs. Any of these dangerous substances can cause liver damage unless the amount of Vitamin E is plentiful.

SOURCES OF E

Wheat germ oil, wheat germ granules, cold-pressed oils, stone-ground whole wheat breads and nuts are excellent sources of Vitamin E. It is found in the oils of all nuts, grains, and seeds. It is also available in leafy vegetables and is found in varying amounts of animal tissues, being most concentrated in the heart and liver. Milk and eggs also contain Vitamin E.

SEVEN TOCOPHEROLS

Vitamin E is composed of seven forms of tocopherols. These are given the Greek names of: alpha, beta, gamma, delta, epsilon, eta, and zeta. So far, only alpha has been shown to be of use to the human. Products containing alpha tocopherols are superior to those having mixed tocopherols. Researchers have found that the Vitamin E dosage must be doubled if mixed tocopherols are used rather than alpha tocopherols.

So read the label carefully before you purchase your Vitamin E. Because of the involved method of extraction, Vitamin E is very expensive to produce. Be certain that you are getting a good quality vitamin before you plunk your money down. Be wary of the "sales" and "specials" on Vitamin E. These are invariably synthetic forms of the vitamin, or at best, mixed tocopherols. A bargain may not turn out to be a bargain if you do not know your source.

REQUIREMENTS

The question of how much Vitamin E is needed is batted back and forth between authorities constantly. Heart patients have taken 1600 units daily after heart attacks with beneficial results. Minimum daily requirements start at 30 units and run to 2000 units daily. Double this latter amount has been taken by some subjects over prolonged periods of time without any signs of toxicity. Our European researchers recommend 1200 to 1600 units daily for athletes in hard training.

I recommend that any athlete who is working out with weights three times a week and doing some cardiovascular, respiratory work at least two other times should have a minimum of 1200 international units of alpha tocopherols daily. This quantity will give him a decent amount of insurance. Most athletes eat a generous amount of fat and the requirement of Vitamin E goes up an additional 100 units for each tablespoon of fat or oil in the diet. Fat is critical for the absorption of Vitamin E, so it must be ingested and should not be avoided. This basic dosage of 1200 international untis can be increased to 1600 I.U. when you are preparing for extra heavy training or for a game. Take the supplement in regulated doses following each meal, i.e., a 400 I.U. capsule after each of your three meals will be sufficient.

The addition of this most important nutrient will give your entire training a "lift." There is little doubt of its necessity for the maintenance of proper health and, equally as important to the athlete, of its usefulness for progress in strength training.   ✦

12

CHAPTER TWELVE
THE BUSY B'S

THE BUSY B'S

THE B-COMPLEX VITAMINS, of which there are now 15 isolated, are some of the most important nutrients to the aspiring athlete. Some have been labeled the "anti-stress" vitamins and although they are not related to one another, either chemically or physiologically, they work closely together to produce better health.

Before the invention of machinery which mills our flour in such a way as to discard valuable nutrients, there was no real problem in obtaining sufficient quantities of the B vitamins from our diet. Breadstuffs served as our staple food, but once the companies began processing grain products they lost most of their B vitamins. Our chief sweetener was B-rich molasses, but this gave way to the more convenient but less-nutritious refined sugar. As you look at your diet you will discover it contains very few foods which are plentiful in the B-complex vitamins. Liver, brewer's yeast, wheat germ, and rice polish are the richest sources, but few people include many of these in their regular dietary regime. There are several other foods which are high in one or two of the B vitamins, but to obtain your daily requirement from the table is practically impossible.

The B-Complex group which I will discuss is made up of the following eleven vitamins: Thiamine, Riboflavin, Niacin, Vitamin B6, Para Amino Benzoic Acid, Vitamin B12, Pantothenic Acid, Biotin, Inositol, Cholin, Folic Acid.

NEEDED BY EVERY CELL

Unlike the other vitamins, the B-Complex groups are needed by every cell in the body. Doctor Roger Williams has pointed out that, "because these vitamins are needed equally by all cells, a deficiency can produce severe damage before the condition can be noticed. The damage is nevertheless real. Instead of one organ showing abnormalities, as do the eyes during a Vitamin A deficiency, the entire body degenerates into a one-hoss-shay collapse. This overall abnormality is difficult to recognize in an adult, but severely stunted growth makes it markedly noticeable in the young."

SYNERGISTIC ACTION

The B's work closely together in the body in what is termed a "synergistic action." Adelle Davis notes that, "It has become increasingly clear that since the B Vitamins occur together in food, no person is deficient in any one B Vitamin without being deficient in all of them. There are, however, as many degrees and variations of B-Vitamin deficiencies as there are different individuals."

Because of this close relationship of all the B's, it is quite unrealistic to speak of a deficiency of just one of the B vitamins. While it may be true that an individual is more deficient in one of the B's than another, the basic problem remains that he is deficient in all of the B-Complex groups.

The B Vitamins can be synthesized by bacteria in the intestine — if these bacteria happen to be present in your system. Yogurt promotes the growth of these bacteria and, hence, is a very useful food for the athlete. These bacteria develop best on milk sugar and must have a certain amount of fat present in order to multiply. Many medications such as antibiotics and sulfanamides destroy these bacteria. When they are destroyed a B-Complex deficiency soon develops.

WATER SOLUBLE

The B Vitamins are water soluble so they cannot be stored in the body. It is important to supply your body with a sufficient quantity of the B Vitamins each day to insure optimum health. You will be able to tell if you are taking more than your body requires as the excess is passed off in your urine. If you find that your urine is a deep yellow just after starting on a B-Complex supplement, cut back on the dosage slightly or break your dosages down into smaller units. It often takes a bit of time for the body to adjust to the B Vitamins in your system, so add them slowly until you build up to the required level.

Later in this chapter, I will go into detail concerning the dosages of the separate B Vitamins, but now I want to mention a difficulty encountered by many athletes and that is overbalancing the intake of one vitamin against another. I

have seen numerous athletes increase their dosage of thiamine, pyriodoxine, or B12 considerably without giving any attention to the other vitamins. As a result they began experiencing fatique and signs of total B-Complex deficiencies. As they upgraded one vitamin, they jacked the others out of kilter. Too much of a good thing is not always best. It is important to keep in mind the synergistic action of the B-Complex group.

I will, in the brief space allotted, attempt to point out the necessity of each of the B Vitamins. Keep in mind that I am only able to touch upon the high spots of each of the nutrients and there are many more important aspects that I will not present.

THIAMIN, VITAMIN B1

Vitamin B1, or thiamin, is most valuable in preventing fatigue. Its basic role in the body is to help change glucose into energy or fat. Adelle Davis tells how this chemical change takes place. "During the breakdown of sugar to produce energy, pyruvic and lactic acids are formed. By the help of enzymes containing Vitamin B1, pyruvic acid is quickly broken down still further into carbon dioxode and water; lactic acid is rebuilt in glycogen. If the vitamin is undersupplied, these changes cannot take place, and the acids remain in the tissues; they accumulate, especially in the brain, nerves, heart, and blood; eventually they are thrown off in the urine. The production of energy from sugar slows down, coming only from half-burned sugar or from fat; the acids irritate the tissues. Since energy cannot be produced efficiently from fat alone, the result is fatigue, lassitude, and a general laziness throughout the body."

Even though thiamin is added to many of our foods, it is still quite difficult to obtain sufficient quantities of it from our diet. Wheat germ is the most excellent source and rice polish is a close second. It is available in all cereal grains, nuts, dry beans, peas, soybeans, and lentils. Peanut butter, breads, and cereals which have not been refined and processed are valuable sources. Kidneys and heart are good sources whereas liver, for a rare change, is not.

Perhaps citing a couple of studies will illustrate just why thiamine is so useful to your body. Dr. Norman Jolliffe of New York University of Medicine studies men living on a diet adequate except for Vitamin B1. After only four days they noticed pain around their hearts, palpitation, and shortness of breath on exertion. They became constipated, usually fatigued, and mentally depressed, the symptoms becoming progressively more severe as they continue on the diet. When adequate Vitamin B1 was given, the symptoms disappeared in three to six days.

Since the brain cells derive their energy exclusively from sugar and since glucose cannot be converted to energy without thiamin, you can readily visualize why mental depression, forgetfulness, and, in general, mental disarrangement takes place when there is a deficiency of this vitamin.

For the athlete, thiamin is essential. Your body constantly needs a high energy level in order to train hard over long periods of time. Your progress is directly related to your ability to put in time in the training room. Should your energy wane, then your poundages will drop and progress comes to a halt.

Most athletes feel a terrific energy lift once they begin a B Vitamin program. They contend that they can train harder and recover faster.

As is the case in all the B Vitamins, it is difficult to fix a necessary dosage for everyone. Since thiamin is essential for changing sugar into energy or fat, the more starches and sugar in your diet the more Vitamin B1 you will need. Obviously, the quantity needed depends on the amount of activity you have, the volume of liquids you drink, your muscular size (stored fat doesn't count as it has no nutritional needs) and the amount of rest you obtain.

As a basic rule, I recommend that you take in at least 100 mgs. of thiamin daily. Your particular need may be somewhat greater but the 100 mgs. will assure you of your basic need. I must reiterate that B1 must be taken in conjunction with all the other B Vitamins as well as with your A, D, C, and E for maximum results.

RIBOFLAVIN, B2, VITAMIN G

It has been stated that a lack of Vitamin B2, or riboflavin, is the most widespread deficiency in this country. Athletes rarely have to worry about obtaining riboflavin as milk is one of the most reliable sources. Most athletes drink plenty of milk and seldom are faced with a lack of this important nutrient.

Liver is the best single source of riboflavin followed closely by yeast. Riboflavin is one of the more unusual vitamins in that it can only be utilized in leafy vegetables after they have been cooked. It cannot be obtained from vegetables such as spinach, lettuce, and kale when eaten raw as in salads.

Riboflavin deficiencies are rather easy to recognize. Your eyes will become extra sensitive to light. If the deficiency is not corrected your eyes will water, itch, and burn. Next, they will become bloodshot due to the lack of sufficient B2.

Tiny vessels also appear on outer layers of the skin on your face if you do not receive enough B2. A riboflavin deficiency will also display itself in an oily appearance on the skin, cracks at the corners of your mouth, and by wrinkles in your lip.

Vitamin B2 is interrelated with the development of enzymes. These same enzymes are made up largely of amino acids. Vitamin B6 is closely associated with any deficiency involving B2. The reason that many deficiencies disappear when B2 is added to the diet is that B2 is generally more lacking than is sufficient protein. The deficiencies, then, are really caused by a shortage of enzymes rather than any one vitamin.

Milk and yogurt are two excellent sources of B2 in that they contain both Vitamins B6 and B2 plus the essential amino acids. The yogurt has the protein and the bacteria to produce the B Vitamins so it is easy to see why this food is a valuable addition to your diet.

The answer to "how much do I need?" is again a difficult one. I place the daily allowance at 60 mgs. per day. Riboflavin is water soluble and must be supplied daily. If you eat plenty of liver, milk, and yogurt you need not be too concerned about obtaining sufficient quantities of B2. Otherwise, be sure that your B-Complex Vitamin has enough for your needs.

NIACIN, NICOTINIC ACID, NIACIN AMIDE, NICOTINIC ACID AMIDE, AND VITAMIN B3

In recent years a great deal of work has been done concerning the relationship of niacin deficiencies to certain forms of mental illness, especially schizophrenia. While the mentally ill may not be a particular concern to the athlete, he still might find some rationale behind those blue days that crop up every so often. They may be linked to a lack of this essential B Vitamin.

Depression, hostility, paranoia, and mental dullness have all been attributed to a lack of niacin in the diet. A diet lacking adequate niacin brings with it personality changes. **In Let's Eat Right To Keep Fit,** a study concerning niacin is presented: "When volunteers have stayed on a diet adequate in all respects except in niacin, the first symptoms noticeable are psychological. The entire personality changes. Persons who were formerly strong, courageous, forward-looking, and unafraid of life became cowardly, apprehensive, suspicious, and mentally confused. They worry excessively and are emotionally unstable, moody, forgetful, and uncooperative. Such persons become depressed; their depression may range from 'blue Mondays' to the point where it is impossible to carry on. They lose their ability to keep going when the going is tough. Fortunately, their depression can be eliminated in a few hours by giving niacin amide."

It is difficult to obtain sufficient niacin in your diet. The best natural sources are: yeast, liver, wheat germ, and kidneys. Fish, muscle meats, eggs, and nuts also provide some, but there is none in milk. Some can be manufactured by the body from the amino acid tryptophane if the diet provides plenty of protein, and Vitamins B2 and B6.

Many people who have taken a niacin tablet experience a flushing sensation on the skin. It becomes hot, itchy, and they are very uncomfortable for 20 minutes to an hour. Most people stop taking the supplement for this reason. Only niacin or nicotinic acid brings on this reaction. Niacin **amide** or nicotinic acid **amide** does not bring on this discomfort so you would do well to check the label closely before purchasing your B3.

I recommend that you get 100 mgs. of niacin amide daily, although I once more must mention the variance between individuals in their vitamin requirements. Niacin plays such an important role in the maintenance of proper mental health. Should you find yourself constantly depressed, I would suggest 100 mgs. to be taken after each meal. Niacin seems to work best when taken in conjunction with Vitamin C and as you might recall, I suggested that Vitamin C be taken with any other supplement.

PYRIDOXIN, PYRIDOXIN HYDROCHLORIDE, OR VITAMIN B6

Vitamin B6 is one of the more interesting of the B-Complex group to the athlete because of its role in the metabolism of amino acids. The amino acids, to quickly review, make up protein and if they cannot be fully utilized by the body, then they are wasted regardless of how much protein you eat. Vitamin B6 is also necessary before the important linoleic acid can be utilized. Without sufficient B6 your muscle tissues cannot rebuild and this is most important to the serious training athlete.

Vitamin B6 is so valuable for the brain, a lack of it results in nervousness, dizziness, insomnia, and mental depression. Of special interest to athletes is the fact that muscle weakness and fatigue are two symptoms of Vitamin B6 deficiency, due to its role in protein and unsaturated fat metabolism.

For individuals who suffer from nervousness and insomnia, Vitamin B6 serves as a tranquilizer. Those who suffer from leg and foot cramps have often been relieved when 25 mgs. of Vitamin B6 are taken with each meal.

The natural sources of Vitamin B6 are: yeast, blackstrap molasses, wheat germ, liver, kidneys, and heart. Cooking, canning, storage, and exposure to light all destroy Vitamin B6 so it is wise to include a supplement to insure that you receive as much as you need.

Your daily intake of Vitamin B6 is largely determined by the amount of protein and unsaturated fat you eat. One authority believes that you should take one milligram of Vitamin B6 for every gram of protein you eat. For example, if you conscientiously eat 200 grams of protein each day then you should also take 200 mgs. of B6 to be sure that you are fully utilizing the protein you take in. It is also recommended that you take your B6 along with your B2 and magnesium, but then again, I recommend that you take all your supplements together just after meal time. Physicians have given as much as 3000 mgs. of B6 daily over an extended period of time without toxicity so my recommendation of 200 mgs. is still within recognized limits.

Vitamin B6 is a most important nutrient for athletes and if you check the label of most B-Complex tablets you will find that they do not contain quite enough for your special needs. An additional supplement is generally in order.

PANTOTHENIC ACID OF CALCIUM PANTOTHENATE

Pantothenic acid is another of the B Vitamins which is needed by every cell in your body. This important vitamin is most noteworthy to athletes who have had to use cortisone for any injury. A deficiency of pantothenic acid prevents the adrenal glands from producing cortisone. During any type of illness or injury when the need for this hormone is most necessary, the requirement for pantothenic acid increases tremendously. Some authorities feel that the addition of pantothenic acid can be just as useful in treating some injuries as the hormone cortisone.

It should also be recognized that prolonged cortisone usage is toxic while the addition of pantothenic acid only assists the adrenals in producing adequate cortisone. So it would make sense to obtain ample pantothenic acid rather than to take the more harmful drugs.

Besides cortisone, over thirty other adrenal hormones need pantothenic acid in order for them to be produced. The adrenals, for those interested, produce a large portion of your sex hormones. Enough said.

Pantothenic acid, like so many of the B-Complex group, is necessary for the production of energy. Sugar or fat cannot be converted to energy without this B Vitamin nor can two other vitamins, cholin or PABA be utilized.

Liver, yeast, kidney, heart, wheat germ, whole grain breads, cereals, and vegetables are the best sources of this B vitamin. It is very unstable in heat and is quickly destroyed by overcooking, canning, or long storage.

Each persons daily requirement of pantothenic acid varies considerably according to the amount of stress, exercise, and other physical and mental problems encountered. Pantothenic acid is never toxic. Dr. E.P. Ralli of New York University College of Medicine studied young men under the stress of swimming in icy water when given no pantothenic acid and again after they had received 10,000 milligrams of the vitamin daily. Her tests showed that the vitamin gave protection in dozens of ways, such as preventing body proteins from being destroyed, blood sugar and blood pressure from dropping, and calcium from being stolen from the bones.

I recommend a daily dosage of 100 mgs. of pantothenic acid. If you have an injury, illness, or allergy, or have been under undue stress, then you should consider taking 100 mgs. after each meal. You should not, however, take a high dosage of pantothenic acid over a prolonged period as this creates a need for more B1. So, if you do take as much as 300 mgs. daily, only do so for 7-10 days and then cut back to the recommended 100 mgs. per day.

FOLIC ACID

Folic acid is very essential for growth. It is necessary for the proper division of our body cells and for the production of the substances which carry on our hereditary blueprints, RNA and DNA.

It, like so many of the other B vitamins, make up enzymes which do so many things in your body. The enzymes it helps to construct are critical for the proper assimilation of amino acids. This, once again, is most important to the athlete who is watching his protein intake.

The necessary folic acid, along with some other B Vitamins, such as pantothenic acid and Vitamin B6, allows your body to fully utilize the amino acids you so religiously ingest.

Sugar cannot be successfully converted to energy in the body without an adequate supply of folic acid. Your body also needs folic acid in order to manufacture antibodies, which of course, are so essential in preventing infections.

Since folic acid plays such a crucial role in cell development, it is not at all surprising that deficiencies have quite a marked effect on the bodies' function. Many of the symptoms of folic acid deficiency are of special concern to the athlete. You become more easily fatigued, experience shortness of breath, and have a tendency to become dizzy after heavy physical training. I have, on several occasions, recommended to a lifter who has experienced light headedness after a heavy set that he take a folic acid supplement. In each case the athlete reported back that the addition of the vitamin solved his problem.

Folic acid derives its name from foliage so, obviously, green vegetables are an ideal source of this vitamin. Broccoli, brussel sprouts, cabbage, cauliflower, sweet corn, kale, parsley, spinach, chard, turnips, potatoes, and squash are all excellent sources. If it has a strange name it generally has plenty of folic acid: kohlrabi, okra, and zucchini are three vivid examples.

Liver is very high in folic acid content, as are yeast and nuts. Being water soluble, much is lost when vegetables are soaked or cooked. Some drugs are known to destroy folic acid in your system immediately, two such being phenobarbital and dilantin.

A strange phenomenon prevails in this country concerning the allowed dosage of folic acid. It is an established fact that folic acid is not toxic . . . yet, the Food and Drug Administration only allows 0.1 milligrams per tablet to be sold without a prescription. We can thank our vegetarian friends for this silly ruling. Vegetarians are almost universally deficient in Vitamin B12, unless they happen to be aware enough to supplement their diet with this necessary nutrient. Most do not and have to be protected from themselves. A prolonged deficiency of B12 results in lifelong and irreversible paralysis. If they take high quantities of folic acid, which most do in leafy vegetables, and then ingest more in supplement form, they do not become anemic or fatigued as it is a lack of both B12 and folic acid that brings on these symptoms. Yet the extra folic acid actually masks the B12 deficiency and keeps them from calling upon medical help.

This is the only country that restricts the sale of folic acid. It would seem more logical to simply add B12 to a folic acid supplement and take the limit off the daily per tablet dosage as it is much too low. Athletes need 5 mgs. of folic acid per day, but currently this is difficult to obtain, even through supplements. Supplements in higher quantities are sold in Canada and can be purchased by mail. But in the meantime, it is wise to eat plenty of greens, preferably raw.

VITAMIN B12 OR CYANOCOBALAMIN

Athletes have been more aware of Vitamin B12 than any of the other B-Complex group. One professional football team some years ago felt that it was so helpful that they gave injections of the vitamin to every player every week during the season. Many weightlifters felt that by including B12 injections in their dietary routine they received a terrific energy lift. One member of the York Weightlifting team used to be so charged after a B12 injection that he litc·ally trained twice as hard that day. Many authorities, however, believe the benefits to be more psychological than physiological.

Vitamin B12 has been used quite successfully in the treatment of lower back pain, a condition that many athletes invariably suffer. The reason that B12 is injected, rather than merely taken orally, is that when you are deficient in B Vitamins, the stomach cannot produce sufficient hydrochloric acid or an enzyme called the "intrinsic factor." Without these two elements the B12, if taken orally, cannot be absorbed into the bloodstream, so an injection is in order. If, however, you are not deficient in the B Vitamins, a tablet will work just as well.

A prolonged deficiency of Vitamin B12 is extremely serious. The first symptoms show themselves in the form of extreme nervousness, an unpleasant body odor, and perhaps lower back stiffness. This is followed by a difficulty in walking and finally irreversible paralysis sets in. As was mentioned in the section on folic acid, this problem is most prevalant among vegetarians. They could very simply avoid the risk of such a disease by including a 50 mcg. tablet of B12 just once a week, or if the deficiency is prolonged, an injection weekly.

A lack of B12 alone does not produce anemia, as was at once suspected. Anemia results only if B12 and folic acid are not supplied in adequate amounts. I recommend that all athletes take a minimum of 500 mcgs. of B12 each and every day. Should you suspect that you are overly deficient in this vitamin, consult your physician and perhaps he will give you B12 injections until you are up to par.

The reason that vegetarians are universally lacking in B12 (if they do not supplement their diets) is that this B Vitamin is only found in animal foods. Liver is very rich in B12. Milk, eggs, cheese, and other meats are also very rich sources. Once again I suggest that you check the label of your multiple B-Complex supplement to insure that you are receiving sufficient B12. If not, add an individual B12 tablet to your supplement list.

BIOTIN

Biotin is one of the B Complex group of which we know surprisingly little, but the facts that we do have are very useful to the athletes. Many athletes, in their quest to obtain large quantities of protein in the simplest manner, include raw eggs in a high protein milkshake. It is very convenient and easy to take.

Unfortunately, there is a potential problem of eating uncooked eggs and this is where biotin comes in. There is a substance in raw egg white called avidin which combines with the biotin and prevents the B Vitamin from reaching the bloodstream. Cooking the eggs removes the avidin and the problem.

Does it really matter? Well, yes. Prolonged use of raw eggs results in a feeling of fatigue, mental depression, a drying of the skin, and sometimes even muscular pain and distress around the heart. Subjects placed on a biotin-deficient diet often experience depression so severe that they become suicidal. This is certainly not a sought-after state for any athlete, or any other human for that matter.

Other studies have indicated that raw eggs only cause problems for those who are already deficient in biotin but my recommendation is for you to avoid eating raw eggs too often. The difficulty generally arises after a prolonged usage but if you have a deficiency it will be multiplied greatly, so make raw eggs an exception rather than a rule.

Animals tested on biotin-lacking diets developed dermatitis, their hair begain to fall out and they were especially prone to heart and lung diseases. Young animals do not grow to full maturity on biotin deficient diets and death results in adults.

The richest sources of biotin is, once more, liver. Kidneys are also very good while soybeans and Brewer's yeast contain small amounts. Dried beans, cauliflower, chicken, whole eggs, hazel nuts, mushrooms, peas, peanuts, and bacon are all reasonably good sources. There is no minimum daily requirement for this important B Vitamin as yet and, even more surprisingly, very few supplements contain biotin.

Some of the better nutritional companies do carry it. The Fiberton Company of Los Angeles, for example, has a 50 mcg. tablet available and they include 15 mcgs. in each of their B-Complex tablets.

I suggest that you have 100 mcg. per day, unless you are doing extra heavy training or have been under some sort of physical or mental stress. Exam time, spring practice, a recent illness — all of these would magnify your need for biotin. At these stressful times, make certain that you get 100 mcg. per day.

PARA AMINO BENZOIC ACID OR PABA

PABA received a great deal of attention some years ago following the reports of studies conducted by Doctor Benjamin Sieve. He restored the color to the hair of 70% of the men studied by giving them 200 milligrams of PABA after each meal. It is often referred to as the "anti-gray-hair vitamin" because black animals lacking it become gray. More recently it has been concluded that four of the B Vitamins, namely: PABA, biotin, folic acid, and pantothenic acid all play an important role in influencing hair color.

Carlton Fredericks, Ph.D. developed the following formula for restoring hair color: PABA, 100 mgs., pantothenic acid 30 mgs., cholin 2 grams, in a natural B-Complex base. Doctor Fredericks presented these views on the subject of restoring hair color: "It may have taken years to gray your hair. Don't expect results in a few weeks. Six months is a more realistic period."

It is recognized that the synthetic B Vitamins do little to restore hair color. The ideal method of obtaining the necessary vitamins is through a diet which is abundant in liver, brewer's yeast, soy flour, and kidneys. If you go the supplement route, be certain that you use a natural product.

PABA has been found to be most useful to folks who sunburn easily. Individuals who previously were not able to sunbathe were able to tolerate as much as 100 times more sunshine after being given 1000 mgs. of PABA daily.

Because of its action within the body, PABA makes sulfa drugs ineffective. So, in its usual backdoor manner, the Food and Drug Administration only allows 30 mgs. of PABA to be sold to everyone without prescription. Actually, PABA serves many of the same functions of the more dangerous sulfa drugs plus many additional ones which sulfa does not, but these facts never occurred to the people who make the rules on nutrition.

PABA has been administered in amounts up to 48,000 milligrams without any signs of toxicity. I have found from the Europeans that they give their athletes who are in hard training 100 mgs. a day. You will have to check the label on your B-Complex supplement to insure yourself of a sufficient quantity. Some companies do sell a 30 mg. PABA tablet and I suggest that you add this important, although relatively unstudied, vitamin to your list.

INOSITOL

Inositol is another of the "anti-stress' vitamins we know so very little about, but this fact does not diminish their importance one bit. Inositol seems to be important for hair growth — a fact all men should be interested in to some degree. Adelle Davis reports on a study of inositol in this connection. "When animals are put on a diet lacking inositol, their hair falls out. If the vitamin is then added to the diet, their hair grows in again. Male animals lose their hair twice as quickly as do females, indicating that the male requirement is higher than that of the female. A hundred times more inositol than any other vitamin except niacin is found in the human body."

Most authorities believe that hair growth is dependant on several, if not all, of the B-Complex vitamins, and a few of the amino acids as well.

Inositol also plays an important role in your vision and heart action. This vitamin is heavily concentrated in the lens of your eyes and in the muscles of your heart.

Inositol is most useful to those who experience digestive difficulties. It helps those with poor appetites, enables food to be digested more thoroughly, and eliminates constipation problems for many.

Inositol prevents the body from accumulating cholesterol. This vitamin helps form lecithin, which in turn breaks up cholesterol into small particles which can then be used by the tissues.

This B Vitamin is found in • er, yeast, wheat germ, whole wheat bread, oatmeal, corn, and unrefined molasses.

Turning once more to Europe for advice, we find that their athletes take 500 mgs. of inositol each day. The better B-Complex supplements contain at least 100 mgs. per tablet so you may be able to obtain the necessary requirement from your multiple tablet.

CHOLIN or CHOLINE or CHOLINE BITARTRATE

Cholin has a special function for any athlete who is troubled with high blood pressure or any type of kidney ailment. Tests have been conducted on individuals with high blood pressure who had been on medication for extended periods of time, without any satisfactory improvement. When cholin replaced the prescribed medicine, the blood pressure returned to normal in less than three weeks. The subjects reported that they could sleep better and tests showed that the heart did not have to work as hard as before.

Cholin can be produced by the body, if certain nutrients are also present. The cholin is manufactured from the amino acid methionine, but only if there is an abundance of it. Then too, folic acid and B12 must be readily available in order for the manufacture to take place.

Cholin is necessary for the manufacture of lecithin. Without cholin the cholesterol level goes up. When cholin is deficient in the diet the kidneys become damaged and nephrities often results.

One of the more interesting aspects of this B Vitamin to the athlete is its role in muscle contractions. Cholin is a part of an enzyme which helps transfer nerve signals to the muscles. A deficiency results in a slow reacting muscle, the extreme being a form of muscular dystrophy. Since a fast-reacting muscle is an asset in any athletic endeavor, the inclusion of this vitamin in your diet becomes very essential.

Your body needs cholin for the production of nucleic acid in the very nucleus of every cell. This center is also responsible for the manufacture of DNA and RNA, so it is quite obvious that cholin should not be slighted.

Cholin is found in wheat germ, liver, yeast, kidneys, brains, egg yolk, and liquid or granulated lecithin. It is not toxic and cases have been reported where individuals have taken as much as 1000 mgs. per day for years with only beneficial results.

Your daily allotment depends to a large extent on how much saturated fat you eat. Our guidelines from foreign athletes show that they take a minimum of 500 mgs. each day and increase this dosage when in extra heavy training or when they are under any kind of stress.

IN SUMMARY OF THE BUSY B'S

Since there are so many B-Complex vitamins and since I do not really expect you to remember exactly what role each performs in your body, I am presenting a chart to briefly summarize their basic functions and my recommended dosages. This chart will enable you to quickly review each vitamin and should you want to dig a bit deeper, then you can refer back to the individual section in this chapter. Some of my recommended requirements will be satisfied in a good high potency B-Complex tablet, but some will not. If the multiple capsule you now use is low in a certain vitamin, then I suggest that you obtain that one separately.

I must, once again, reiterate the very involved action of all the B Vitamins with one another. An overdose of one B Vitamin will only create new problems. Remember the synergistic action of these vitamins and keep your dosages in proper balance. The taking of one or more increases the need for all the rest, because any one of the B's alone cannot increase the activity of each body cell.   ★

SUMMARY OF THE BUSY B'S

VITAMIN	FUNCTION	DAILY RECOMMENDED DOSAGE FOR ATHLETES IN HEAVY TRAINING
Thiamin, B1	Production of energy. Necessary for growth, appetite, digestion, normal functioning of the nervous system. Needed for proper metabolism of carbohydrates.	100 mgs.
Riboflavin, B2	Aids proper growth and tissue function. Along with B1 needed for metabolism of sugars and starches.	60 mgs.
Niacin, B3	Eliminates mental depression. An essential part of enzyme system.	100 mgs.
Pyriodoxine, B6	Aids in amino acid and fat metabolism. Prevents various nervous disorders, muscular weakness, and fatigue.	200 mgs. (One mg. for each gram of protein eaten)
Pantothenic Acid	Building of body cells and maintaining normal skin, growth, and development of the central nervous system. Involved in formation of antibodies.	100 mgs.
Folic Acid	Essential for growth. Necessary for the proper division of body cells and for the production of RNA and DNA. Needed for production of enzymes which help assimilate amino acids. Used in conversion of sugar into energy.	5 mgs.
Biotin	Considered a growth-promoting factor. Essential to the vital life processes. Relationship to the metabolism of fats and amino acids.	100 mcgs.
Vitamin B12	Increases physical vigor and mental alertness. Used in treatment of lower back pain. Deficiency of B12 and folic acid produces anemia.	500 mcgs.
PABA	Known as anti-gray-hair vitamin. Prevents sunburn. Anti-stress vitamin. Important for growth.	100 mgs.
Inositol	Important for hair growth. One of the anti-stress vitamins. Plays important role in vision and heart action. Prevents body from accumulating cholestrol.	500 mgs.
Cholin	Regulates blood pressure and alleviates many kidney problems. Needed for the manufacture of lecithin. Necessary for muscle contractions.	500 mgs.

13

CHAPTER THIRTEEN
THE MIGHTY (AND MISUNDERSTOOD) MINERALS

IT MAY BE A MISTAKE to put this chapter so near the end of the nutritional section as it might be misconstrued that the minerals are less important to your total nutritional program than the amino acids, fatty acids, and various vitamins. Nothing could be further from the truth. The minerals are, by all standards, on a par in importance to your body as are all the other nutrients I have covered so far.

The minerals are certainly the most neglected nutrients, and perhaps the most misunderstood. When I question an athlete about his nutritional program, he generally gives a good account of the vitamins and protein he takes, but he seldom mentions minerals at all. When asked why minerals are not included in his diet in supplement form the usual reply is, "I didn't know that they were important." Not just important, but critical for health and total fitness. Many nutritional researchers contend that the minerals are actually **more** necessary to the hard-training athlete than many of the more well-thought-of vitamins.

MINERAL REQUIREMENTS

The human animal requires: calcium, phosphorus, magnesium, sodium, potassium, sulfur, chlorine, iron, copper, cobalt, iodine, manganese, zinc, and fluorine in his daily diet. Molybdenum and selenium have been proven essential for experimental animals and may yet be proven a requisite for man. The duties of the various minerals are closely interrelated to one another as well as with all the vitamins, amino acids, fatty acids, and carbohydrates. I am not in a position to suggest that minerals supersede vitamins in importance. Rather, I believe the relationship between vitamins, minerals, and all the other essential nutrients should be stressed. My philosophy is that you should be conscious of all your nutritional requirements and attempt to provide your body with adequate quantities of each and every necessary nutrient. It is not, then, a battle of priorities, but rather a venture of cooperative, understanding, and applying the sound principles of nutrition to further your athletic prowess.

I will explain some of the functions of the various minerals, but as a preface I would like to discuss the minerals in general. Table II on this page gives a listing of the minerals found in your body. I will discuss a dozen of these in this chapter, omitting sulfur, aluminum, molybdenum, fluoride, vandium, cadmium, and selenium.

TABLE II

APPROXIMATE ELEMENTARY COMPOSITION OF THE BODY

ELEMENT	PERCENTAGE
Oxygen	65
Carbon	18
Hydrogen	10
Nitrogen	3
Calcium	2●
Phosphorus	1.1#
Potassium	0.35
Sulfur	0.25
Sodium	0.15
Chlorine	0.15
Magnesium	0.05
Iron	0.004
Manganese	0.00013
Copper	0.00015
Iodine	0.00004
Cobalt	*
Zinc	*
Fluoride	*
Aluminum	*
Molybdenum	*
Vandium	*
Cadmium	*
Selenium	*

● estimates vary
percentage varies with that of calcium
* quantitative data not yet available

MACRO-MINERALS

The mineral elements which the body needs in substantial quantities are called macro-minerals and these are: calcium, phosphorus, magnesium, sodium, potassium, sulfur, chlorine, and iron. The body also needs, in smaller amounts, "trace" or micro-elements: copper, iodine, manganese, cobalt, zinc, aluminum, fluoride, other "trace" minerals such as vanadium, selenium, cadmium, and molybdenum are still under study and it is not certain if these are needed to maintain health.

TRACE MINERALS

The "trace" or micro-elements (also referred to as "cligo" elements from the Greek root meaning "a scanty") are designated as such because they exist in foods in very minute amounts. Because they are so scanty, the reader may be left with the impression that they are not as important as the more abundant micro-minerals. This is not necessarily true. Research has pointed out the relative importance of many of these elements. Even the rather conservative **U.S.D.A. Yearbook** makes this comment on the "trace" minerals:

"At the present stage of our biological knowledge we cannot ignore the possibility that some of the trace elements we now think of as nonessential do have as yet unrecognized functions in the body's process. One of the great problems today is to set standards for fixing the need for trace elements or any constituents of diet. The old attitude was that a constituent is essential if slow growth, or zero growth, or death results from failure to include it in the diet. It has been apparent for some years that the definition is not good enough. The establishment of mineral dietary requirements for the trace elements is a difficult problem, for many factors may affect their absorption and utilization."

For this reason I will be using the terms "trace elements" and "micro-elements" interchangeably. Actually, the latter term is more definitive and will eventually come into popular usage.

MINERALS ARE INTERRELATED

The minerals are very much like the B-Complex vitamins in that they play an important role in relationship to one another. Copper, iron, and cobalt are all interrelated in the synthesis of hemoglobin and the formation of red blood cells. Both magnesium and calcium are needed for nerve cell functions. Body fluid maintenance is dependent on five minerals: sodium, potassium, chlorine, phosphorus, and calcium.

It is critical that you obtain adequate amounts of the various minerals, but it is also important that they be obtained in a definite proportion to one another. The ratio of calcium to phosphorus, for example, should be 1 to 1.5 or 2. An excessive amount of phosphorus in your diet will form insoluble salts with calcium and, in effect, create a deficiency of calcium.

So the role of each mineral is not only intertwined with that of the other minerals, but also with that of the organic elements such as proteins, fats, and carbohydrates. They all work together as a team when supplied in adequate and balanced amounts.

I will highlight a dozen of these inorganic substances, but once more I must mention that I am merely skimming the surface of facts on these important nutrients. I hope to whet each reader's appetite sufficiently so that he will continue his study of this segment of nutrition further.

CALCIUM

One of the more important minerals for all athletes to be aware of is calcium. It serves so many functions which directly affect your performance. When insufficient calcium is taken into your body the muscles become irritable and cannot contract properly. This irritability often displays itself in the form of muscle cramps. Most individuals discover these cramping sensations in their extremities first; like the feet, hands, and face. Should the calcium deficiency continue unchecked, these cramps become spasms and may even occur internally. An extreme case of calcium deficiency will result in convulsions.

Calcium is extremely important for maintaining muscle tone. The strength of your muscle contraction is directly dependent on adequate supply of this mineral. Studies have shown that calcium helps to prevent fatigue and enables the body to recover from strenuous training more rapidly. Calcium plays an important role in influencing the excitability of the motor system and the motor system is of great interest to all athletes.

The transportation of nerve impulses in your body is dependent on an adequate supply of this mineral. A lack of calcium produces nervous tension. You become irritable and quick-tempered. It becomes more and more difficult to concentrate on what you are doing and you find it difficult to relax. Often insomnia follows.

CALCIUM AS A PAIN KILLER

Calcium has been found to be an excellent pain killer. Migraine headache victims, given a combination of calcium and Vitamin B6 find welcomed relief. Calcium has been used for many years to help relieve the pain of toothache, pleurisy, and even child birth. It is much safer than aspirin or the more potent pain killers and should be kept available in every household.

A RELAXANT

This mineral has also been found to help those who cannot relax or sleep properly. Milk is the best single source of calcium so you can easily understand how the folk remedy of warm milk at bedtime came into practice. The heat aids in the digestion process and should you want absolute results, just take 2 or 3 calcium-magnesium tablets along with the warm milk at bedtime.

While the importance of calcium in the structure of your bones and teeth has long been recognized, it was felt for some time that this mineral was only necessary while the bones and teeth were being formed. Now researchers know that your body constantly needs an adequate supply of this, as well as other nutrients such as phosphorus and Vitamin D, in order to keep your teeth from decaying and your bones from becoming brittle and weak.

Just about every athlete has had the misfortune to have some degree of bursitis, arthritis, a calcium deposit, or calcium spur somewhere in his body. Weightlifters accumulate calcium spurs generally in the wrists and most have had one case of bursitis of the shoulders. Most are told by medical men to avoid eating foods high in calcium to avoid building up more of a deposit. Actually, the condition cannot improve until the calcium intake is increased, rather than diminished. Magnesium is also important as is Vitamin E, but when all three of these nutrients are provided in the proper amounts, the calcium deposit often disappears.

More people lack calcium than any other single nutrient. This might be a surprising fact to many since milk and milk products are our richest sources of calcium. Milk products such as sour milk, buttermilk, yogurt, and unprocessed cheeses are excellent sources. Soybeans, blackstrap molasses, turnip greens, almonds, parsley, Brazil nuts, dandelion greens, and beans are also good.

RICH SOURCES OF CALCIUM

Thus, green vegetables, milk and milk products, nuts, and legumes represent the richest sources of calcium. The mere fact that a food is rich in calcium does not necessarily follow that eating such a food will result in 100% absorption and assimilation. Human beings absorb calcium inefficiently. A growing rat may absorb nearly all ingested calcium, but in humans the absorption is usually only 20 to 30%. The availability of calcium from vegetable sources, for example, is reduced by interfering stubstances, sometimes to such an extent that the calcium is not available at all. The absorption of calcium is increased by the presence of hydrochloric acid (all the more reason to avoid alkaline substances for an upset stomach). This is true of all mineral elements by the way. That is, they are more soluble in acid solutions.

Food proteins which contain lactose, increase the absorption of calcium. This sugar is found in milk and milk products. Moderate levels of fat favor the utilization of calcium. Vitamin D, possibly by stimulating the utilization of calcium from the intestine, influences the extent to which the body uses the element. Phosphorus, too, is essential for the absorption of calcium and these two minerals have to be kept in a proper balance to each other. The ratio of calcium to phosphorus should be 1:1.5 or 1:2. An excessive amount of phosphorus will form insoluble salts with calcium and the latter mineral will be lost in the urine. Some typical American diets contain 10 times as much phosphorus as calcium, thus creating a shortage of the latter mineral.

I recommend that you take in at least 2 grams of calcium per day. This is the equivalent of eight glasses of milk, but naturally you will be ingesting some of this requirement from other food sources. Most athletes drink four glasses of milk anyway. If you choose to take your calcium in supplement form, be certain that you also take in the other necessary nutrients to help you utilize the mineral, such as Vitamin D, Vitamin B6, magnesium, phosphorus, and fat. A multi-mineral tablet is a sound solution as it has the necessary elements in balanced proportions.

If you plan to purchase a supplement form of calcium you should be aware that calcium gluconate and calcium lactate absorb more readily than does either calcium phosphate or calcium chloride. So check the label before you buy it.

I want to reiterate the fact that as little as 20% of the calcium eaten is finally utilized by the average body. With this fact in mind, it should be very evident to every athlete that a planned nutritional program is necessary if you are to insure your body of obtaining a sufficient amount of these necessary nutrients. You will need to eat adqequate amounts of calcium-rich foods and keep a check on the other minerals to see that they are all ingested in the proper proportion to each other.

PHOSPHORUS

Phosphorus is present in every cell of your body. Not only is phosphorus found in the inorganic combination such as bones, teeth, and blood, but also in organic combination such as nucleic acid and various enzymes.

Phosphorus has many functions in your body; it is involved in keeping the chemical balance of your blood, the acid-base balance, the skeleton growth, tooth development, muscle metabolism, and is responsible for the intermediary metabolism of carbohydrates, fats, and protein. It is important in helping construct and regulate the activity of the various enzymes in your system.

Since phosphorus plays a central role in the structure of cytoplasm and the cell nuclei, all biological disorders involve phosphorus metabolism to some extent. Fortunately for everyone, the element is widely distributed in food. Wheat germ, cheeses, Brazil nuts, soybean flour, walnuts, almonds, beans, rolled oats, wheat, peanuts, peas, lima beans, lentils, liver, corn meal, fish, chicken, eggs, and milk all supply adequate phosphorus. Basically, if a food is high in protein content it is also high in phosphorus.

PHOSPHORUS' RATIO TO CALCIUM

The problems arise, not from too little phosphorus in the diet, but when there is more phosphorus ingested than calcium. These two nutrients are very interdependent, as was mentioned previously. The ratio should not be over one part calcium to 2 parts of phosphorus, but it has been found that the American diet supplies much more phosphorus than calcium, thus creating a deficiency in this latter mineral.

More than 70% of the phosphorus ingested in foods is absorbed from the intestine into the blood. Thus, food phosphorus is utilized much more efficiently than is food calcium. Calcium is used in combination with phosphorus in the building and maintenance of teeth and bones. Without a sufficient supply of calcium, the phosphorus is at a loss and is excreted. The problem magnifies itself when calcium is drawn into the blood from the bones to unite with the more abundant phosphorus. This leaves the bones and teeth depleted. If this situation continues for a prolonged period of time, the bones and teeth weaken and decay.

If you eat large amounts of foods that are especially abundant in the element phosphorus and low in calcium, then a calcium supplement is in order. Yeast, liver, wheat germ, and lecithin are four such foods. It is a wise idea to include plenty of milk products in your menu if you are eating the high phosphorus foods. In this way the phosphorus and calcium balance is upheld and you are way ahead of the game. It is rather difficult to set a requirement for phosphorus. The U.S. National Research Council in 1964 recommended that the "phosphorus intake should be at least equal to that for calcium in the diets of children and of women during the latter part of pregnancy or in lactation periods." I might add that athletes be included in this needy group. A dietary survey conducted by H.C. Sherman in 1947 showed that the dietary phosphorus intake by adults is approximately 1.5 times that of calcium.

The National Research Council bulletin states in conclusion: "In general, it is safe to assume that if the calcium and protein needs are met through common foods, the phosphorus requirement also will be covered, because the common foods richest in calcium and protein are also best sources of phosphorus." I suggest that you attempt to regulate your phosphorus intake to no more than 4 grams daily.

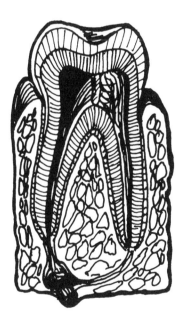

MAGNESIUM

Magnesium is another mineral which should be of special interest to all athletes as it does so many things for your body which can affect performance. It is very much like calcium in that it is involved with the nervous system. Magnesium is needed by every cell in your body. Magnesium functions chiefly as an activator of numerous important enzymes, especially enzymes involving ATP reactions. Since ATP is required in muscle contractions, in the synthesis of proteins, fats, nucleic acid, and in glucose metabolism — just to name a few — you can readily see why this mineral is all important to general health. Magnesium is needed to help form the enzymes which provide the body with an energy source, and without energy you will do little training.

At one period in the history of our country, sufficient magnesium could be obtained from the foods in the market.

During the past few years, studies have clearly shown that our national diet is no longer adequate in magnesium. If chemical fertilizers are used on the soil the resulting foods contain no magnesium. For some reason soils east of the Mississippi are lacking this vital mineral. Then, to add more woe to the problem, magnesium is lost if the foods are soaked or boiled.

Should you be far enough ahead of the game to insure yourself of an adequate intake of magnesium, then you still have to be careful that you retain it. If you drink alcohol you lose a great deal of this mineral. If you take any diuretics, more is lost. Diarrhea really depletes the supply, so you can readily see why it is a tough task to supply your body with adequate amounts of magnesium.

MAGNESIUM AND THE NERVOUS SYSTEM

Since magnesium is so involved with the action of the nervous system, a lack of it creates many psychological-type problems. Extreme nervousness, apprehensiveness, irritability, and sometimes belligerent behavior results. If magnesium is severely deficient, then the brain is affected and mental confusion and marked depression follows.

Magnesium is very closely related to many of the other vital nutrients and you should attempt to keep these in correct proportion to one another. Vitamin B6 and magnesium have been used together to get good results in epileptic cases. Individuals taking antibiotics or diuretics, which destroy B6 and increase the loss of Magnesium actually induce an epileptic-type reaction. Vitamin B6 cannot be absorbed unless magnesium is present and when either of these two nutrients are deficient, convulsions may result.

All magnesium deficiency difficulties are greatly magnified when there is also a deficiency of calcium and an abundance of phosphorus. Unfortunately, this is the very type of diet eaten by most Americans. When there is a magnesium deficiency in the body, calcium is lost in the urine, and tooth decay, poor bone development, and even osteoporosis occurs in extreme cases. Calcium and magnesium are very interdependent, as are most of the essential elements. A magnesium deficiency also interferes with protein synthesis, so it is very important for the athlete to obtain adequate amounts of this mineral.

Magnesium is found in: cocoa, cashew nuts, almonds, Brazil nuts, soya flour, lima beans, whole barley, peanuts, whole wheat, pecans, oatmeal, hazelnuts, walnuts, corn, and brown rice. It is evident that nuts, cereals, and legumes are important sources of magnesium.

MAGNESIUM RATIO TO CALCIUM

Your magnesium intake should always be kept in proper proportion to your calcium consumption. The more calcium you eat, the more magnesium you must take in. You should obtain twice as much calcium as magnesium or a 2:1 ratio. I recommend that you get one gram of magnesium per day which fits in well with this ratio as I also advocated two grams of calcium. You also need to be aware of how much phosphorus you obtain and not let this get over four grams per day, to keep the calcium-phosphorus ratio of 1:1.5 or 2 intact. If your phosphorus consumption goes up, then you must pull your calcium and magnesium intakes up accordingly.

It is a wise idea to take all of your supplements with your meals each day so that all the nutrients can work together. Vitamin B6 and E need to be taken so that the magnesium can be utilized fully. You have already been advised as to the recommended dosages for these two vitamins. A general summary will be presented at the conclusion of this section with all the recommended dosages, so if you are getting slightly lost, don't worry about it.

MAG-CAL TABLETS

Most health food stores carry a magnesium-calcium tablet compounded to the correct proportion. Usually they go under the name Mag-Cal or some other such original title and you should check to see if they are in correct ratio (some are not) and also check to be sure that the calcium is in the form of calcium gluconate or calcium lactate as these forms absorb better than calcium phosphate or calcium chloride. The magnesium-calcium tablets are most handy to have around the house as they make excellent, safe tranquilizers. In fact, magnesium is often referred to as "nature's own tranquilizer." Use these tablets instead of the more harmful opiates or prescription tranquilizers when you need to rest or when you are unusually irritable or depressed. It's a safe way to get where you want to go.

Table III lists a number of foods and the approximate analysis of these three important minerals.

TABLE III

Approximate amounts of calcium, phosphorus, and magnesium in 100 gm. of food

FOODS	CALCIUM	PHOSPHORUS	MAGNESIUM
Beef(lean)	0.007 gm.	0.218 gm.	0.024 gm.
Eggs	0.067	0.180	0.011
Egg Yolk	0.137	0.524	0.016
Milk	0.210	0.093	0.012
Cheese	0.931	0.037	0.680
Wheat	0.045	0.423	0.133
Potatoes	0.014	0.058	0.028
Corn Meal	0.018	0.190	0.084
Oranges	0.045	0.021	0.012
Almonds	0.239	0.465	0.251
Spinach	0.067	0.068	0.037
Beans (dried)	0.160	0.470	0.156

From Schmidt and Greenberg, Physiological Review, 15:300.

POTASSIUM

Just as calcium, phosphorus, and magnesium work hand-in-hand in your body keeping the nervous system stable, potassium, sodium, and chlorine are critical for the control and regulation of glandular secretions and the composition of body fluids. Potassium has a special place in every athlete's nutritional plan because this mineral is essential for muscle contractions. Actually, it is through the activation of certain enzymes that influences the muscle contractions, but none the less, sufficient potassium starts this process.

Adelle Davis explains this process in **Let's Eat Right To Keep Fit**: "Without potassium, sugar in the form of glucose cannot be changed into energy or into body starch (glycogen) to be stored for future energy. When sugar cannot be utilized or glycogen held in the cells, energy production comes to a standstill. Like a motor out of fuel, the muscles can no longer contract, and paralysis or partial paralysis results. Nor is that the only harm done. Under normal conditions potassium stays largely inside the cells and is balanced by sodium outside the cells. If potassium is deficient, however, sodium enters the cells, taking with it so much water that many cells actually burst. The result is water retention (edema), damage to muscles and connective tissue, and extensive scarring."

POTASSIUM/SODIUM BALANCE

The balance between potassium and sodium is most critical. When lots of fresh fruits and vegetables are eaten there is seldom any difficulty, but very rarely is this the case today. People prefer the more convenient canned products, and they are very high in sodium, but severely lacking in potassium. When there is an excess of sodium, the potassium is lost. The opposite is also true, but very rarely occurs, that is, an excess of potassium creates a sodium deficiency.

For those athletes who have used diuretics as a means of losing bodyweight, you should be aware of the effect they have on your potassium level. Diuretics create a tremendously rapid loss of potassium. The drop in the potassium level causes a lowering of the blood sugar and fatigue is the inevitable result. To add insult to injury, when the blood sugar is lowered, stress usually follows and this too taps into the already depleted potassium reservoirs. Fatigue is soon followed by cramps and often muscle spasms. Some of these suffering athletes are given salt tablets, but since they are deficient in potassium rather than sodium or chlorine, it actually accelerates the problem. I have witnessed some sad cases of severe cramping during and following competition all because the individual chose to make weight via the diuretic route.

SUGAR DESTORYS POTASSIUM

A high intake of sugar will destroy the potassium in your cells. The relationship of potassium to heart attacks is one which is being researched in depth at present and it appears as if there is a very direct coorelation between heart disease and potassium deficiency. Potassium is strongly linked with magnesium in this case as a lack of the latter mineral allows both the cholestrol level to rise in the blood and the potassium to leave the cells. Again, we see the critical inter-relationship of the essential nutrients. Calcium is interwined with phosphorus, phosphorus to magnesium, magnesium to potassium, potassium to sodium, sodium to chlorine, and on and on. The one truism that I hope to present in this nutritional section is the fact that the whole is very dependent on all of its parts.

Potassium has been found to be very vital to the liver, keeping it stimulated and functioning properly. Muscles cannot respond quickly or become highly toned without this nutrient.

SOURCES OF POTASSIUM

Some foods containing potassium are: bacon, cereals, eggs, fish, apples, pears, bananas, fruit juices, pork, beef, lamb, nuts, oatmeal, prunes, carrots, beets, corn, peas, and spinach. Fruits grown on foreign soils are especially high in potassium. These include: bananas, papayas, mangos, dates, and figs. Potassium is water soluble so any food cooked in water will lose a great portion of this mineral.

Individuals vary tremendously as to their potassium needs. Anyone who sweats a great deal has to be especially conscious of his potassium needs. Drinking an excessive amount of fluids, such as every athlete does after a grueling session in the weight room or on the practice field, also washes away much of the potassium from your cells. Alcohol depletes the potassium level, so if you drink be aware of the fact that you need more than the recommended requirement of potassium.

It has been calculated that Americans ingest approximately 20 grams or 5 teaspoons of sodium daily. You should be taking in slightly more potassium than sodium, but if you can keep them on a par you are ahead of the game. Few people are ahead of the game, however, as it is estimated that the average diet provides but 4 to 8 grams of potassium per day. This means that you have some catching up to do. For each teaspoon of salt (4000 mgs.) you eat you should obtain 5000 mgs. of potassium. As your salt intake rises, as it will if you eat refined foods such as catsups, luncheon meats, TV dinners, salted nuts, potato chips, sodas, and canned foods, then your potassium intake should rise accordingly. Potassium-chloride salt substitutes are available and will enable you to increase your potassium intake considerably. Supplements are also available, but the amount of potassium is limited by federal regulations to 180 mgs. per tablet. My recommendation is for you to limit your intake of sodium to no more than two teaspoons of salt (8000 mgs.) per day and make every effort to obtain 8000-10,000 mgs. or 8-10 grams of potassium daily. Lots of vegetables and fruits should be on your menu, and both should be eaten raw.

SODIUM

Sodium and potassium, as was just mentioned, must be in constant balance in order to do their jobs properly. Ample sodium is found in our diet in the form of sodium chloride, or table salt. Very rarely will you be deficient in sodium, but athletes do deplete their supply every so often. During games or in heavy training sessions in which you sweat profusely, you may lose excessive sodium. A salt deficiency results in nausea, dizziness, a feeling of exhaustion, cramping in the hands and feet, and even vomiting.

Salt tablets, or even better, salt tablets plus a potassium supplement, will relive these symptoms quickly. Some teams are now giving their players mixed mineral tablets before, during, and after each game. These work much better than the traditional salt tablets as they supply the body with all the lost nutrients rather than just one. Merely drinking lots of water when you are sweating a great deal will not alleviate the problem. In fact, it will accentuate it.

During very hot weather it is a good idea to take a mixed mineral supplement before, during, and immediately after each training session.

FUNCTIONS OF SODIUM

Sodium, basically, has two important functions in your body: 1) to contribute towards the acid-base balance of the body and 2) to be responsible in a large measure for the total osmotic pressure of the fluids which reside outside the cells.

The American diet is relatively high in sodium and the problems usually arise from too much rather than too little of this mineral. An overabundance of sodium, without a correspondingly high intake of potassium will create a potassium deficiency as was pointed out in the previous section. Sodium is found in all our canned foods — a can of clam chowder contains over 1100 mgs. of sodium — our drinking water, baking powder, baking soda, and all the foods preservatives which have a sodium nitrate or sodium nitrate base. Foods high in sodium are: cold cuts and luncheon meats, butter and margarine, cheddar cheese, dehydrated prunes, and all types of breads. Then, of course, there is our table salt.

SODIUM/POTASSIUM 1-1

As was suggested in the previous section, you should attempt to balance your sodium and potassium intake on a one-to-one basis. If you perspire a great deal, then increase the intake of both of these elements, but do not merely add more of one of them to your diet to less than 10 grams of sodium per day or you will simply magnify the deficiency. Restricting your diet to less than 10 grams of sodium per day is a wise idea as this will enable you to balance this intake with an equal amount of potassium.

CHLORINE

Chlorine is so closely related to sodium that the two can hardly be separated. In the form of sodium chloride (table salt) chlorine plays a role in osmotic pressure relationships and in maintaining the water content of the body.

Chlorine is especially critical in the acid-base relationship of the body since only the chlorine ion can readily pass through the cell membrane; the sodium or potassium ions cannot.

Chlorine, like sodium and potassium, is responsible for drawing the nutrients you eat from the intestines to the blood and finally from the blood into the cells. Without adequate chlorine, this process would not take place and your cells would not be supplied with nutrients.

Chlorine is necessary in the formation of adequate hydrochloric acid in the stomach. Basically, sodium and chlorine are fraternal twins, the metabolism of one cannot be separated from the other, although each provides slightly different contributions to your body.

Sufficient chlorine is available in salt and the foods which I mentioned as being high in sodium also contain chlorine. There are very few problems in obtaining an adequate amount of this mineral.

THE TRACE OR MICRO-MINERALS

The amount of minerals in plant and animal tissues range from grams to micrograms per 100 grams of substance. Those that are present in abundance have been called micro-elements, while those that are present in very small quantities have been referred to as micro — or trace elements.

In the **Science of Nutrition** we find the following comments on the subject: "Many food chemists and nutritional biochemists have stopped using the term 'trace element' because it is misleading. Mineral elements are equally essential whether needed in milligram or microgram quantities. Some elements occur in trace amounts in some tissues, but in rather high concentrations in other tissues. Also, scientists cannot agree on the definition of a 'trace element,' primarily because some elements cannot easily be placed in such a category. For instance, in a recent publication Underwood in 1962 placed iron and iodine in the 'trace element' category while Moore in 1964 excluded them."

The two words will be used interchangeably in the remainder of this book.

COPPER

Copper is detected in all tissues of plant and animal origin. It is required for the synthesis of hemoglobin and the production of ribonucleic acid (RNA), the nucleus of every cell. Copper is an important component of several enzymes and oxygen-carrying proteins. Copper plays a role in bone formation and is a part of several respiratory enzymes, such as ascorbic acid oxidase.

Copper has been found to play a fundamental role in the utilization of iron, hence a deficiency shortens the life span of the red blood cells and anemia results. This mineral is also involved in skin color. Tests conducted on animals show that black animals turn gray when they are deficient in copper.

Oysters are the best single source of copper, followed by liver, kidneys, and brains. Beans, peas, wheat, oats, avocados, corn, kale, prunes, and eggs also contain small amounts.

Your diet should provide you with adequate amounts of copper if you are eating plenty of protein-rich foods and avoiding refined products. It is estimated that most diets supply between 2 and 5 mgs. of copper per day which is sufficient. The rule of thumb is 0.05 to 0.1 mg. per kilogram (2.2 pounds) of bodyweight per day. A two-hundred pounder (90 kgs.) would use 4.5 to 9.0 grams daily. The mineral molybdenum seems to have a profound effect on copper metabolism. Too little molybednum creates a copper toxicity and too much a copper deficiency, so it seems the inter-relationship of these two minerals is critical.

ZINC

The essentiality of zinc for human growth and development was first established in 1934. Zinc is found in all the cells of the human body and a high level is in the testes, seminal vesicles, prostate, and semen. It is also highly concentrated in the eyes. Zinc plays a role in the synthesis of protein so should have a special place in every athlete's diet.

A study conducted by Stain, Dutton, Heyer, and Ramsey at the University of Rochester in 1953 showed that Zinc promoted the healing of burns and wounds. It has since been used for this purpose in many hospitals.

Zinc deficiencies were reported by Prasad, Schubert, Mirale, Farid, and Sandstead in the **American Journal of Clinical Nutrition**, 1963, on populations in Egypt and Iran. Male subjects showed dwarfism, severe anemia, and interference with the growth and development of the testicles and penis. Facial and pubic hair did not grow. The study showed that the addition of zinc normalized these conditions.

Zinc is found in: oysters, herring, oatmeal, wheat bran, liver, peas, milk, egg yolk, beets, and corn. As in the case of copper, if you are eating a diet high in protein foods you should be receiving a sufficient supply of this important mineral.

COBALT

Cobalt is an essential element to all animals as it is a vital component of Vitamin B12. You may recall that Vitamin B12 was unique in that it is the only vitamin to contain metal as an integral part of its structure.

The cobalt content of plant tissue is determined largely by the cobalt content of the soils in which they grow. E.L. Smith in his book **Mineral Metabolism** points out a study showing that the cobalt content of lettuce raised from 0.03 to 0.50/100 grams. by adding cobalt sulfate to the soil.

E.J. Underwood conducted a study on cobalt deficient animals in Australia and New Zealand and found that when the land becomes depleted of cobalt, the animals suffer from anemia and die.

A cobalt deficiency results in pernicious anemia since adequate Vitamin B12 cannot be synthesized by the body without it.

Spinach, turnip greens, beet tops, buckwheat, cocoa, cabbage, pears, and figs are good sources of cobalt while: onions, chard, spinach, tomatoes, milk, and corn contain some.

It is estimated that the average diet provides 5-8 mgs. of cobalt daily, but since only 10 to 20% of this amount is absorbed, only about 1 to 3 mgs. are actually utilized.

IRON

The ancient Greeks believed the great god Mars had endowed iron with a special strength and those who ate this mineral would become strong and masterful.

Most people realize that a severe iron deficiency results in anemia, but anemia is actually a very late sign of iron deficiency, since it does not become evident until the iron supply is completely exhausted.

A slight deficiency brings with it dizziness, muscle weakness, lack of endurance, and a constant state of fatigue. This condition may linger for months and even years if not corrected and it is certainly not the best state of affairs for an athlete who plans to train hard and heavy.

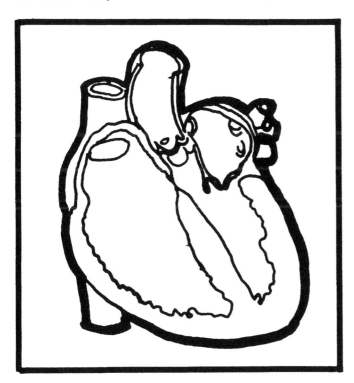

ANEMIA

Anemia refers to the condition where the body does not produce sufficient red blood corpuscles or hemoglobin. An iron deficiency generally results in that form of anemia in which the hemoglobin concentration is decreased more than the red blood count.

Iron should be of great interest to athletes in another regard also — as this mineral is critical for the structure of myoglobin, the hemoglobin of the skeleton and heart muscles. Myoglobin stores oxygen released by hemoglobin in the tissues and serves as a reservoir for the oxygen. Iron must be adequately supplied in order to build and maintain this vital structure.

Iron is found in: brewer's yeast, wheat germ, eggs, potatoes, prune juice, whole wheat bread, dates, apricots, soybeans, kidneys, liver, pork, and lamb. The efficiency of absorption of food iron varies with the types and amounts of foods eaten, with the amount of physical activity, and especially with the adequacy of iron stored already in the tissues. The iron from muscle meats and organs such as liver, kidneys, and heart is much better absorbed than that derived from eggs and vegetables.

Johnson reports in the **Journal of Nutrition** that 50% of the iron in beef is utilized by the human body while Moore and Dubach found only 4% of the iron in eggs was utilized.

Foods high in acid content such as buttermilk, yogurt, and all citrus fruits aid in the absorption of this mineral. Ascorbic acid increases the absorption of iron also. Conversely, refined carbohydrates prevent iron absorption, primarily because they increase the alkaline digestive juices.

Dr. Robert Harris, in the **Science of Nutrition,** writes: "It is evident that the availability of the iron in various foodstuffs is quite variable, that normal people absorb only 5 to 10% of the food iron, and that deficient patients absorb perhaps 10 to 20%. On this basis, a diet which contains 12 mgs. of iron daily actually contributes only about 0.6 mg. of iron to normal subjects and possibly as much as 2 mg. to deficient subjects."

Since it is so difficult to retain iron, a daily intake of 15 mg. is needed to supply the body with 0.7 to 1.5 mgs. of the absorbed mineral. Iron should be taken in conjunction with all the other essential nutrients for best results. Your diet should supply you with a sufficient supply of this mineral.

IODINE

When you think of iodine, think of the thyroid gland and you will be able to remember what this mineral does in your body. The thyroid tissues are literally iodine-seekers, concentrating the iodine from the blood to such an extent that the thyroid/blood ratio is 25 to 1 in humans.

If you supply your body with a sufficient supply of iodine, the thyroid can produce adequate amounts of the thyroid hormone, thyroxine, and the body functions normally. Come up short and there are problems. Your energy level will drop off, all physical and mental development ceases, the activities of the endocrine glands (such as the gonads) stops, and the metabolism of carbohydrates, proteins, and fats is disturbed. Sounds as if you're near death, and actually people who lack this hormone do move about as if they were more dead than alive.

GOITER RESULTS FROM IODINE DEFICIENCY

A severe deficiency of iodine is generally easy to diagnose as it results in a goiter. A goiter, simply speaking, is an enlargement of the thyroid glands which are located in your neck. Goiters can be both prevented and reduced by the addition of sufficient iodine to the diet.

In 1918, two doctors, Kimball and Marine, conducted a test on the effects of iodine on goiter development on school girls in Akron, Ohio. Their findings, reported in the **Archives of Internal Medicine** that same year, revealed that small doses of iodine given during a 10-day period twice yearly would greatly reduce the incidence of simple goiter in children. Because of this and similar tests, the addition of iodine to salt has become an accepted public health practice.

This essential mineral element was first discovered in 1811 by Courtois while he was attempting to extract saltpeter from seaweed vats for Napoleon's army. It is the heaviest element known to be required for animal growth and development and is found primarily in sea life. Cod and haddock are the richest of the fish sources and shrimp and lobster the highest of the shellfish. Clams, oysters, crabs, sea perch, mackerel, bacon, pork, beef, eggs, butter, and cheese also contain some iodine.

KELP

Kelp is an extremely rich source of iodine and can be obtained in supplement form. Besides iodine, kelp contains some 22 minerals, such as: calcium, phosphorus, iron, copper, potassium, magnesium, sodium, manganese, and sulphur. If you feel your energy level dragging, you might consider using this supplement. Iodine should always be taken along with the other essential nutrients, especially magnesium, Vitamin E, and Vitamin B6.

Your diet, especially if it contains plenty of protein-rich foods, will afford you 0.15 mg. of iodine per day, which is sufficient.

MANGANESE

Manganese is another of the trace or micro-elements you hear very little about, but which does play a role in total health and fitness. Manganese is involved in activating several enzymes. It plays a distinct role in the development of the testicles and humans and animals lacking this element become sterile. This mineral has a function in helping the body to utilize fats.

Of special importance to those involved in athletics are the studies done on manganese which reveal that a deficiency results in uncoordinated movements and a loss of equilibrium. Certainly the factor of balance is of prime consideration to all athletes and it appears that this mineral has a bearing on this attribute.

Foods which contain manganese are: lettuce, pineapple, beet tops, blueberries, blackberries, spinach, wheat germ, nuts, and unrefined breads and cereals. Manganese is not absorbed into plants which are grown on soils impregnated with chemical fertilizers. As is the case in many of the other minerals, a diet high in phosphorus reduces the absorption of manganese.

While a standard has not been set for this micro-element, many authorities feel an addition of .10 mg. per kilogram (2.2 pounds) of bodyweight would be valid. Hence, a 150-pounder would need approximately 7 mgs. and a 200-pound athlete 9 mg. Because of its role in balance and coordination, I definitely recommend that you include manganese in your dietary schedule. Most mixed mineral supplements contain a sufficient quantity of this essential element.

SUMMARY

I sincerely hope that I have impressed upon you the importance of the minerals in your diet. The minerals are so closely intertwined with each other and all the other essential nutrients that they cannot in actuality be separated if you are seeking total health and fitness. The nutritional functions of these inorganic elements are usually very complex and interrelated with one another as well as with all the vitamins, amino acids, fatty acids, and carbohydrates. As Doctor Robert Harris so aptly states in **The Science of Nutrition**, "Calcium and phosphorus are principally involved in the formation of bones and teeth, yet each has many functions of a very different nature. Iron, copper, and cobalt are interrelated in the synthesis of hemoglobin and the formation of red cells, yet each has other activities. Sodium, potassium, chlorine, phosphorus, and calcium are involved in the maintenance of body fluids; magnesium and calcium are concerned with nerve cell functions; iodine is a constituent of thyroxine, a thyroid hormone; and manganese, molybdenum, zinc, and other minerals serve as activators of a number of enzymes that are concerned with a variety of metabolic reactions."

Since I have covered a dozen mineral elements rather quickly, and realize that one becomes easily confused with these nutrients, I have prepared a summary chart as I did for the B-Complex vitamins, showing the elements primary function and my recommended dosage.

As you become further interested in each of these minerals you can leaf back to the more detailed information contained in this chapter. While I fully realize that I have but skimmed the surface of information on the minerals, there is sufficient information presented to enable you to build a solid diet for your individual athletic needs. ★

SUMMARY OF THE MIGHTY MINERALS

MINERAL	FUNCTION	RECOMMENDED DAILY DOSAGE FOR ATHLETES IN HARD TRAINING
Calcium	Builds and maintains bones and teeth. Needed for muscle contraction and tone. Excellent pain killer. Closely interrelated to phosphorus and magnesium absorption.	2.0 grams
Phosphorus	Critical to acid-base balance, skeletal growth, tooth development, and muscle metabolism. Also plays a role in intermediary metabolism of fats, carbohydrates, and proteins.	4.0 grams
Magnesium	Vital to bones and teeth. Activator of numerous enzymes, including ATP, which is needed for muscle contractions and synthesis of proteins, fats, and nucleic acid. "Nature's own tranquilizer!"	1.0 gram
Potassium	Necessary for normal muscle tone. Associated with carbohydrate metabolism. Energy level dependent on this mineral. Stimulates the liver.	10.0 grams
Sodium	Contributes to acid-base balance. Responsible for osmotic pressure of fluids outside the cells. Close relationship with potassium and chlorine.	10.0 grams
Chlorine	Delicate balance with potassium and sodium in maintaining water content and osmotic pressure in the body. Needed to form hydro-chloric acid in the stomach.	10.0 grams
Copper	Required for synthesis of hemoglobin and ribonucleic acid. Role in bone formation and is part of respiratory enzyme. Involved in skin color and utilization of iron.	5.0 mg.
Zinc	Essential for growth and development. Valuable for healing burns and wounds. Deficiency produces underdeveloped sexual glands. Plays a role in protein synthesis.	1.0 mg.
Cobalt	Vital component of Vitamin B12. Deficiency results in pernicious anemia.	5.0 mg.
Iron	Important in formation of hemoglobin and red blood cells. Helps build myoglobin. Needed for the transportation of oxygen.	15.0 mg.
Iodine	Necessary for thyroid gland to produce hormone, thyroxine. Thyroxine regulates mental and physical energy levels, activates endocrine glands and helps in metabolism of fats, proteins, and carbohydrates.	0.15 mg.
Manganese	Involved in activating many enzymes. Role in development of testicles. Influences factors of coordination and equilibrium in the body.	10.0 mg.

14

CHAPTER FOURTEEN
SUPER FOODS AND SUPPLEMENTS

ANALYZING YOUR INDIVIDUAL REQUIREMENTS

HOPEFULLY, YOU HAVE NOW been convinced of the importance of the various nutrients. Your next step is to put these theories into actual everyday practice. Unfortunately, this is not quite as easy as it may appear, for a number of reasons.

Individuals vary tremendously as to their basic nutritional needs. There is no such thing as a minimum daily requirement that applies to everyone. Your special need for certain essential nutrients, such as potassium, might be ten times higher than the need of another person of the same age and body build. Your activity level has a bearing on your daily nutritional requirements. If you are in two-a-day practice sessions, then your body needs much more nutritional attention than it does if you are training but once a day, or three times a week.

BASIC METABOLISM

Your individual basic metabolism rate influences your nutritional needs. Some people utilize the ingested essential nutrients much more effectively than others. Two people training side by side in a gym. Both are doing the same program, yet one will be dripping wet with sweat while his partner looks like he just walked in the gym. Your metabolism changes with age so what worked so well for you as a teenager no longer does the job at twenty-five. If your body is still maturing and forming muscle, bones, ligaments, and other tissue, then your needs will be especially high in magnesium, calcium, phosphorus, protein, and a host of vitamins.

If you are attempting to gain functional bodyweight, then you certainly have special dietary needs. Should you be attempting to drop a few pounds while trying to increase your strength, then you do not have average nutritional requirements.

Dr. Roger Williams, perhaps the world's foremost authority on the nutritional uniqueness of each individual, puts it this way in his book, **Free and Equal**: "We have lived too long with the idea that there must be a **best** way for a man to do everything. We have said either everyone should eat a heavy breakfast or else no one should. If eight hours sleep is right for one, it is right for all."

ATHLETES' HIGH NEEDS

One of the most important facts to consider is that you are an athlete and this puts you in a category all by yourself. It is as if you are supplying a four-barrel carburetor, an overhead cam, the Offen Hauser engine of the species. Your body is the machine to be tested at Indy each weekend. Just as the super stocks do not run on ordinary fuel, athletes do not perform well on ordinary diets. Your requirements are a great deal higher than those of the non-athlete. To compare your Vitamin C or Vitamin E or protein needs with that of an insurance salesman, or postal clerk, or business executive is pure foolishness. To complete the analogy, it is like putting regular gasoline in Andy Granitelli's finest. It just doesn't correlate.

So what I am saying is that it is a tough task to outline a single nutritional program that will relate to every individual. What I will present is a program that should be pertinent to every athlete to some degree. Your final dietary schedule must, however, come from adapting the ideas and principles presented here with lots of personal observation and some experimentation. Maybe this seems like an unnecessary and hopeless task, but it isn't really, and it will be worth the effort to your overall health and athletic performance.

Review your nutritional program constantly and make changes when you see them necessary. Check through the individual chapters periodically — they will serve as a short review course on the subject — and read as much as possible from other nutritional resources. In a short period of time you will be able to learn the various signs of deficiency of the various elements. Perhaps you are low on energy. This could be due to a number of factors from a lack of iron, potassium, iodine, the B-Vitamins, or a lack of eating enough energy-producing foods in general. Do a little detective work in order to find out the source of the problem. Increase the dosage of just one of the suspected nutrients at a time. If that one doesn't produce any results, then try another. Then try some in combination. Check the balance of your nutritional intake as too much of one element can produce a deficiency in another. If you are overdoing one of the B-Complex vitamins, such as thiamine or pantothenic acid, then you could bring on symptoms of a B-Vitamin deficiency. Remember the balance of all the essential nutrients is as critical as the amount taken.

EXPERIMENT

Experiment and record the results. Soon you will develop a nutritional program that suits your needs exactly. You will learn when to add more potassium and sodium chloride to your body, when to increase calcium, phosphorus, and magnesium and when to take extra large amounts of Vitamin C and E.

Always keep in mind that you have very specific individual requirements. Use the information you read and hear about as a guideline, not as hard and fast rules. What works well for your training mate may not work as effectively for you. Develop your own plan to supply your body with its nutritional needs. It may seem like a troublesome process, but it is well worth the time and effort. It will make you a better athlete and that's what it's all about.

Table I on page 98 lists all the thirty essential nutrients that are described in some detail and that are presently known to be required by your body and the dosages that I recommend for the hard training athlete. I have not included the many trace elements which may also have value. I mentioned earlier that nearly all of the recommended allowances exceeded those set up by organizations in this country. Those standards are meant for the average person and not for athletes. My standards are derived from those set forth by the European authorities and by recent research in this country. The communist countries in Europe have done extensive studies on the nutritional needs of their athletes and I feel their standards are much more relevant to your needs than the minimum daily requirements set forth by the more conservative American Medical Association or the Federal Drug Administration. None of my recommendations exceed a toxic level, however, so you need not be concerned that you are endangering any portion of your health by following my standards. They are definitely mega-dosages, but well within safe limits.

SOME SUPER FOODS

Every athlete should be aware of a few foods which I call "super foods" because they supply so many of the essential nutrients. All of these foods should be included a few at a time. I will talk specifically about supplements later on in this chapter, but if you include enough of these super foods in your diet you will not have to supplement your diet nearly as much.

These super foods should slowly, but surely, start taking the place of foods of lesser nutritional value. Begin to avoid all foods that do not add to your nutritional needs. Junk foods like candy, soda, pasteries, starchy foods, and sweets of all sorts should be eliminated from your diet. Learn to snack on foods of higher nutritional value. Fruits make excellent snacking, and are filled with essential nutrients. Fruit juices should replace the less valuable sodas. Nuts of all sorts and sunflower seeds can easily be eaten instead of popcorn, potato chips, or candy bars. It's merely a matter of substitution. You can learn to enjoy nutritional foods just as well as the junky ones in no time at all.

LIVER IS A SUPER FOOD

Your liver does so many things for your body that listing them is like recording all the functions of your body. Linda Clark in **Stay Younger Longer** lists a few: "The liver is basic to the strong heartbeat, the wide-open channels of your blood vessels, the soundness of your digestion, the sharp-ness of your brain, the strength of your life. Your kidneys would be unable to dispose of waste nitrogen if the liver didn't first turn it into urea for excretion. The liver acts as a storehouse for vitamins, it balances hormones, builds amino acids, it secretes bile to govern intestinal activity. The liver controls bleeding, combats dangerous clotting, fights viruses and bacterial poisons, releases energy from food, and performs an amazing variety of functions. It is able to regenerate itself over and over, and this is where nutrition helps."

You can easily see why you need to give this vital organ all the help that you possibly can. The best food to supply the liver with all the nutrients it needs is liver itself. For the hard training athlete it is of paramount importance that you get plenty of this organ food in your diet in some form or other. It supplies so many essential nutrients like: protein, fatty acids, phosphorus, iron, copper, zinc, iodine, Vitamin A and D, inositol, cholin, folic acid, Vitamin B12, pantothenic acid, Vitamin B6, niacin, thiamine, and riboflavin. In fact, liver is a source of all the B-Complex Vitamins and is a most excellent way to obtain an abundant supply of the B group. The proteins found in liver are complete so it is an excellent source of this nutrient.

ANTI-FATIGUE VALUE OF LIVER

The test conducted by Dr. B.H. Ershoff in 1951 on the value of liver in combating fatigue is now a classic study in the necessity of liver for the athlete. Dr. Ershoff was testing for an anti-fatigue diet in his laboratory. He used three groups of rats on three different diets which he fed for 12 weeks. The first group ate a laboratory diet to which he added nine synthetic and two natural vitamins. The second group of rats had this same diet plus all the B-Complex Vitamins. The third group ate the original diet with 10% desiccated liver added instead of the B-Vitamins.

Each rat was placed in a drum of water from which he could not climb out. He had to keep swimming or drown so it was a genuine test of endurance as the motivation was of the highest order. The first group swam for an average of 13.3 minutes before they gave up and indicated positively that they had no energy left. The second group swam for an average of 13.4 minutes before drowning. In the third group, the desiccated liver group, three were able to swim for 63, 83, and 87 minutes before retiring while the remainder of the group were still swimming vigorously at the end of two hours. The message is clear enough for the most "Doubting Thomas."

Many people do not have the taste for this organ food, but I have found that if it is prepared correctly the taste is no longer a barrier. Generally, people overcook liver in hopes of improving its flavor. It should be slightly undercooked rather than overcooked because a hard, tough piece of meat is distasteful to everyone. Liver can be cooked with many different things to add to its flavor, such as mushrooms, onions, bacon, or tomatoes. One athlete I know just could not handle the taste of liver, but realized its nutritional value. He cut the meat into small bite-sized pieces and froze them. Then he swallowed them like pills with a glass of milk. In this manner he was able to ingest a half pound of liver every day and his lifting ability improved noticeably.

LIVER SUPPLEMENTS

Should you be stymied completely as to how to eat liver, then a supplement might be the answer to your difficulty. Desiccated liver powder and tablets are available for those who prefer this route. The better products contain ½ gram of protein per tablet and you can regulate your protein intake exactly by utilizing this supplement. Select a product that has not been tampered with if at all possible. There are a few good ones around, and there are also a few duds. Select the undefatted variety over the defatted kind. There is only a trace of fat in liver and the chemical process used to distract the fat also destroys some of the amino acids and some of the B-Vitamins. The better products are merely compressed and are not touched with either heat or chemicals.

The powder form of desiccated liver is more concentrated, but alas, harder to take as it has a strong liver flavor. It has to be mixed with vegetable juices, such as tomato or V-8 juice, or put in meatloafs or stews to get it past most taste buds. Even though I admit that the power form of any nutritional supplement is more economical than the tablet form, I still recommend that you choose the tablets in the case of liver. The monetary difference is very slight and at least you'll have a chance of taking the tablets. With the powder, I'm not so sure.

WHEAT GERM

Wheat germ comes in two commercial forms, granules and oil. Both are valuable sources of the following essential nutrients: Vitamins C, D, and E, protein, fatty acids, thiamine, riboflavin, niacin, inositol, folic acid, cholin, pantothenic acid, Vitamin B6, Vitamin B12, phosphorus, iron, magnesium, and sodium. The granules can be used as a cereal or added to salads, soups, gravies, or meat dishes. It makes an excellent substitute for flour to roll chicken, steak, or other meats before baking or frying. Check to see if the wheat germ has been processed or had things added to it. The best has not been toasted nor has sugar or honey been added. The natural form is recommended.

The germ of the wheat is the center of the wheat kernel. It is the most vital part of the grain and the most nutritious. One half cup of granulated wheat germ contains twenty-four grams of protein, the same amount provided by four large eggs, or three eight ounce glasses of milk.

The oil should be cold-pressed and while it is extremely high in Vitamin E, it does not contain as much protein, B-Vitamins, or minerals as the wheat germ granules. The oil can be taken in liquid or capsule form. The capsules are the most expensive because you are paying for having the oil placed in the gelatin, but if you have trouble swallowing the oil then this is the best method for you. I find that if you swallow a fruit or vegetable juice immediately behind the oil, there is no aftertaste.

WHEAT GERM COMBATS FATIGUE

Dr. Thomas Cureton, Director of the Physical Fitness Institute at the University of Illinois, has conducted numerous studies on the value of wheat germ oil for athletes. He has found wheat germ oil to be most beneficial in combating fatigue. One such test showed that the addition of one teaspoonful of wheat germ oil per day raised the oxygen level in the heart, the muscles, and the other body tissues some 30%. This, in his calculation, was the same as putting the subjects in an oxygen tent. Certainly the ability to retain oxygen is a great asset to any athlete.

MIXED OILS

When you go to the health food store you may find some mixed germ oils alongside the wheat germ oil. You may be tempted to purchase these because a combination of many oils, such as rice, soy, wheat, and fish liver should be better than just one oil. Right? Wrong. The mixtures do not contain the nutritional potency of the wheat germ oil alone. Studies have indicated that by mixing many of the germ oils the benefit of any one is counterbalanced by the others and, actually, some of the original value is lost. Some of the Vitamin E, for example, is destroyed when the oils are combined. The mixtures are just another sales gimmick. The mixed oils are cheaper to produce than pure wheat germ oil since the mixtures contain very little of the wheat germ oil (the most potent) and lots of the less nutritious oils such as rice oil and fish liver oil. The manufacturers push a heavy advertising campaign to make you believe they are better, but they aren't, so stick with the genuine article. Unrefined, cold-pressed, raw wheat germ oil is the best value for your dollar.

BREWER'S YEAST

Brewer's yeast is surely one of the "super foods" and may go a long way to providing for the world's hunger problem someday. Yeast can be grown in a matter of hours and is a storehouse of nutrition. Brewer's yeast contains sixteen amino acids, thiamine, riboflavin, B6, niacin, cholin, inositol, pantothenic acid, PABA, biotin, folic acid, phosphorus, calcium, potassium, magnesium, copper manganese, zinc, sodium, aluminum, iron, cobalt and iodine.

Quite a line-up. This food supplies you with more nutrients than any other except liver. Linda Clark summarizes a study which was first published in the **Journal of Nutrition**. She writes: "The study involved ten healthy men, ranging from twenty-three years to forty. They were allowed to choose anything they wished to eat from a diet which was inadequate in the B-Vitamins. They had a choice of white bread, soda crackers, macaroni, butter, egg white, ice cream, puffed rice, and coffee. However, twice a week they were given a small amount of fish, meat, or poultry. All of these men were required to do hard work. At the end of the first week they showed the following symptoms: laziness, inefficiency, depression, fatigue, muscle and joint pains, poor appetite, irregular bowel habits, constipation, and irritability. When brewer's yeast was given to them, they began to feel better within forty-eight hours. From then on, their improvement was sudden and dramatic. In five days, despite their otherwise deficient diet, all complaints had disappeared."

Brewer's yeast takes a bit of getting used to and because of its high B-Complex content it will often produce intestinal gas. This is an indication that you are deficient in the B-Vitamins and it is best to increase the dosage slowly. Brewer's yeast can be used as a flavoring, much like salt. By adding a little of it to your diet each day you will increase your nutritional intake a good deal without any great stress on your part.

For those who cannot take the powder, then tablets are available, but remember that a powder form of any supplement is always better than a tablet form. This is because in order to make a tablet a binder must be used and you end up paying for this binder. The best buy is always powder but sometimes taste must be considered over economy.

YOGURT

Yogurt has always been associated with health food freaks, weirdos, and strange cults. Yet, it too has a definite place in every athlete's diet. Yogurt is merely a form of fermented milk. It is made from goat, cow, or soy milk. The best yogurt is that which has not been processed. Try to select the unpasteurized and unhomogenized version if at all possible. Only a couple of states, at present, have unpasteurized dairy products available although every state should soon come to the realization of their nutritional superiority.

Yogurt's greatest value is that it aids in the digestive process. It helps you to utilize all the nutrients you have been eating. Yogurt helps your body manufacture many of the B-Vitamins. As in the case of brewer's yeast, many people experience intestinal gas when they first add yogurt to their diet. This, again, is a sign of a B-Vitamin deficiency. If this occurs, then take the yogurt in smaller doses, perhaps just half a cup at a time rather than a full cup, until the body adapts to the new influx of bacteria.

The acidic content of yogurt aids in the digestion of many minerals, such as calcium, as all minerals need an acid base in order to be utilized properly. Yogurt is also a good source of protein, and this protein is predigested so it absorbs more rapidly. It is also a complete form of protein.

There are many ways to add yogurt to your diet. Mix it with fruits or fruit juices in your blender. For a super high protein milkshake, combine eight ounces of milk, a cup of milk solids, a banana, a cup of yogurt, and two scoops of vanilla ice cream. You end up with a delicious drink which contains approximately fifty grams of high quality protein. It's a great way to add weight and all sorts of varieties can be thought up. Like using strawberry ice cream and fresh strawberries. Let your taste buds and your imagination be your guides.

The addition of fruit or fruit flavoring does not alter the nutritional effect of yogurt, contrary to what some people believe. It would be much wiser, however, for you to buy the plain unflavored variety and add your own flavoring of fresh fruit. Why pay a high price for blueberry sauce which is mostly sugar and artificial flavoring? If you look closely at some of the flavored yogurts you will discover more flavoring in the container than yogurt. Syrup is cheaper than yogurt.

KEFIR

Kefir is a first cousin to yogurt, and is being sold in more and more stores across the country. Kefir, like yogurt, is a cultured milk product and also aids in the digestive process. A Danish scientist, Dr. Orala-Jensen, even goes so far to contend that: "Kefir has an even higher nutritional value than yogurt, due to the abundance of the yeast cells which are digested, and by the beneficial effects on the intestinal flora."

The kefir culture can be kept active for many years and oven dried for future use. At present, this product is grossly overpriced, I suspect because it is a new product and the public does not understand enough about it to know they are being had. Actually, kefir is much simpler to make than yogurt, and it requires no special equipment to make. In the future I expect to find kefir being used in place of yogurt, as it is easy to make at home and will provide you with many of the nutrients you need for health, vigor, and vitality.

SUNFLOWER SEEDS

Sunflower seeds make excellent snacks. They contain all the B-Vitamins and are especially high in cholin, PABA, and inositol. They contain iron, phosphorus, calcium, copper, manganese, potassium, magnesium, and iodine.

One quarter of a pound of sunflower seeds will yield 92 units of Vitamin D, 31 units of Vitamin E, 25 grams of protein, and 42 units of unsaturated fatty acids. Certainly it could be considered one of the better snack foods on the market.

Once again, the less processed the merchandise, the better the end product. Sunflower seeds can be added to salads, vegetables, or fruit dishes. Have them around for guests to nibble on or use them as snack foods when watching TV. Because of their high protein content they make for excellent quick energy foods during the day. Instead of reaching for a sweet or pastry, learn to make sunflower seeds your snack food.

KELP

Kelp is another of those foods which you may associate with health faddists, but it does fit into the athlete's overall dietary program.

Kelp is a rich source of minerals, containing calcium, potassium, phosphorus, iron, copper, magnesium, manganese, sodium, and sulphur, plus twelve other trace elements. Kelp is available in powder and tablet form. The powder can be added to foods as a seasoning much like salt and is especially good on soup and salads. This is an easy and most economical way to add to your nutritional needs without a whole lot of difficulty. These little nutritional extras start to add up, by the way. A few extra B-Vitamins for breakfast, a few extra amino acids at snack time, and a few extra vitamins and minerals before going to bed all improve your chances of meeting your bodies nutritional requirements.

LECITHIN

The addition of this "super food" to your dietary program may be one of the wisest things you ever do in your entire life. Lecithin is found in every cell in your body. By eating a sufficient amount of it daily you can assist your body in quickly rebuilding these cells.

Lecithin has received a great deal of attention in recent years because of its role in helping to neutralize excess cholestrol in the body, but that's only a trifling of what it does. It helps to lower blood pressure. It has helped to eliminate acne, eczema, and other skin diseases. It relieves nervous tension and acts as a tranquilizer. Lecithin aids in the assimilation of Vitamins A and E. Seminal fluids are rich in lecithin, and it has been used in Germany as a sexual aid.

Lecithin is very high in phosphorus, inositol, cholin, and linoleic acid. I suggest that you obtain lecithin in the liquid form, as this is the most concentrated and is quite inexpensive.

It is also available in granules and in capsules. The granules look and taste a great deal like wheat germ. They can be added to soups, salads, juices, and meat dishes. The more concentrated liquid has the consistency of melted caramel. It has a nutty flavor and is quite easy to take. Milk and fruit juices seem to make the best chasers. It tastes fine but sticks to the roof of your mouth until you perfect the technique.

Two tablespoons of Fern's Liquid Lecithin will supply you with 770 mgs. of phosphorus, 750 mgs. of inositol, 770 mgs. of cholin, 5,500 mgs. of linoleic acid and 800 mgs. of linolenic acid, the latter two being essential fatty acids. It is a wise addition to any diet.

THE VALUE OF SUPPLEMENTS

Are food supplements really necessary? Some authorities say, "definitely not, just eat a balanced diet." Other nutritionists reply that "you have to supplement your diet in order to obtain the needed nutrients because of the way our food is being processed to death." What is the answer, are they or aren't they necessary? Let me reiterate one point before making my declaration on the subject. The authorities who advocate the balanced diet route are never talking about the special needs of the athlete. It may be possible, although I believe it quite unlikely, that an average person with average nutritional requirements can obtain sufficient nutrients from the foods he purchases in the supermarket,

but it is not even remotely possible for the hard training athlete to do so.

The nutritional needs of the athlete are just too great to be fulfilled with the foods purchased in the market place. His requirements for Vitamin C, Vitamin E, and potassium are sometimes ten times higher than the less-active individual. These elements may, theoretically, be obtained from table foods but realistically it is nearly impossible. You would have to spend all day with some sort of food in your mouth. Supplements are an easier and surer way of obtaining the high nutritional requirements for an athlete, and in the long run, they are less expensive.

LOTS OF PILLS!

"But it's so much trouble to remember to take so many different pills and tablets every day." I have heard this complaint constantly and it has never registered as making sense from a person who willingly spends three to four hours a week pushing and pulling weight so as to improve his athletic performance. Not to mention the jogging, handball, basketball, paddleball, or volleyball he plays in order to improve his cardiovascular fitness. I figure an athlete who is serious about getting into top condition must spend a minimum of ten hours a week, (counting undressing, dressing, showering, and training) on becoming physically fit.

The chore of taking supplements may consume a total of ten minutes a day, based on a three minute session after each meal, and this time may prove to be just as important to your total state of fitness as the other 10 hours. It is merely a matter of accepting the importance of nutrition. If you do not feel that it has value, then it will seem like a bother and a waste of time. On the other hand, once you genuinely believe in the value of taking all the nutrients each and every day, the routine will become a regular part of your life. It's just a simple fact of making it an everyday habit. Get up from the table, take your supplements, and then brush your teeth. No big thing, if you really want to be a superior athlete.

By using supplements you can accurately control and regulate exactly how much of each vital nutrient you are taking into your body each day. It eliminates guesswork. You set up a nutritional program which includes X-grams of protein, X-amounts of minerals and vitamins and through the use of supplements insure yourself of obtaining the necessary amount. Otherwise, it's a hit and miss situation. One day you may be able to obtain your needed supply of protein from the foods you eat, but the next you may come up 50-75 grams short. So on the first day you can skip taking a protein supplement but on the second it will fulfill your protein quota quickly and efficiently.

The supplements insure control and this is important to the athlete as he wants to supply his body each and every day. He is not just interested in maintaining a certain level of health, but must push his body to the highest levels of fitness. Only by adequately supplying his nutritional needs day in and day out will he be able to do so. A day of deficiency will slow his progress and a steady upgrading of progress is most important.

Let the foods you eat from the table act as bonuses. Should you be fortunate enough to eat lots of protein foods, fresh vegetables and fruits, then you are ahead of the game. But the way our society functions, few have the time or the situation to plan each meal properly. So have the supplements handy in case you come up short. I certainly recommend that you obtain all the nutrients you possibly can from natural sources, like dairy products, fresh meat, vegetables and fruits, but this is the "ideal" and is not the "real" situation. You will, realistically, have to get the majority of your nutritional needs from the supplements and add to them from the table. It's a reverse of how nature intended it, but it's the only practical approach to solving the problem of obtaining the essential nutrients in today's food-tampering, profit-oriented culture.

WHAT YOU NEED

Actually, if you chose your supplements wisely you will not have to take lots of them. I recommend that every athlete should have available the following supplements: 1) a multiple vitamin, 2) a multiple mineral, 3) Vitamin C, 4) Vitamin E, 5) a B-Complex Vitamin, 6) an unsaturated fatty acid, and 7) a protein supplement. I'll examine each of these separately.

MULTIPLE VITAMIN

Since you will be taking a separate tablet for many of the various nutrients it may seem a bit redundant, and also expensive, to take a multiple vitamin tablet too. Not really. The better multiple vitamins have lots of little extras not included in the individual products. The product I use contains such things as the bioflavonoids, rutin, glutamic acid, more potassium than my multiple mineral tablet, plus various trace elements from bone meal, water cress, wheat germ oil, and soya lecithin. It is Ken Patera's "Super Strength Multiple."

This product forms the backbone of my nutritional program. The extra-good products contain lots of the essential nutrients. After checking the quantities of each ingredient you can add to them with specifics to bring your daily intake up to the recommended level.

Label reading is most important when you are purchasing a multiple vitamin. Don't be fooled by brand names or pushy advertising gimmicks. Madison Avenue has a finger in the nutritional market too. Check to be sure the ingredients are natural. They'll attempt to trick you if they can. Some flash the words "naturally best" or from "nature's own." Misleading, but not enough for the FDA to make them change the wording. Read the label all the way to the bottom. If one or two of the vitamins is derived from synthetic sources then

you can bet they all are. The easiest to remember are Vitamins A, D, and C. The A and D should be from fish oil and the C from something natural such as rose hips. If the C is ascorbic acid, then it's a good bet that the rest are synthetic or unnatural.

Some multiple vitamin tablets also contain minerals and you may not feel the need to purchase a multiple mineral tablet in this case. Before making such a decision, check and see if the amounts of minerals contained are sufficient to meet your daily requirements. Some companies add just enough minerals to be able to list them on the label. The quantities are so low that they are practically useless. Just another sales trick. There are some, however, that do include a worthwhile portion of all the necessary minerals. If this is the case, then you may decide to bypass the multiple mineral. But do not be too anxious to do so. Your need for minerals is very high and the minerals are just as important to your body as the vitamins.

MULTIPLE MINERAL TABLET

A good multiple mineral tablet will contain ample quantities of the eleven essential elements I mentioned in this book. You will not find all the recommended requirements in any one product but by checking the label you will be able to differentiate between poor, fair, good, better, and best. Select the one that has the highest quantity of minerals per dollar spent. If you have a special need, like potassium, then pick one which has plenty of this mineral in the tablet.

It is a wise idea to purchase a multiple mineral tablet that is in a natural base, such as yeast, kelp, or even chlorophyll. This way you pick up a few of those micro-elements that may be of nutritional value, but which aren't on any of the charts as yet. Another ingredient often added to some multiple mineral tablets is hydrocholic acid. This is a most useful addition as hydrocholic acid aids in the absorption of all the minerals and especially in the absorption of calcium.

Some labels are tricky — on purpose. Read the small print. Do you have to take just one of these tablets per day to receive the listed nutrients or two tablets three times a day? It does make a difference. Once again I caution against indiscriminate buying of name brands. They usually cost more and do not supply any more of the vital nutrients than the less advertised brands. They may have a fancier label and a more prominent place in the health food store, but that doesn't make them better for you. Check things out before you buy.

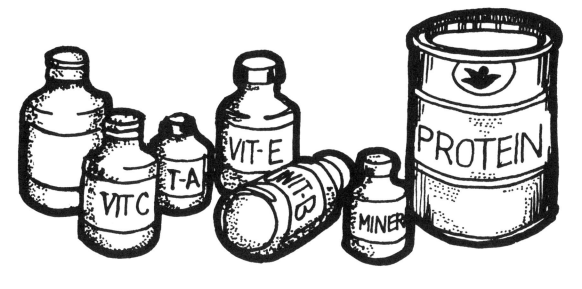

B-COMPLEX VITAMINS

The B-Complex Vitamin supplements are most essential for the athlete because it is very difficult to obtain sufficient amounts of them from the foods he eats. If you eat liver every day or take liver tablets, then you can skip this supplement. Otherwise, I feel it is necessary to be included in your supplement list.

Most B-Complex supplement products are prepared so that the vitamins are in a balanced proportion. This, as you will remember from the chapter dealing with the B-Vitamins is most critical.

I do not recommend that you take the B-Complex Vitamins as separate vitamins unless you spend a great deal of time studying the subject so that you understand fully the correct balance of each to the other. To take a high dosage of one of the B-Complex group, such as niacin or pantothenic acid, without taking a corresponding dosage of all the rest will result in an overbalancing and, in many cases, a deficiency will result. It is far better for the athlete to take the B-Vitamins in a complete capsule.

Check the label on the B-Complex Vitamins. Again, look for the natural ones. See that all the eleven B-Complex Vitamins are included and match the quantities per price to the other brands available. I should mention that there isn't just one company that makes the best in all supplements. While one may have a superior mineral tablet, that same company may produce an inferior brand of B-Complex Vitamins.

Take some time to see what each line has to offer. Take this book along with you to the health food store and read right down the ingredients on the label. Is it natural? How many do you have to take per day to receive the potency listed? Does it have all of what you are after? Is it competitively priced? It pays to take a few extra minutes to check out these particulars.

UNSATURATED FATTY ACIDS

I have already explained the importance of the fatty acids in your daily diet. It is essential that you receive these regularly and the best method is, again, through supplement form.

The three fatty acids you are after are: linoleic, linolenic, and arachidonic. They cannot be synthesized in your body and must be supplied in your diet. Of the three, linoleic is the most important. Be sure that any product that you puchase contains a good deal of linoleic acid. These products are usually derived from linseed or soy oil and are quite inexpensive. Taking one such capsule with each meal insures you of a sufficient supply and will do much to add to your total energy requirement for the day.

Liquid lecithin, mentioned earlier in this chapter as a "super food," is a very good source of the fatty acids. Two tablespoons of lecithin contains 5,500 mgs. of linoleic acid and a pint costs less than $1.50. One of the genuine bargains on the health food shelf.

Some people still prefer to take their fatty acids in the form of a liquid cooking oil such as safflower or sesame oil. A tablespoon after each meal, quickly satisfies this requirement. Capsules are still the favorite for most people, however, because they are convenient and easy to take.

VITAMIN E

Because of an athlete's high requirement for Vitamin E, it is virtually impossible for him to obtain sufficient amounts of this nutrient from his diet or from the multiple vitamin tablet. Even the better multiple vitamins only contain 75-100 I.U. of Vitamin E and, as you recall, an athlete needs anywhere from 1200-1600 I.U. per day.

You may feel if you eat a diet which is rich in meats, dairy products, fruits, and vegetables that you should be able to obtain a sufficient amount of this vitamin. I doubt it. Herbert Bailey points out the reasons in **Vitamin E: Your Key To A Healthy Heart:** "Vitamin E has been slowly but inexorably processed out of the American diet. For instance, present-day bread and flour, rice, corn, and the other cereal foods contain little Vitamin E. The Vitamin E which is available in fruits and vegetables is a poor source of alpha tocopherol, which is the only form of the vitamin which has been shown to be active in animals and in man. Also, the so-called 'unsaturated' fatty oils derived from grains, such as corn, actually deplete the body of Vitamin E, even though paradoxically, they contain fair amounts of the vitamin. Further, there is the problem of utilization. Meats such as steak and liver contain fair quantities of alpha tocopherol, but processing, storing, and cooking lower the Vitamin E content. It has been ascertained by researchers that Vitamin E is poorly utilized in the body."

HIGH NEED FOR E

The athlete's need for this vitamin is extremely high. Many studies have been conducted showing the value of Vitamin E to the athlete's diet. Dr. A. Goria of Italy has performed some of the more classic studies involving athletes and Vitamin E. She used the electrocardiograph to check the "before" and "after" of subjects taking this supplement. The subjects given Vitamin E had much more stamina and endurance, during periods of hypoxia (deprivation of oxygen). One subject's pulse rate, without Vitamin E rose during one three-minute experiment, from 68 to 107, but with Vitamin E it rose only from 58 to 87. Numerous other experiments have brought home the point that this vitamin is a most necessary one for athletes and the only practical way to supply it to your body is through supplements.

Vitamin E is expensive because the extraction process is most involved. It is generally derived from wheat germ oil and it takes a lot of wheat germ oil to make a few units of Vitamin E. Because it does cost the most of all your supplements you may be tempted to go after a bargain. Don't. They are throwing synthetic Vitamin E at you if it's discounted, you can bet on it. **Synthetic Vitamin E is one fifth as potent as the natural kind.**

It should tell you on the label whether its natural or synthetic, but don't always count on it. There are other ways to check in case they don't. The prefix d- signifies natural and dl- means synthetic. Likewise, the best Vitamin E is alpha tocopherol. The mixed tocopherols (alpha, beta, gamma, and delta usually) are only one half as potent as the alpha by itself. So see just how much alpha tocopherol is involved if the label states that it is mixed. Sometimes it's a sufficient amount, while at other times it is very low in proportion.

I suggest that you purchase your Vitamin E in 400 I.U. capsules. Then you can take one with each meal and meet your daily requirement easily. A larger potency becomes unhandy and a lesser one necessitates taking more capsules each day and you will want to avoid this, if possible.

VITAMIN C

As in the case with Vitamin E, an additional supplement is required for Vitamin C in order for you to meet your extra-high requirement. The athlete's needs for this vitamin are just too high to expect to receive it in the diet. You would have to be drinking fruit juices constantly and this would, in turn, add to your carbohydrate count to such an extent that you would gain lots of unwanted weight. It is practically impossible to obtain the suggested 4-5 grams of Vitamin C from the foods you eat. Very few foods contain a very large amount of the vitamin in the first place, and those that do, once processed, have lost the majority of it. It's best to turn to a supplement in the case of Vitamin C.

The question immediately comes up concerning synthetic forms of the vitamins versus the natural kind. A bit of examination is necessary here because it will not always be in your best interest to purchase the natural form of the vitamin. I will explain why this is so. The advantage that natural Vitamin C has over synthetic Vitamin C is that the natural contains some bioflavonoids. These are most useful in increasing the strength of the capillary walls, reducing inflamation, and decreasing the seepage of blood cells and proteins into the tissues. The bioflavonoids have a special spot in every athlete's diet as they help heal slight muscle strains and minor joint injuries. They are not found in the juice of citrus fruits, but rather in the pulp and rind. If you should eat an orange or grapefruit each day and peal away the white portion and eat it you will supply yourself with an ample quantity of this needed nutrient. It is a good idea to obtain some bioflavonoids each day, but it does not have to come from the same source as your Vitamin C or in the same quantity, although it should be taken at the same time as it makes the Vitamin C work better.

Many multiple vitamins contain sufficient bioflavonoids so a synthetic Vitamin C is just as good as a natural one in this instance. If your multiple vitamin does not list bioflavonoids, then there is yet another economical solution. Purchase a small bottle of natural Vitamin C, with bioflavonoids, in a small dosage, such as 100 mgs. Then buy a larger supply of 500 mg synthetic Vitamin C, or ascorbic acid. Take on of the little ones and two of the big ones after each meal. Presto, you have your bioflavonoids, ample Vitamin C to meet your high requirement and a penny or two left over.

PROTEIN SUPPLEMENT

Some athletes will not need a protein supplement as they will be able to obtain a sufficient amount of this essential nutrient from their diet, but for most it is necessary. If you eat plenty of eggs, cheeses, milk, and meats you can ingest the recommended 200-250 grams of protein each day. I have seen plenty of examples of this, but in each case the individual had control of his meals. He ate at the same place each day and saw to it that his protein requirements were met.

Unfortunately, not everyone can do this. If you have travel, work, or school responsibilities, quite often you are skipping meals or eating foods which you really don't care to eat. The professional players are always complaining because of the banquets, business engagements, and friends dropping in to break up their dietary plans. College players are faced with institutional meals, and a general lack of continuity of eating habits. High school players are faced with an even more hectic schedule. Some rarely even eat and when they do it's often no more than a rushed hamburger or

something even less nutritious.

If your eating schedule is not regular you might want to have a protein supplement available in case you missed meeting that requirement on a given day. I recommend desiccated liver tablets very highly. Should you find that you come up short, say 50 grams of protein, then just take a hundred liver tablets with a glass of milk. Liver tablets are much preferred over the other protein tablets. The protein tablets are usually made of soybean and they do not have the nutritional benefit of liver. Liver gives you a bonus of B-Vitamins, along with Vitamins A, D, and E, plus a host of minerals.

Should you prefer a powder to be mixed with milk in the traditional high protein milkshake, I recommend a protein powder made from milk and egg sources over one derived chiefly from soybean powder. The milk and eggs are much more readily assimilated by the human body than are soybeans. Animals, other than humans, utilize soybeans protein much better than Homo sapiens and while the protein content is high, it still does little good unless it gets all the way to your cells. Your digestive system breaks down milk and egg protein better.

I also know that most soybean protein products are not strained, that is, they do not take out the fiber but merely leave this undigestible portion in to add bulk and weight to the product. The milk and egg variety may cost a bit more than soybean products but is nevertheless a better dollar value in the long run.

Another way to add to your protein intake very economically is merely to add a cup of dried milk solids to a quart or half gallon of your regular milk. One cup of powdered milk will supply you with an additional 27 grams of protein, 968 mgs. of calcium, 1160 mgs. of phosphorus, 200 mgs. of potassium, 1160 units of Vitamin A, plus many of the B-Vitamins. You can also mix the dried milk in with a milkshake to add an extra bonus of protein to that supplement.

SOME FLEXIBLE OTHERS

There are a few other supplements that you maybe want to have available for your special nutritional needs. Because of their role they are especially valuable to the athlete. They do certain things in your body which merits attention from anyone who places extra heavy demands on his body, such as every athlete does. But, then again, these supplements will not be necessary for everyone.

POTASSIUM

It is not healthy or wise to let your body run low on potassium and it is rather difficult to obtain enough in your every day diet. Especially during hard training sessions you will lose a great deal of sodium, chlorine, and potassium in your perspiration. The first two minerals can be replaced quickly by taking salt tablets, but potassium is not that available unless you plan ahead.

Potassium supplements can be taken in tablet or powder form. The powder is far superior since federal controls restrict the quantity of each tablet to just 180 mgs. of potassium, whereas a teaspoon of potassium chloride salt supplies approximately 4,000 mgs. of potassium. This will balance nicely with a salt tablet or a teaspoon of sodium chloride, which yields 4,000 mgs. also, and these three minerals must be kept in balance.

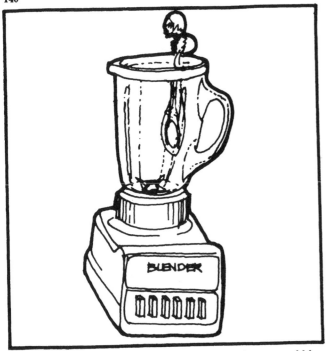

On a hot day when you perspire a great deal, you would be most wise to have a teaspoon of potassium chloride mixed in water along with a couple of salt tablets. The difference it makes in your recovery rate is truly remarkable.

This is basically the formula for the so-called "thirst quenchers" such as Gatorade, Energade, Olympade, and Instant Replay. A 12-ounce container usually consists of 11 ounces of water, 1½ ounces of sugar and dextrose, plus a blend of sodium and potassium salts. You can make your own much cheaper and by adding a couple of mineral tablets you are one step ahead.

VITAMIN B6

Many athletes have found it beneficial to take an additional Vitamin-B6 tablet since this vitamin is so important for the utilization of protein. You need approximately one gram or milligram of B6 for every gram of protein you eat each day. Most athletes are quite successful in obtaining some 200 grams of protein but few are equally successful when it comes to Vitamin B6. If you come up short on this vitamin, then you are in effect, wasting some of the protein you eat.

Most B-Complex tablets carry only about 30-50 mgs. of B6 in a daily requirement so you might want to add another 100 mgs. in the form of an additional supplement each day. I recommend obtaining these in 50 mgs. size so that you can add a couple to your diet each day.

VITAMIN B12

Here is another vitamin that some athletes feel is most beneficial to them in an extra amount. By taking a 50 or 100 mcg. tablet each day they are insuring themselves of an extra supply of this energy vitamin. If your B-Complex tablet or your multiple vitamin contains an ample quantity of B12, then you are ahead of the game. If not, you may want this one available.

MAG-CAL TABLETS

The magnesium-calcium tablet is another nutritional supplement which every athlete will find useful at one time

or another. It is a terrific pain killer and tranquilizer rolled into one safe tablet. On those days when you have some muscle aches or when you simply cannot relax and rest because of physical tension or tiredness, a couple of mag-cal tablets will work wonders.

These need not be taken on a regular basis, but only when the need arises. I think it's a good investment and they are much safer than aspirin, or any of the prescription tranquilizers or sleeping pills.

HOW TO TAKE YOUR SUPPLEMENTS

Since so many of the nutrients work closely together, it naturally follows that you should take all your supplements together just after mealtime. In this way the added nutrients go to work with the vitamins, minerals, proteins, fatty acids, and carbohydrates from the food you eat.

Break your supplements dosage into three equal parts so that you are taking the same amount after each meal. Should you want to take in an additional 1200 I.U. of Vitamin E during the day, then three 400 I.U. capsules after each meal will get the job done.

On certain occasions you may want to increase the dosage on some of the nutrients and on others, skip them entirely. For example, if you have just returned home from a strenuous practice or training session dripping wet with perspiration and totally exhausted you may want a glass of potassium chloride and a teaspoon of salt immediately to satisfy your bodies' deficiency. On the other hand, should you have a rest day with little or no activity, then you may want to cut back on your supplement intake for that day. Let your needs dictate your intake of nutrients.

Regulate your intake according to need and not to some preconceived plan. Should you put your body to a great deal of physical stress then be certain that you supply yourself with ample nutrients. If you are lazing around reading or watching TV then you only will need one-third or one-half as much fuel to keep the machine humming. Use a bit of logic on your nutritional program and you will come out ahead.

IN SUMMARY

I urge each reader to carefully examine his daily food intake. Be sure that you are eating plenty of the more nutritious foods and avoiding those of little or no value. No sense spending time in the weight room or on the track burning off those useless calories that you've stored away as body fat through poor eating habits. Getting into top condition is difficult enough without adding to the problem.

Be sure that you include plenty of fresh fruits and vegetables in your diet. Add lots of meats and dairy products, such as milk, cheese, eggs, yogurt, and cottage cheese. Include some form of grain cereal in your diet as it adds to your overall nutritional count. Select your breads and cereals with care as most are loaded with preservative and supply little nutrition.

Remember the "super foods" and include them in your diet regularly. Slowly, but steadily, let these "super foods" replace some of the other foods in your diet of lesser value. Let wheat germ replace a commercial cereal. Eat sunflower seeds instead of popcorn or potato chips. Replace ice cream with yogurt and fresh fruit. Then add the supplements to be sure that you are supplying your body with all the fuel it needs for the task ahead. Do not underestimate the value of good nutrition when you are engaging in a strength program. It can help make you a stronger athlete and I sincerely believe a stronger athlete will be a better athlete. ★

15

CHAPTER FIFTEEN
A FEW SPECIAL NUTRITIONAL SITUATIONS

THE GENUINE ADVANTAGE OF understanding nutrition is that you can apply that knowledge to specific situations. The problems of weight control, pre-game and post-game meals can be solved much more easily if you consider the facts presented in the preceding chapters. By utilizing this information, plus some research data on each specific subject, you will be able to improve your performance and this is the ultimate goal of every athlete.

Entire books have been written on the subjects of weight control, i.e. gaining and losing weight, so I will not be able to cover all the points in this brief dissertation. Nevertheless, there are certain basic rules which I will present which, when applied, will prove to be most helpful to every athlete.

GAINING WEIGHT

Since more football players are more interested in putting on pounds of bodyweight than in taking them off, I will examine this situation first. To add bodyweight is very simple, it's merely a matter of eating everything in sight. You can look around you and see plenty of examples of people who have successfully gained weight. In fact, one of the biggest health problems this country faces is that of obesity. The athlete has a somewhat different goal in mind. He wants to add **functional** bodyweight and in order to do this certain scientific principles must be followed. Gaining bodyweight boils down to taking in more calories than you utilize.

A CALORIE

Energy in the human is expressed in terms of the heat unit or calorie. A calorie, as you might recall from your general science or biology class, is defined as the amount of heat required to raise the temperature of 1 gram of water 1°C. I will not be counting calories, but rather the types of foods which produce these calories.

Fats, carbohydrates, and proteins all yield a specific amount of calories upon oxidation. Most fats average about 9.0 calories per gram, most proteins 4.1 calories and most carbohydrates 4.0 calories. I use the term "most" as not all compounds of the same class yield the same caloric values. The carbohydrate glucose, for example, yields 3.7 calories per gram while starch and sucrose yield 4.1 and 4.0 calories per gram. For our purposes I will use the "Atwater factors," a set of caloric standards applied to the various nutrients some 50 years ago. These are: 4.0 calories per gram for protein and carbohydrate 9.0 calories per gram for fat.

PROTEIN-FOODS

When you are attempting to add muscular bodyweight there are three important factors to keep in mind: 1) you must eat plenty of protein-rich foods, 2) you must also eat a sufficient amount of carbohydrates, but specifically ones which give you a nutritional bonus over ones which merely add calories and 3) you must cut back on your energy output. The first rule is rather self explanatory. The protein foods are needed to build the muscle tissue and if you expect to put on muscular bodyweight then you certainly must provide your body with lots of this essential nutrient.

EAT CARBOHYDRATES

The reasoning behind the second rule may not be as clear. You may wonder why you need to eat lots of carbohydrates as they do not build muscle. The carbohydrates are needed for energy. If you eat a diet totally lacking carbohydrates, the body will convert the protein into energy. The desire is for you to utilize the protein, not for energy, but for building tissue. "But how about fats?," you might be asking. They are higher in caloric content than either proteins or carbohydrates, so why not use them as the energy source? You will and should increase your unsaturated fat intake but it is rather difficult to obtain large amounts of unsaturated fat without also taking in equally large amounts of the saturated variety. This you do not want as the saturated fats cause problems with which you do not want to contend.

I reiterate that the carbohydrate foods should be ones which provide a nutritional bonus. By this I mean that they should do more than merely provide calories. I prefer carbohydrate foods that come from natural sources, such as fruits and vegetables over those found in breads, pastries, candies, sodas, French fries, spaghetti, pizza, and so forth. A banana has the same carbohydrate count as a piece of cake but the banana also supplies valuable vitamins and minerals, the cake does not.

CUT BACK ENERGY OUTPUT

The last rule may need little clarification. You are going to want to store as many of those calories as you possibly can. By slacking off on your exercising you will be able to gain much easier. I do not mean that you should suddenly become lazy and stop physical training altogether. Rather, I suggest that you cut back on the time you spend in the weight room or perhaps drop one day of running from your program, at least until you get your weight to the desired level.

I have found that it is best to gain weight and then try to harden it up rather than attempting to put on each pound of solid muscle. It appears to be easier to pack on the pounds and then solidify them rather than doing it in a slow, one-half pound a week process.

Just before you begin this program, record exactly all the foods you eat in a three-day period. Then check the carbohydrate, protein, and calorie count. If you find that you are eating some 3000 calories per day, and are still maintaining your weight, then you must be burning off this amount. Increase the foods you eat so that you are eating 4000-5000 calories a day. At the same time, cut back on your physical activities so that you are not burning off as much energy as before. Your weight should start to go up.

SMALL MEALS

Eat many small meals rather than three huge ones each day. Some people make the mistake of gorging themselves at each of the three meals. They leave the table uncomfortable and bloated. Their digestive systems cannot handle this volume of food and passes off most of it. It is much better to eat normal meals and then snack inbetween.

Have something to eat every two hours, preferably a piece of fruit. An apple, banana, or pear is very portable and each contains about 100 calories each. Eat a dozen extra pieces of fruit a day and you have taken in an additional 1200-1500 high quality calories.

MILK

Milk is still one of the best ways to add bodyweight. An extra half gallon of milk a day will add some 1300 calories to your diet. You'll also get a bonus of 64 grams of protein plus vital fatty acids, minerals, and vitamins.

I know of one athlete who adds one half pound to his bodyweight each day simply by drinking a protein milkshake before going to bed. He eats only his three normal meals per day plus this high protein milkshake. It is enough to elevate his bodyweight slowly but surely. The milkshake consists of eight ounces of milk, two scoops of ice cream, one cup of dried milk solids, a banana, and a cup of yogurt all mixed in a blender. Others, who do not gain as easily, take this mixture twice a day. Mixed in the morning, it is drunk along with each meal instead of a regular glass of milk. A convenient and very simple way to add some additional pounds.

Eggs are another excellent method of increasing your total food intake without a lot of trouble. An egg contains 75 calories with ample protein, fat, vitamins, minerals. Hard boil a dozen each day and snack on one or two in between meals. You'll be able to add close to 1000 calories to your intake quite easily.

CONSISTENCY

The one most important factor to remember when you are trying to add weight is that of consistency. You cannot eat heavily for two days and then skip the next. You must keep up the high food intake day in and day out. After a time your body chemistry slowly changes almost as if it has figured out what you are trying to accomplish and gaining becomes easier.

Teenagers have the most difficulty in putting on pounds because their energy requirements are so high. After you reach twenty it becomes easier; after twenty-five, much

easier and after thirty, fantastically simple. Few people over thirty ever want to gain weight, however, so the metabolic switch doesn't really serve much purpose. Even the teenager can gain if he consistently eats more food than he burns off. Miss a few days of watching your diet, however, and the scale will drop back down.

IMPORTANCE OF REST

When you are in the process of gaining weight, rest whenever possible. Add an hour's sleep each night and take naps as often as you can. Conserve your energy when you are not engaged in weight training or actual practice. Cut out as many of the superflous activities as you can. This conservative process will only last for a short period of time but you will need to give your body a little extra help to get it started in the right direction.

Few people realize that it is much more difficult to gain useful bodyweight than it is to lose it. You have to eat constantly and you have to select your foods very carefully, since you don't want to become a butterball.

To recap, you must: 1) eat more food than your body utilizes each day, 2) eat plenty of protein-rich foods, 3) eat lots of carbohydrate foods but select the ones that afford a nutritional bonus like fruits and vegetables, 4) you must cut back on your energy expenditure, and 5) you must stay constantly on the program.

LOSING WEIGHT

The process of losing bodyweight is the reverse of gaining weight, that is, you must take in fewer calories than you expend. The solution to losing weight however, does not revolve around calories, but rather carbohydrates as carbohydrate calories store in your body as body fat. While it is a fact that an excess of protein will store in your body, the realistic fact is that this rarely happens for the simple reason that you utilize all the protein you eat if you are an athlete.

The fat you ingest does not store as fat but is converted to energy, so it is only the carbohydrates that present a problem if you are trying to shed pounds.

Although Dr. Atkins in his book **Diet Revolution**, contends that the body does not need any carbohydrates, I do not agree. My findings indicate that some few carbohydrates are needed as they act as starting materials for the synthesis of other compounds in the body, such as fatty acids and the amino acids. In addition, they play a role as part of the structure of other biologically important materials such as nucleic acids, glycoproteins, and glycolipids. So the carbohydrates should not be thought of as merely an energy source, although that is their primary function.

I do believe, however, that you must restrict the amount of carbohydrates in your diet if you desire to lose weight. My research reveals that a maximum of sixty grams per day is sufficient to meet your bodies' nutritional requirements, but is not too much to be stored as excess.

CARBOHYDRATES BELOW 60

Keeping your carbohydrate count to sixty grams is not an easy chore, but if you do so you will lose weight, especially if you are active in athletics. You can, and should, continue to eat all the foods you desire which contain protein and fat. You will need the fat (the unsaturated variety) as an energy source since you are restricting the carbohydrate intake.

The protein foods are necessary for the maintenance and building of the tissues.

What foods are best? Eggs are excellent. They are high in protein and unsaturated fat and have no carbohydrates. Be careful with dairy products. Some are good for dieters while others are not. Cottage cheese contains 30 grams of protein and only 6 grams of carbohydrates per cup so it is a good food for dieters. Yogurt, on the other hand, is not a great diet food for you as it has 12-13 grams of carbohydrates per cup and only 8 grams of protein. Milk has more carbohydrates than protein, 48 to 32 per quart.

PERILS OF FRUIT

Fruits pose as problems for the dieter as they are highly concentrated forms of sugar or carbohydrates. An innocent-looking apple has 18 grams of carbohydrates, a banana 23, and an orange 16. Many dieters run into a snag and can't figure out where they are taking in the extra carbohydrates. It's usually from fruit or fruit juices. A glass of fresh orange juice has 25 grams of carbohydrates and the concentrated form has even more.

All meats are excellent foods for dieters. Fish is super good, eat it as often as you wish. A 7-ounce can of tuna makes a nice lunch and contains 58 grams of protein and no carbohydrates. Liver is great for dieters, a slice yields 30 grams of protein and but four grams of carbohydrates.

At the end of this book I will present a listing of foods along with their nutritional content. By checking with this chart you will be able to select those foods which you enjoy and space your carbohydrate foods out so that you are taking in some throughout the day. A glass of juice in the morning and a vegetable at night with a glass of milk will just about get you to the 60-gram limit.

Be certain that you are obtaining all your other nutrients via supplements while you are in the process of shedding the pounds. Otherwise, you will be asking for problems. With a little practice, you will be able to put together a diet which will prove to provide 200 grams of protein and less than 60 grams of carbohydrates. One such sample diet is listed below.

SAMPLE DIET		
	Carbohydrates	Proteins
Breakfast		
3 eggs	trace	18
2" wedge of cheddar cheese	trace	8
eight ounce glass of milk	12	8
Lunch		
seven ounce can of tuna fish	0	58
one tablespoon mayonnaise	trace	trace
1 piece whole wheat bread	10	2
Dinner		
1 large slice of liver	8	58
1 cup brussel sprouts	12	6
1 cup cottage cheese	6	38
1 glass of milk	12	8
TOTAL	60	204

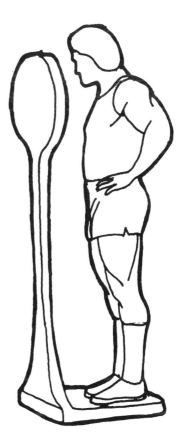

SHEDDING A FEW POUNDS QUICKLY

Ever so often, for a variety of reasons, the athlete is faced with the problem of dropping a few pounds very rapidly. Some teams have weight checks based on what the coaches have decided is the player's ideal playing weight. Various professional teams check weights periodically, some weekly, and others monthly, and slap a fine on the athlete who is over the limit. Colleges or high schools usually do not fine players, but often keep them out of the line-up if they fail to meet specific weight requirements.

The players generally need to knock off 2, 3, or 4 pounds quickly without tapping into their strength. Ideally, they would prefer to drop the weight overnight so as not to have to go on a two or three week diet or sit in a steam room for five straight days.

The problem is not a new one to those in sports which have weight classifications such as boxing, wrestling, and weightlifting. These athletes usually train three or four pounds over the class limit and knock off the excess the last 24 to 48 hours before weigh-in. The lost weight is usually in the form of body fluids and are quickly replaced as soon as the scale is satisfied.

Various studies have been conducted, especially on wrestlers, to see if this quick weight loss had adverse effects on their performance. One of the most complete, conducted by Roger Singer and Steven Weiss of Illinois State University was reported in the May, 1968 edition of **Research Quarterly**. The ten subjects studied showed that up to 7% of body weight may be lost without adversely affecting factors apparently related to wrestling performance — strength, cardiovascular endurance, and response time." These same three factors relate very directly to the sport of football.

So an athlete can drop some quick pounds and not be adversely affected — if he goes about dropping the excess bodyweight correctly. There are right and wrong ways of losing these extra pounds.

DIURETICS

Let's examine a couple of the wrong ways first. The taking of diuretics is a wrong way. Diuretics play havoc with many of your essential nutrients, especially potassium. The diuretics do increase the urine output but only temporarily as the cells quickly try to retain water because of the lack of potassium.

A person deficient in potassium will experience fatigue because of the rapid drop in blood sugar level. When potassium is low in the cells, the blood sugar is correspondingly low. If too many diuretics are taken the muscles will fail to contract properly, the pulse rate drops, fatigue and intestinal pains develop. All in all, it's not a wise route to take when attempting to lose weight.

Another poor avenue to follow is to stop eating completely. Fasting before competition is not a wise idea for the athlete. Some individuals deprive themselves of all foods for two or three days prior to the weigh-in. When it comes time to perform they are so listless that they can barely get their gear on. Fasting is great for meditation but not for those engaged in strenuous physical activities.

The right way revolves around counting carbohydrates. Stop eating all carbohydrates, limit your other foods to a moderate intake, and eliminate all fluids for the final twenty-four hours before you weigh-in. How long before weigh-in you begin this routine depends entirely on how much weight you have to drop. If, for example, you have to lose six pounds in six days and the weigh-in is on Saturday at 12 noon, then on Monday you should stop eating all carbohydrate foods. This act alone may be sufficient for you to drop three quarters of a pound to a pound a day and may be enough for you to make the desired weight without eliminating fluids the last 24 hours.

If, however, by Thursday you are still about three pounds over limit, cut back on the protein foods a bit more. I still want you to continue eating and generally, you can eat all the protein foods that you wish and still make weigh-in satisfactorily. On Friday, exactly 24 hours before weigh-in, stop taking in all fluids. You will not have to steam or run the body fluids out as they will be used internally. You will drop two or three pounds the last day in this manner. The lungs, for example, utilizes a great deal of fluids, so the weight will drop without any overt action on your part. Should you find that you make the desired weight well before weigh-in then you can start eating some carbohydrate foods and drinking fluids before the weight check.

As soon as you make the weigh-in, drink some liquids which contain potassium, sodium, and chlorine so as to insure yourself of supplying your body with these essential nutrients before the game or practice session.

By dropping excess weight in this manner you will retain all of your strength and endurance and still meet the necessary requirements of the coaches. Be sure that you are taking all of your vitamins and minerals during this dieting period as you are not securing the normal quantity from your diet as you usually would.

MAINTAINING YOUR BODYWEIGHT

Once you get your body weight to the desired level you should find it rather easy to maintain. Drop back on your carbohydrate intake to 100 grams or less per day and continue to secure at least 200 grams of protein daily. Adjust your activity schedule so that you are utilizing all the calories you eat.

Check the scales frequently, daily if possible. If you find that your weight is moving up, then cut back on your carbohydrate intake even more and increase your activity level. If your weight starts dropping back lower than you wish, eat more and train a little less. After a bit of practice, you will be able to hold your body weight at any figure you choose.

PRE-GAME MEAL

Traditionally, football teams have sat down to a hearty meal consisting of a steak, baked potato, and salad some two hours before game time. This is the pre-game meal designed to fulfill the athlete's nutritional needs on the playing field. Lately, however, research has indicated that the traditional meal is not the best for optimum performance. Dr. P.V. Karpovich, in his book, **Physiology of Muscular Activity** states that solid food should not be consumed for three to four hours prior to competing. Authors L.E. Morehouse and A.T. Miller concur in their book, **Physiology of Exercise.** They contend that when vigorous exercise is attempted while the stomach is distended by food, both diaphramatic and cardiac action may be impaired.

The solid foods need to be replaced by liquids and more attention given to carbohydrates and fats rather than to proteins. Many competitive weightlifters utilized this data and mixed a drink consisting of: orange juice, ice cream, dried milk solids, and wheat germ oil. If they ate anything solid at all, it was usually at least four hours before competition and consisted of a food high in carbohydrate, such as fruit, rice, or cereal.

LIQUID FOODS

Liquid foods have been found to be very beneficial to the athlete prior to any form of exercise. Cooper, Bud, and Blair writing in **The Journal of the Oklahoma Medical Association,** May of 1962, demonstrated that the replacement of the solid foods pre-exercise with a liquid meal was both psychologically and practically sound. They reported an absence of muscular cramps and pre-game and game time vomiting. These investigators did their testing on football players.

Researchers Asprey, Alley, and Tuttle of the University of Iowa have found the following meal to be most beneficial. Subjects ate this prescribed meal ½ hour, 1 hour, or 2 hours before competition (running various distances up to one mile) and found no adverse affects in the form of nausea or stomach cramps during or after the run. The same meal was tested on swimmers by Ball with the same results. This prescribed meal consisted of:

1 cup of cereal
2 slices of toast
sugar
butter
1 glass of whole milk

The meal contains 16 grams of protein, 70 grams of carbohydrates, and 20 grams of fats.

A slight change of thinking is in order for the pre-game meal. If you are to play a game, practice, or workout in the early afternoon, then a recommended eating schedule might be as follows. Have a breakfast loaded with protein and carbohydrates. An example of this type of breakfast would be: two or three eggs, bacon, toast, potatoes, cereal, fruit, and milk. Take whatever supplements you plan to take

immediately after the meal. For your noon meal have the following foods mixed in a blender:

1 quart of orange juice
1 cup of dried milk solids
2 tablespoons of wheat germ oil
1 banana
1 scoop of ice cream

This highly-concentrated drink will yield approximately 50 grams of protein, 115 grams of carbohydrates, and 50 grams of fat. Add your supplements once again and you will be ready for action.

This dietary schedule should set you in fine fiddle for your game or practice session. You have included sufficient protein from breakfast to carry you through to the game and have supplied your body with an abundance of carbohydrate and fat foods to be utilized for energy. You should not feel full or stuffy at game time but neither should you feel empty. It provides a sensible balance to take care of your nutritional needs under physical stress.

PROTEIN QUICKLY

The European researchers have found that if their athletes ingest protein, preferably in a liquid form, in less than 30 minutes after exercise, their recovery rate is three times faster than if they wait past this time period. The Europeans give their athletes a mixture of milk, milk solids, and a flavoring which is taken immediately after training or competition. Many weightlifters put this information to wise use and have a high protein milkshake ready as soon as they shower. Add some mineral tablets, with special attention to potassium and sodium, and you'll feel fully recovered in no time at all.

The longer your body remains deficient of the nutrients it has used up during the exercise period, the longer you will feel tired. Replace the used nutrients quickly and the deficiency will be short-lived. Wait for a prolonged period of time and you may experience extreme weariness, cramping, and even nausea.

After this quick ingestion of some protein rich foods, you can relax and go out for a full meal. This meal, like the quick post-game drink, should be laden with proteins and mineral foods. Have a good portion of meat, some eggs, dairy products, and a vegetable or salad.

You'll find that by following this procedure your body will recover remarkably fast and you'll feel none of the usual post-exercise aches and pains. It's just a matter of putting nutritional findings into actual practice.

THE FINAL WEEK

You should really begin your dietary preparation for the game some two or three days prior to the contest. Start increasing your carbohydrate intake by Thursday, if it's a typical Saturday game. This will help increase the glycogen content of the muscles.

Dr. Roy Shephard in his book **Alive Man!** makes this suggestion concerning the diet prior to competition: "The optimum regime seems a bout of vigorous exercise several days before a contest, a short period on a protein/fat diet, and then when the muscle cells have developed a maximum hunger for glycogen one or two days of a high carbohydrate diet."

DURING EXERCISE

You can also enhance performance by making sure that your body is supplied with the proper nutrients during a workout, practice, or game. Should the game be played in hot weather or be extremely long in duration it has been concluded by several researchers that a high power output is enhanced by regular hourly doses of a diluted sucrose or glucose solution. Water, sodium, and potassium also need to be supplied to the depleted cells to maintain a high level of activity.

This, as I mentioned previously, is the basic formula for the "thirst quenchers" drinks such as Gatorade, but it can be prepared as the individual or team trainer just as easily.

Those athletes who eagerly ingest high dosages of some form of sugar (dextros tablets, fructose tablets, or honey) are actually hindering their energy output rather than helping it. Small dosages of concentrated sugar works fine, but if you overdo it and take in concentrations over 40% you actually delay the digestion of such sugars so it does your body little good.

POST-GAME MEAL

The intake of large quantities of nutritional foods is most important immediately after exercise — the more strenuous the exercise, the more your body needs the lost nutrients. A weight training work-out will tap into some of your nutritional reserve; a practice session a bit more; and a game a tremendous amount. You need to resupply your body with the lost nutrients and the faster the better.

★

TABLE IV

SUMMARY OF THE NUTRITIONAL REQUIREMENTS
OF HARD-TRAINING ATHLETES

NUTRIENT	RECOMMENDED DOSAGE
Protein	one gram per pound of body-weight of complete protein
Carbohydrates	one half gram per pound of bodyweight
Fatty Acids	Three tablespoons of un-saturated fat oils containing the essential fatty acids: linoleic, linolenic and arachidonic.
Vitamin A	25,000 units
Vitamin D	5,000 units
Vitamin C	4,000 mgs.
Vitamin E	1200 I.U.
Thiamine, B1	100 mgs.
Riboflavin, B2	60 mgs.
Niacin, B3	100 mgs.
Vitamin B6	one milligram for each gram of protein eaten
Vitamin B12	500 mcgs.
PABA	100 mgs.
Pantothenic Acid	100 mgs.
Biotin	100 mcgs.
Inositol	500 mgs.
Cholin	500 mgs.
Folic Acid	5 mgs.
Calcium	2.0 grams
Phosphorus	4.0 grams
Magnesium	1.0 grams
Potassium	10.0 grams
Sodium	10.0 grams
Chlorine	10.0 grams
Copper	5.0 mgs.
Zinc	1.0 mgs.
Cobalt	5.0 mgs.
Iron	15.0 mgs.
Iodine	0.15 mgs.
Manganese	10.0 mgs.

It must be reiterated that these recommendations are for athletes who are spending 2-4 hours of physical training each day. If the athlete is not participating in spring ball, summer camp, the actual season, or an off-season weight program, then his nutritional needs will be much lower.

REFERENCE LIST — NUTRITIONAL SECTION

Abrahamson, E.M. and Pexet, A.W. **Body, Mind, and Sugar.** New York: Henry Holt and Company, 1951.

Airola, Paavo. **Are You Confused.** Phoenix, Arizona: Health Plus Publishers, 1971.

Altschul, A.M. **Proteins, Their Chemistry and Politics.** New York: Basic Books, 1965.

Bailey, Herbert. **Vitamin E, Your Key To A Healthy Heart.** New York: ABC Books, 1964.

Bajusz, Eors. **Nutritional Aspects of Cardiovascular Disease.** Philadelphia: J.B. Lippincott Company, 1965.

Borgstrom, George. **The Hungry Planet.** New York: Collier Books, 1967.

Chen, P.S. **Mineral Balance in Eating for Health.** Emmaus, Penna.: Rodale Books, 1969.

Clark, Linda. **Stay Young Longer.** New York: Pyramid Books, 1968.

Crain, Lloyd. **Magic Vitamins and Organic Foods.** Los Angeles: Crandrich Studios, 1971.

Davis, Adelle. **Let's Eat Right To Keep Fit.** New York: Harcourt Brace Javonovich, 1970.

Davis, T.R.A., et al. "Review of Studies of Vitamin and Mineral Nutrition in the United States," **Journal of Nutrition Education,** 41, 1969.

Guthrie, Helen. **Introductory Nutrition.** St. Louis,: The C.V. Mosby Co., 1967.

Hoffer, A. and Osmond, H. **How To Live With Schizophrenia.** New Hyde Park, New York: University Books, 1966.

Johnston, W. "Vitamin E for Athletes", **Lancet.** I:882, 1960.

Kervran, Louis, **Biological Transmutations,** Binghamton, New York: Swan House, 1972.

Klenner, F.R. **The Key To Good Health: Vitamin C.** Chicago: Graphic Arts Research Foundation, 1969.

Lappe, Frances Moore. **Diet For A Small Planet.** New York: Ballantine Books, 1971.

Margolius, Sidney. **The Great American Food Hoax.** New York: Dell Publishing Co., 1971.

Nizel, Abraham. **The Science of Nutrition and its Application in Clinical Dentistry.** Philadelphia: W.E. Saunders, Company, 1968.

Pauling, Linus. **Vitamin C and the Common Cold.** San Francisco: W.H. Freeman and Company, 1970.

Prokop, L. "The Effect of Natural Vitamin E on Oxygen Consumption and Oxygen Debt," **Sportarztl Prax.** (Germany), 1:19-25, 1960.

Robinson, M.H. **Big Brother and His Science: A Report on the FDA.** 10121 Chapel Road, Potomac, Maryland, 1969.

Roels, O.A. **Present Knowledge of Nutrition.** New York: The Nutrition Foundation, 1967.

Seelig, M.S. "The Requirement of Magnesium by the Normal Adult," **American Journal of Clinical Nutrition,** 14, 1964.

Seneca, H., et al. "Bactericidal Properties of Yogurt," **American Practitioner and Digest of Treatment,** 1252, 1950.

Sherman, H.C. **Chemistry of Food and Nutrition.** New York: The MacMillan Co., 1952.

Shute, W.E. and Taub, H.J. **Vitamin E for Ailing and Healthy Hearts.** New York: Pyramid House, 1969.

Smith, Evelyn. **Dictionary of Health Foods.** New York: Dell Books, 1972.

Starr, Bill. "Protein Needs for the Athlete," **Strength & Health,** May, 1970.

Von Itallie, Sinisterra, and Stare. "Nutrition and Athletic Performance," **Journal American Medical Association,** 162:1120-1126, 1956.

Wilder, R.M. "A Brief History of the Enrichment of Flour and Bread," **Journal American Medical Association,** 162: 1539, 1956.

Williams, Roger. **Alcoholism: The Nutritional Approach.** Austin, Texas: University of Texas Press, 1959.

ibid. "We Abnormal Normals," **Nutrition Today,** 2:19:23, 1967.

ibid. **You are Extraordinary.** New York: Pyramid Books, 1971.

Wood, Curtis. **Overfed but Undernourished.** New York: Tower Publications, 1971.

THE STRONGEST SHALL SURVIVE...

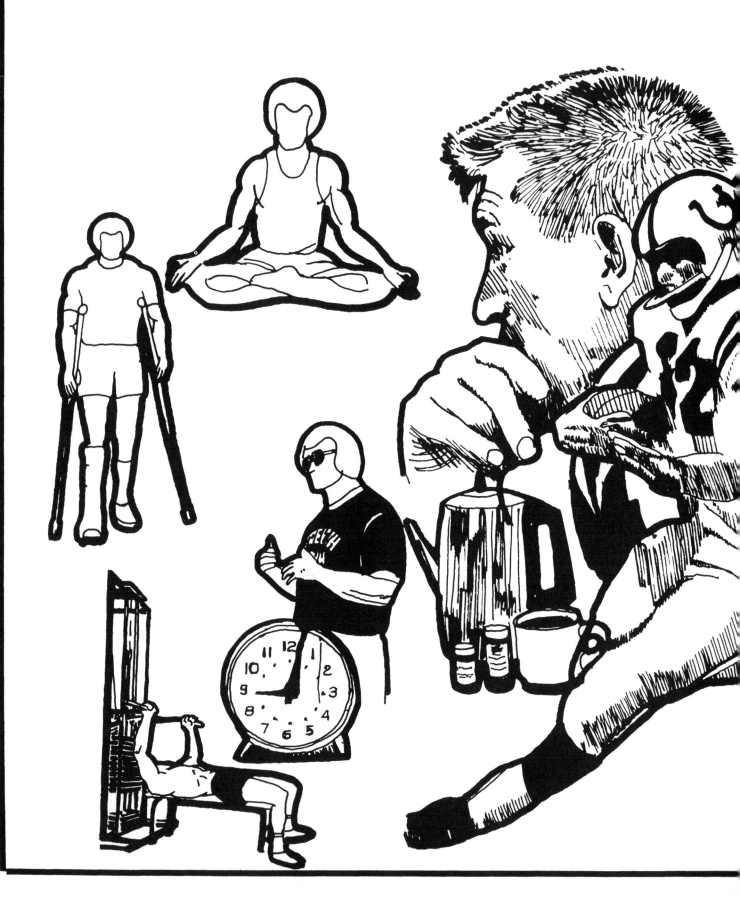

STRENGTH TRAINING FOR FOOTBALL

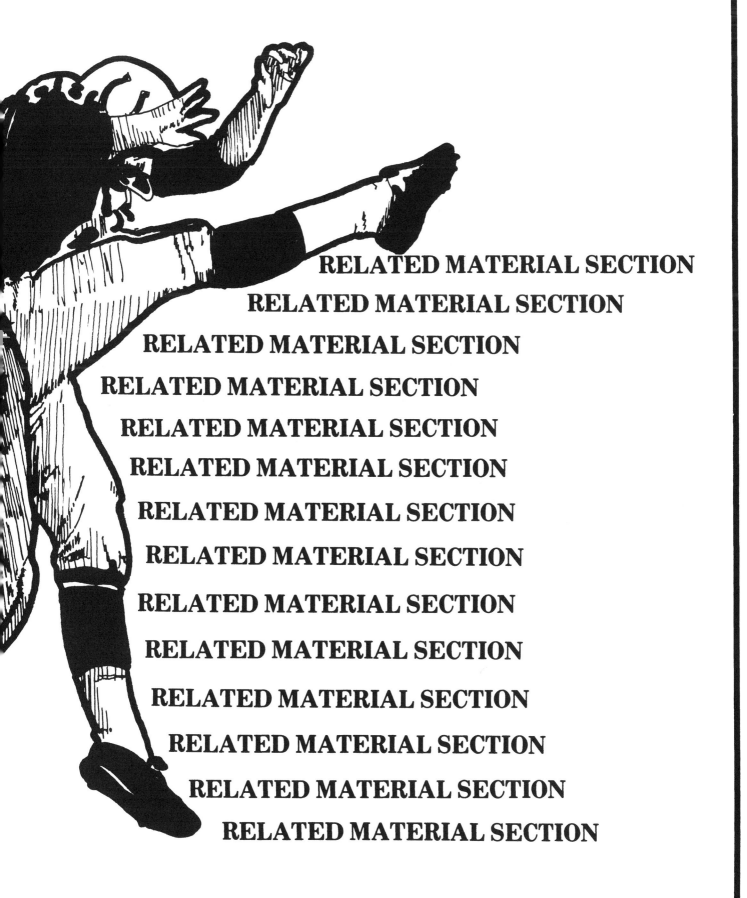

RELATED MATERIAL SECTION

RELATED MATERIAL SECTION

RELATED MATERIAL SECTION

RELATED MATERIAL SECTION

RELATED MATERIAL SECTION

RELATED MATERIAL SECTION

RELATED MATERIAL SECTION

RELATED MATERIAL SECTION

RELATED MATERIAL SECTION

RELATED MATERIAL SECTION

RELATED MATERIAL SECTION

RELATED MATERIAL SECTION

RELATED MATERIAL SECTION

16

CHAPTER SIXTEEN
PRINCIPLES FOR
REHABILITATING INJURIES

INJURIES ARE A PART OF ATHLETICS

PERHAPS THE GREATEST FEAR confronting any athlete is that of sustaining an injury which will put him out of action for an extended period of time. Minor injuries can cause major set-backs. Serious injuries can end athletic hopes and careers. Every athlete is aware of these facts and, for the most part, takes all the precautions he possibly can to avoid injuring himself. It can be safely stated that no one actively solicits an injury.

Yet every athlete does get injured because sports and injuries go hand-in-hand regardless of the precautions taken. This is especially true in a contact sport such as football. There just isn't enough padding available, save enclosing the player in mental armour, to keep him from being injured at some time in a year of hard-hitting games and scrimmages.

Warm-ups, stretching, protective devices, and attentive behavior all help to cut down the percentages but, nevertheless, the highly-motivated player still leaves himself open to injury each time he involves himself in a play.

Most injuries on the field are a result of some freak play — an unexpected move, an unavoidable collision, a blind-side hit, being stepped on, or being twisted in a pile-up — for which preparation just does not make any difference. It is a truism that a well-conditioned player will be less severely injured than a poor-conditioned one, but even the best conditioned player can and does get injured.

THE STRENGTH COACH AS REHABILITATOR

While it is a fact that the responsibility of rehabilitating an injured player does fall rightfully on the shoulders of the team's medical expert, it is often the Strength Coach who is actually given the duty of getting the player back on the field in a fit condition. The medical authority diagnoses and treats the injury and, in most cases, turns the player over to the Strength Coach to be physically rehabilitated.

This is becoming the practice in more and more instances for two very specific reasons. The first being that the team doctor and trainer are extremely busy and cannot afford the time to outline and administer an exercise program. Secondly, the Strength Coach is — or should be — the expert on how resistive exercise affects the muscles and joints. His expertise in rehabilitating athletes, coupled with the medical expert's diagnosis on the extent of the injury, goes a long way in helping the athletes to become physically healthy more quickly.

Before attempting to treat any athletic injury with resistive exercises, there are ten basic principles that every Strength Coach should understand and remember.

TEN PRINCIPLES OF REHABILITATION

1] **Do not diagnose an injury.**
2] **Refer all cases to the medical expert for diagnoses.**
3] **Do not exercise any injury that results in acute pain.**
4] **Use high repetitions for the first week of rehabilitation.**
5] **Go directly at the injured area.**
6] **Exercise the injured area every day during rehabilitation.**
7] **The injured area should receive exercise priority.**
8] **Progressively lower the repetitions and increase the weight.**
9] **Emphasize nutrition during the recovery period.**
10] **Keep in constant contact with the medical expert.**

Each of these ten principles will be explained in some detail so that the weight trained athlete and Strength Coach can go about setting up a rehabilitation program for themselves or for others whenever the need arises.

DO NOT DIAGNOSE AN INJURY

A word of precaution to the Strength Coach or athlete who is in a position of setting up a rehabilitation program for himself or for others. Do not become a doctor and a diagnostician. The injury, even minor bruises or sprains, should be checked by a medical professional. For the Strength Coach to assume this responsibility is both irresponsible and dangerous. In many cases only a trained expert can tell the difference between a minor and major injury. To begin exercise therapy to an injury which may be considered minor to the untrained eye and to later discover that it is, in fact, quite a serious injury is certainly bordering on criminal irresponsibility.

In a great many instances the injured player will come to the Strength Coach and ask him for assistance. The Strength Coach's first step should be to immediately refer him to the medical authority available. It is very easy for the Strength Coach to assume the medical role as it affords him a tremendous ego boost, but it is also rather foolish. Once the player's injury is diagnosed, then the Strength Coach can consult with the medical person concerning the extent of the injury and together they can map out a course of action to help the player get back into action promptly.

University of Hawaii Trainer, Dean Adams, attends to a fallen Rainbow Warrior, Stan Berry.

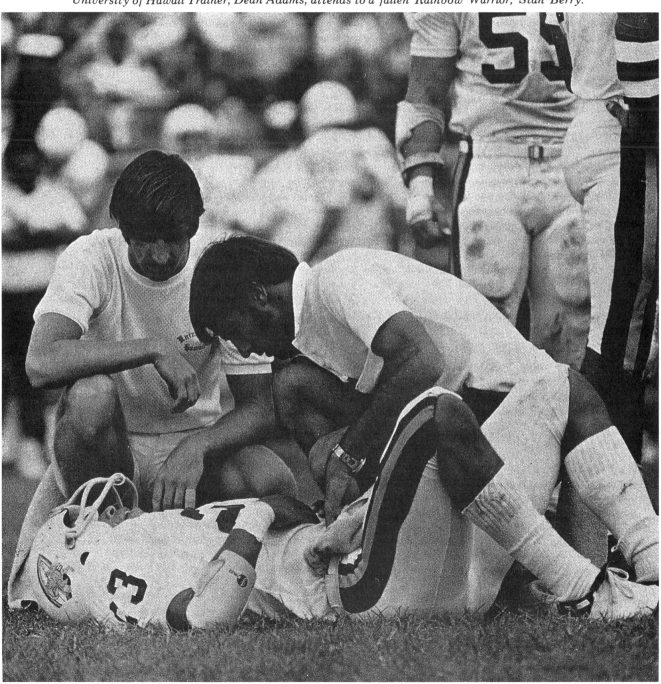

REFER ALL CASES TO THE MEDICAL EXPERT FOR DIAGNOSIS

This second principle, quite obviously, is tied in directly with the first, but it needs to be reiterated often enough so that the ambitious and foolhearty Strength Coach remembers it well.

The Strength Coach is, in actuality, a physical therapist. And, like the physical therapist, he does not diagnose, but simply sets up approved programs of corrective exercises for the injured player. The emphasis is on the word "approved." The Strength Coach is to set up a program in consultation with the medical expert. To short-cut this procedure may seem harmless, but it can be quite dangerous. Without full knowledge of the extent of an injury it is impossible to know the correct procedure to follow in order to rehabilitate a player. There is a vast difference between treating a shoulder separation and treating bursitis of the shoulder joint, for example.

The following story was related to me by the Strength Coach involved and may help to bring home this point more forcefully. An assistant football coach in West Virginia was given the responsibility of setting up exercise programs for injured football players. The quarterback of the team came to him one day complaining of pain in the deltoid region of his shoulder. He had been experiencing this problem for almost a week and decided that some light weight training might help the situation.

The Strength Coach, assuming that the injury was a minor muscle tear, set up a series of shoulder exercises that had worked on previous cases. The player began the program. The pain increased steadily. Finally, after another five days of weight training, the quarterback went to his family physician for a diagnosis. The team did not have a regular doctor or trainer. It took the medical man about twenty seconds to discover that the young quarterback had a dislocated clavicle. It had slipped where it attaches itself to the sternum, a common occurrence among quarterbacks. The doctor simply pressed the bone back into place and the pain disappeared.

This tale ended on a relatively happy note as there was no additional damage done by the exercise program. Had the injury been more severe, then the exercise program could have had serious repercussions. As it was, the player suffered needlessly five days longer than he should have because of the unwise behaviour of the coach and this is not a burden anyone would like to carry.

DO NOT PERFORM EXERCISES ON AN INJURY THAT RESULTS IN ACUTE PAIN

The Strength Coach must be able to differentiate between pain of acute nature and pain of a chronic nature. Acute pain is the sharp, stabbing kind and it does not subside during the exercise. Pain which is dull and throbbing, but which subsides after five or six repetitions is considered chronic. Chronic pain can be dealt with through exercise; acute pain cannot.

There is typically acute pain associated with a new injury and it generally lasts for three to five days depending, of course, on the extent and severity of the injury. During this time, exercise programs are not recommended as they can cause further damage. This is the period when medical treatment such as drug therapy, hot and cold therapy, ultra-sound, and so forth are used. When the acute pain subsides, then the injured area can be effectively exercised.

The Strength Coach must be able to differentiate between pain of acute nature and pain of a chronic nature.

Again, when in doubt, the following rule of thumb allows the Strength Coach to differentiate between the two types of pain. Chronic pain goes away after five or six repetitions of an exercise that directly affects the injury. Pain which is acute does not subside. As long as acute pain exists, resistive exercise is not recommended as further tissue and joint damage can result.

USE HIGH REPETITIONS THE FIRST SEVEN DAYS

High repetitions are therapeutic. They force large volumes of blood into the damaged area. The arterial blood brings tissue-building nutrients to the muscles, tendons, and ligaments. The venous blood caries away waste materials and enables the area to be reconstructed much more rapidly.

By high repetitions, I am referring to twenty-five or more. A minimum of three sets is in order with as much resistance as possible on the final set. The injured area is literally gorged with blood. It is rested and the blood evacuates. Another set and it is flooded with blood again, rested, filled again, and rested. Three sets are sufficient as the muscles and supportive structure begin to become fatigued at this point and there is no desire to proceed past the point of fatigue.

Select a poundage for this recovery period which is approximately 50% of the trainee's maximum for five repetitions for the first set of twenty-five. The second set will be performed with 60% and the third with 70-75%. For example, should the player be squatting with 200 x 5 at the time of the injury (assuming that it is a leg injury) then he would do 100 - 25 for his first rehabilitation set, 125 x 5 for his second, and 150 x 25 for his third. Increase the second and third sets slightly each successive day for the five days. Amazingly enough, some players move their 25 repetitions higher and higher and almost approximate their best for five repetitions at the end of the week. It is a most demanding program and cannot be continued for too long a period of time, however.

GO DIRECTLY AT THE INJURED AREA

It must be reiterated once again for the sake of absolute clarity that the injured area is not to be exercised at all as long as there is excessive swelling or sharp pain present, but once these subside, then the injury responds best to exercise therapy if it is attacked head-on.

Our guide in weightlifting was always to reconstruct the injured areas with the exact exercise that caused the damage in the first place. If the back was injured doing a dead lift, then the dead lift was used to rebuild the area. If presses caused the problem, presses were used to solve the problem. This rule is not always 100% true, as is the case of most rules. Some injuries of more severe nature would not allow this method to be employed. When this was the case we circumvented the injured area and came as close to it as possible with other exercises. But as soon as the injury came around sufficiently enough so that we could come directly at it, we did so.

Lower back injuries are most common in competitive weightlifting because of the great demand placed on the lower back through squatting, pressing, jerking, and pulling movements. When the lower back is seriously damaged, perhaps through a heavy pulling exercise, all pulls must be discontinued for the time being. Such exercises such as back hyperextensions, and good mornings are then substituted to keep a constant blood flow to the injured area and to keep the surrounding muscles toned. The injury is stimulated but not directly. As soon as possible, however, direct exercises are filtered into the rehabilitation program. Light, high repetition dead lifts, cleans, high pulls, etc. are employed — coming straight at the injured area.

EXERCISE EVERY DAY WHEN REHABILITATING

The basic idea behind this principle is to insure an adequate blood supply to the damaged area. The high reps are literally feeding the injured tissues with rebuilding materials and carrying away the unwanted products. Working the muscles, tendons, and ligaments every day allows this reconstruction process to occur much more rapidly.

Certain cases could even be exercised more than once a day. Dr. John Zeigler of Olney, Maryland, was the team doctor for the York Barbell Club during the time that I was with the team, and I witnessed some almost miraculous recoveries as a result of his methods. Dr. Zeigler was most original in many of his methods and he produced amazing results. Utilizing his medical knowledge and the latest techniques in the field of physical rehabilitation, he could put athletes back together in a manner of days, whereas normal medical procedure would have taken months. Dr. Zeigler believed that the body could be exercised every six hours, if proper nutrition and rest were provided.

THE BILL ST. JOHN STORY

One case is well worth mentioning as I watched the proceedings and know the facts are most valid, although they were never reported in any medical journal, as Dr. Zeigler unfortunately does not take the time to pass on his findings other than verbally. Bill St. John of Glassboro, New Jersey, was preparing for the Mr. America Physique contest and was in heavy training. While on his job at a naval ship yard near Philadelphia he broke his ankle. It was X-rayed, diagnosed as a fracture, and he was given six weeks leave of absence. Bill called Dr. Zigler in Olney, a small town just outside Washington, D.C., and the doctor told him to come to his house immediately. This was on a Thursday. By the time he drove to Maryland, his foot was swollen twice its normal size and he could not put any weight on it. In fact, he was barely able to drive.

Dr. Zeigler began exercising the ankle immediately using an electro-stimulator which he developed himself. The machine contracts the muscles involuntarily and is used medically to treat bed-ridden patients. He supplied Bill with tissue-rebuilding drugs and other pharmaceuticals to promote healing. He fed him high protein foods plus all the necessary vitamins and minerals and had him rest when he was not exercising. Bill exercised the injured ankle every six hours around the clock for five straight days. On Tuesday, he was able to do a full squat with 500 pounds and had complete mobility in the ankle. He returned to the company doctor and had his ankle reexamined. They would not buy the story and contended that they had misdiagnosed the injury — yet the X-ray with the break showing was still before them.

The body can, in fact, be exercised quite often if all the other variables are taken care of, such as diet, rest, and therapeutic drugs. Two-a-day exercise bouts will prove beneficial to some athletes, but the Strength Coach must be very cautious and keep in close touch with the medical expert when directing this accelerated routine. The Strength Coach should not attempt to go about setting up such a program on his own. If the medical person you are currently dealing with does not have sufficient knowledge of athletic injuries, then find one who does. Results are what you should be after.

The Strength Coach must keep the patient under extremely close surveillance to insure that he is doing everything absolutely correct. The player must warm-up and stretch thoroughly, do each set picture-perfect, stretch out afterwards, and pay close attention to his rest and nutrition. Nothing can be left to chance when the player is recovering from an injury.

INJURED AREA RECEIVES PRIORITY

When a player is in the process of rebuilding an injury, then that portion of his body takes priority over all others. The rehabilitative exercises are done first in the program so that maximum attention and energy can be delegated to the injury. The reader may recall the principle of priority training which states that the exercise which is performed first in a program has the greatest developmental effect on the body.

This principle is most useful when rehabilitating an injury, as we want to give full attention to getting the athlete whole once again. It may mean dropping a few exercises for other portions of the body so that more energy can be diverted to the trouble spot.

After a thorough warm-up, go immediately to the therapeutic movements. After the necessary sets for that day are completed, the athlete may feel fatigued. If this is the case, it may be wise to forego the remainder of the program for that day.

Performing exercises, especially high repetitions directly on an injury can be most fatiguing because a great deal of mental as well as physical energy is required. There is usually some pain involved and pain in itself can be tiring. Be aware of these facts and if the trainee expresses a feeling of fatigue or you observe that he is extra tired, then skip the other exercises.

Also be very careful that the trainee does not do any exercises that might risk more injury to the damaged area. Sometimes, a player will not be aware that a certain exercise affects a specific area, even slightly, and will attempt to perform it while injured.

One player in our program pulled a leg biceps muscle, but wanted to continue training on the remainder of his program while the muscle was being rested. He wanted to do bench presses and power cleans until his leg came around sufficiently to start the rehabilitative squat program. He did not check with the Strength Coach or medical expert before going ahead with his idea and on his first set of power cleans he nearly fainted from the pain as he quickly discovered that the leg biceps comes very much into play on the power clean.

PROGRESSIVELY LOWER THE REPETITIONS AND INCREASE THE WEIGHT

In our attempt to reconstruct a damaged area we must progressively overload the muscles, tendons, and ligaments. The high repetitions are most therapeutic, but for peak strength we must use a higher weight than is allowed with the higher reps. In a contact sport such as football, the attachments must be strengthened and this can only be done with a heavy overload.

The general rule of thumb is to keep the injured player on twenty-five repetitions for three sets for 5-7 days, working the program every day.

The general rule of thumb is to keep the injured player on twenty-five repetitions for three sets for 5-7 days, working the program every day. The rule is flexible, naturally, as its application depends on the nature and extent of the injury. Some injuries take a bit longer while others can be accelerated. The time of year often dictates the length of time the player will stay on the high repetitions. If, for example, the player is injured in early summer and there are two or three months left to get him whole before summer camp, then the luxury of taking a few extra days can certainly be afforded. If, on the other hand, a key player is injured during season and he is sorely needed back on the field in a week or two, then the program may be accelerated.

It should be noted that all of these cases refer to injuries that can be helped with corrective resistive training. Certainly not all athletic injuries can be treated via the weights — at least not immediately. Some injuries of the more severe nature will require rather drastic medical treatment and long periods of rest and recovery before the patient is allowed to start on a therapeutic exercise program. This, once again, is a medical decision and does not fall under the responsibility of the Strength Coach.

Generally speaking, an athlete should be on this program for a minimum of two weeks in order for the program to have its full effect and three weeks is even better. For the first five days, have the player perform three sets of 25 repetitions, increasing the top weight each day. Rest the sixth day, then start six days of training performing five sets of five repetitions alternating with five sets of ten repetitions resting between each training day.

EMPHASIZE NUTRITION DURING THE RECOVERY PERIOD

The prescribed exercises will enable more nutrients to be supplied to the injured area but if the nutrients are not present in the blood supply then it logically follows that the effect of the exercise program will be limited.

During rehabilitation, upgrade the intake of all nutrients but especially those which are necessary for tissue building. Specifically, more protein, B-vitamins, minerals, and vitamins C and E. What I usually recommend is for the player to double his nutritional intake during this two-week recovery period. If the player is not taking supplements, then he should start immediately. If he is serious about wanting to get himself back into shape, then the money can be found for the nutritional supplies. In some cases, there may be an excess of nutrients which are not utilized by the body, but it is far better to have too much rather than too little when recovering from an injury. Too much may mean a loss of a few cents, but too little will retard progress.

The nutritional aspect of rehabilitation is often overlooked and as a result the recovery comes much more slowly than it could otherwise. When a player is injured he typically settles into a state of depression. He stops or slows down on his eating and neglects taking his supplements. This action only accentuates his problem and it is up to the Strength Coach to counsel and motivate the player to get back on a full nutritional schedule immediately.

If the injured player is not taking supplements, then by all means have him begin as the tissues must be supplied in abundance with the rebuilding materials. Do not short-change the body or it will not be able to reconstruct itself nearly as rapidly.

JUNIOR OL
DAVE PERNA

A four-year starter and two-time captain at Johns Hopkins, Dave Perna was 1st team All Centennial Conference: '97, '98, '99; 1st team All American Football Gazette: '98, '99; Hewlett Packard All American '99; and Huddle Club's Most Valuable Player in '99. Dave is also an exceptional Olympic lifter, winning regional and state titles, including The Garden State Games. He competed in the Collegiate Nationals and has qualified for the Seniors. Soon to be an M.D., he is still active in Olympic lifting while doing his surgical residency at Stony Brook University on Long Island.

My last principle relates directly to the first; do not go about playing doctor. Keep the medical expert informed as to what you plan to do each day and also inform him of the results from each phase of your rebuilding program. He, in turn, may want to incorporate some drug therapy, such as enzymes or steroids, to promote the healing process. Or, he may be using ice therapy, ultrasound, whirlpool treatments, or galvanic current and this therapy must be coordinated with the exercise program in order for it to be effective.

The Strength Coach and medical expert, then, have to work closely together in order to reconstruct the player. One cannot go about treating the injury in one fashion while the other goes ahead blindly doing his therapy. The athlete may be caught in the middle and end up being more damaged than before.

Communication between the two helping parties is most critical and the Strength Coach must be aware that he is merely carrying out a medical duty when he is rehabilitating an injured player. He must always give way to authority and do what he is instructed to do by the medical expert. His own concepts and ideas must be relegated to second spot behind the medical expert, whether it be the team trainer or doctor. To attempt to treat an injury in a manner which is not approved by the medical expert is both dangerous and foolish.

There is very seldom any conflict between the Strength Coach and the team medical person since both are seeking the same result. The Strength Coach should take the time to fully explain what he proposes in the way of an exercise routine for the injured area and he usually has the full support of the medical expert. Two heads are generally better than one. The basic point should be reiterated — the Strength Coach should not play doctor.

A SAMPLE REHABILITATIVE PROGRAM

Since the legs seem to be the biggest problem in football, I will outline a program for the rehabilitation of a pulled muscle in the quadriceps group. Specifically, a tear in the high portion of the rectus femoris. Our patient could perform five sets of five repetitions with 225 pounds at the time of his injury. He has rested the injury for three days. The majority of the swelling and tenderness has disappeared and the medical expert has given him the go-ahead to start an exercise program. He is able to perform full squats, although there is still some pain associated with the movement.

Monday: Full Squats: 115 x 25, 135 x 25, 145 x 25
leg biceps curls: 20 x 25, 30 x 25, 40 x 25

Tuesday: Squats: 115 x 25, 135 x 25, 155 x 25
leg biceps curls: same as Monday

Wednesday: Squats: 115 x 25, 135 x 25, 165 x 25
leg biceps curls: same as Monday

Thursday: Squats: 135 x 25, 155 x 25, 175 x 25
leg biceps curls: same as Monday

Friday: Squats: 135 x 25, 155 x 25, 185 x 25
leg biceps curls: same as Monday

Saturday: Squats: 135 x 25, 175 x 25, 205 x 25
leg biceps curls: same as Monday

Sunday: light jogging, about one-half mile

Monday: Squats: 135 x 25, 175 x 25, 205 x 25,
225 x 25
leg hyperextensions: 80 x 25, 100 x 15, 120 x 10
leg biceps curls: 40 x 25, 50 x 15, 60 x 10

Tuesday: light running, up to one mile

Wednesday: Squats: 135 x 10, 155 x 10, 175 x 10, 195 x 10, 215 x 10
leg hyperextensions: 80 x 25, 100 x 15, 130 x 10
leg biceps curls: 40 x 25, 50 x 15, 65 x 10

Thursday: jog one-half mile and stride five 100-yard dashes

Friday: Squats: 135 x 5, 175 x 5, 215 x 5, 235 x 5, 265 x 5
leg hyperextensions: 80 x 25, 100 x 15, 130-140 x 10
leg biceps curls: 40 x 25, 50 x 15, 70 x 10

Saturday: should be at full strength

If the player is to scrimmage or play in a game on this Saturday, then he should forgo the Friday workout and rest.

It may seem a bit farfetched to schedule the injured player to be squatting with more weight just two weeks after his injury than he could do before he was hurt, but this will be the case if he strictly adheres to the program. The high repetitions and the priority given the injured muscle will enable it to respond extremely quickly. You will note that the weight used for the leg biceps curls remains constant the first week and then progressively increases the second. In the same train of thought, leg hyperextensions and some running are added the second week after a sufficient strength base has been established.

This method of rehabilitating an injured muscle allows for plenty of work, but it does not push the muscle to the point of fatigue. At the end of the two weeks, the player should be at full strength and be fully able to play in a game or to practice at 100%.

Arnold greatly impressed the Kansas City Chiefs on his second try in the NFL. He tried out with the Chargers as a free agent in 1976 but was waived and sat out the season. When his second opportunity came, Arnold was ready. He was especially impressive in the Chiefs' '77 pre-season victory over Pittsburgh, catching five passes, one for the winning touchdown. He also scored the winning touchdown in the '78 opening game upset of the Bengals.

THE ARNOLD MORGADO STORY

Before closing this chapter, I would like to document a case which happened just after I assumed the position of Strength Coach at the University of Hawaii. The principles outlined in this chapter were put to the test. Our outstanding running back, Arnold Morgado, tore his hamstring muscle while running a pass pattern on Thursday, March 7th, just eleven days prior to the opening of spring practice. The coaches wanted him ready and Arnold wanted to be ready as he had transferred from Michigan State and had not yet proven himself to this staff.

The team trainer, Dean Adams, iced the injury immediately. The following day, Arnold went to see George Fujio, a licensed masseur who specializes in getting athletes back on their feet fast. George treated the injury with galvanic current on Saturday, after the tenderness in the injury had subsided. I conferred with George and told him of my plans for an accelerated training. We coordinated our programs so that Arnold would not be fatigued from the resistive training on the days of treatment and, likewise, he would have plenty of rest after weight training before having another galvanic treatment.

On Monday, he was able to do a full squat without a great deal of pain, although there was some discomfort. At the time of his injury, he was doing five repetitions with 285 pounds. That first day, he did 135 x 25, 175 x 25, and 205 x 25. The first set was done very slowly and deliberately to make certain that no acute pain was being experienced. The first half dozen repetitions hurt him, but then the pain disappeared as the reps increased.

On Tuesday, Arnold did 135 x 25, 175 x 25, and 225 x 25. Again, care was taken on the initial set to insure that the movement did not irritate the injury. It did not, so we proceeded. Wednesday found him performing 135 x 25, 205 x 25, and 255 x 25. On the final set he was working to 100% capacity. Correct position was stressed and he reported a "pump" in his legs like he had never experienced before.

He rested on Thursday and on Friday did 135 x 5, 205 x 5, 255 x 5, 295 x 5, and 325 x 5. Exactly one week after his injury he was able to squat with 40 more pounds for five repetitions than he could before his injury. The leg biceps was not only rehabilitated, but was actually stronger than it was prior to the injury. Arnold ran on Saturday, rested on Sunday, and was able to go through the opening day of spring practice on Monday, March 18th, at full speed.

All other exercises were curtailed during this rehabilitation period. Arnold did not perform any exercises for the shoulders or back so that all of his energy could be directed to the injured muscle. I did not include leg hyperextensions as I felt that they would be a bit taxing as he was already working the injury to its maximum. A little more may have been too much. Mr. Fujio administered four galvanic treatments during this period and Arnold doubled his intake of supplements, notably protein, liver tablets, B-vitamins, and vitamins C and E. He rested whenever he was not going to class or to some other important function. His full cooperation was a most contributing factor in his rapid recovery.

The reader might note that I broke the rule of doing high repetitions for a full week, but this was done in this case because of the closeness of spring practice. Ideally, it would have been preferred to have 5-7 days of high repetitions before moving on to the heavier weight. Arnold, however, did so many things right during this rehabilitation program that it turned out just fine.

The next chapter outlines some specific exercises for certain types of athletic injuries. By utilizing the principles outlined in this chapter along with the selected exercises described, the Strength Coach should be able to provide a genuine service to his team.   ★

17
CHAPTER SEVENTEEN
REHABILITATION EXERCISES
FOR FOOTBALL PLAYERS

THE VALUE OF PROPER AND RAPID REHABILITATION

ONE OF THE GREATEST contributions that the Strength Coach can make to his team is to get an injured player back on the field quickly. A healthy team greatly increases the chances for victory in the game. Winning teams bring in larger crowds. Filled stadiums spell m-o-n-e-y and money is essential to building an even better team in the future.

By successfully rehabilitating just one key player a week or two earlier, the Strength Coach can earn his salary for the entire year. A key player put back into action can turn a game around. State championships, bowl bids, and professional playoffs are very often determined by the outcome of one game. One of the secrets of the many successful coaches is to field as many healthy players as possible for every game. Those teams which are crippled by injuries stand little chance in the tough games.

Complete teams win games. Winning attracts people on any level of football. People spend money and that money is refunneled into the football budget. The chain starts with an able body. It is the designated role of the Strength Coach to make these able bodies stronger and also to piece them back together rapidly when they break.

Each of the following sections in this chapter deals with a series of exercises for the various parts of the body. Obviously, there is not adequate space in one chapter of a book to cover every possible injury, plus all the many variables to a typical injury. An injury to the knee might be a result of almost a dozen different segments tearing or being stretched in some manner.

The exercises recommended in this book are for typical injuries and can be most helpful to either the athlete who coaches himself or to the Strength Coach. By adhering to the general principles from the preceeding chapter and administering these suggested movements, a program of therapy will be most useful.

PROGRAMS ARE FOR TRAUMATIC INJURIES

The programs suggested are specifically for injuries of the traumatic nature. Exercises for congenital and pathological conditions are not covered here. The principles related in this book for the recovery of injuries do not necessarily apply to handicapped conditions such as those involving deformations of an orthopedic nature. These conditions **can** be helped by a rehabilitative program with resistive exercise, but it is not within the scope of this book to cover that subject.

Trauma injuries are those resulting from a blow by some outside force. The injured portion of the body is typically compressed or elongated. Fractures and damage to the softer tissue fall under the compressed classification while tearing and straining the connective tissue or muscle fibers is an example of an elongated type of injury.

SPRAINS

The most frequently occurring injuries to athletes are: sprains, strains, dislocations, and fractures. **Sprains** are injuries to the ligaments surrounding given joints. These occur when the joint is forced beyond a point usually held by the ligaments. Since ligaments are non-elastic, they stretch or tear when forced beyond their normal range of motion.

STRAINS

A **strain** generally refers to an injury which damages a muscle, although tendon fibers can also be strained. Since the tendon is actually an extension of the muscle, damage usually affects both types of fibers. One of the more common strains occurs at the point where the muscle joins the tendon. When the belly portion of a muscle is strained, it is generally called a "pulled muscle."

DISLOCATIONS

A **dislocation** occurs when the articular surfaces of a joint are completely separated. When the joint surfaces are only partially separated, it is called a **subluxation**. Quite often, severe sprains are a result of dislocations, but the joint surfaces realigned themselves so that only the tissue damage remains. Dislocations are quite serious as the adjoining muscles, tendons, ligaments, synovial membranes, nerve and blood vessels are also damaged.

FRACTURE

A **fracture** is simply a break in the bone, in which the continuity of the bone's surface is disrupted. As in the case of the dislocations, a fracture usually has accompanying damage to the surrounding tissue. Sprains, strains, and even dislocations are not at all uncommon in the sport of football.

One of the major responsibilities of the Strength Coach is to put together a set of corrective exercises for these various types of injuries. The selected exercises will enable the damaged tissues to become stronger and, in the case of dislocations and fractures, allow the joint or bone to function properly without fear of a recurrence of the same injury.

REVIEW OF KINESIOLOGY IS IN ORDER

Before embarking on any corrective exercise program for an injured athlete, I would suggest that the Strength Coach review the chapters on the anatomy, physiology, and kinesiology of the various muscles and joints involved. Do not blindly, or even half-blindly, go about treating a knee injury without fully comprehending exactly how that joint functions and how the knee was specifically damaged. Also be aware that the human brain only retains information for a short period of time. Even though you may have had a most complete knowledge of the anatomy, physiology, and kinesiology of the human body in the past does not necessarily mean that you still have full retention of all that information currently.

KNOW YOUR MUSCLES AND JOINTS

When you are setting up a rehabilitation program, you will be dealing with muscles and joints. Muscle tears, sprains, dislocations, and fractures are the injuries with which you will be treating. The athletes who are rebuilding after operations will also fall under the Strength Coach's rehabilitation program. It is quite important to have a thorough working knowledge of all the joints in order to successfully direct such a program.

Whenever a ligament, tendon, or muscle is injured the joint involved must be rested for a certain period of time. In the case of severe injuries, such as shoulder dislocations or damaged vertebrae, the rest is rather extensive. Inactivity always results in muscle atrophy and this means a loss of strength.

The purpose of the rehabilitative exercises is simply to make the attachments stronger. They should, in fact, be made much stronger than they were prior to the injury to provide some added insurance against a recurrence of the same problem. Only by strengthening the muscles, tendons, and even the ligaments surrounding the damaged area will the joint be made stable. And stability is the key to keeping the body all in one piece.

EXERCISES FOR SPECIFIC INJURIES

SHOULDER INJURIES

There has to be a distinction made between exercises designed for rehabilitating shoulder dislocations and all other injuries involving muscles, tendons, and ligaments of the shoulder. Because of the action of the shoulder joint, no exercise should be used that allows the arm to be raised **above shoulder level** when treating a dislocation or separated shoulder. This action could result in a recurrence of the dislocation and this, of course, would mean further damage to the injured area. Too many recurrences and you have a surgical problem on your hands.

Shoulder Dislocations and Shoulder Separations

A clarification of terminology is usually made between shoulder dislocations and shoulder separations. Partial dislocations, (subluxations) of the acromio-clavicular joints are called separations. A dislocation of the shoulder refers to a dislocation only at the gleno-humeral joint. A shoulder separation at the third joint of the shoulder, the acromio-clavicular joint, is commonly called a shoulder point.

Injuries to the acromio-clavicular joint are the most frequent followed by gleno-humeral and sterno-clavicular joints. Sprains and strains also result quite often to the shoulder in football since this part of the body is fallen on so frequently.

I will outline a series of exercises which specifically work the muscles which surround the shoulder joint. When setting up a rehabilitation program you may only want to select two or three from the group and work them extensively. Basically, the exercises will be for the deltoids, the trapezious, and the pectorals with primary emphasis on the three heads of the deltoids.

Rehabilitating Exercises for the Shoulders

Front Raises with Dumbbell

A dumbbell is used in all of these exercises up to the point where the damaged shoulder is equal in strength to the undamaged one. At that point a barbell can be substituted for many of the movements, although it is not necessary. The dumbbells work just as well in almost all cases.

Select a dumbbell which is light enough for you to perform the required number of repetitions (25 initially). Stand erect and hold the dumbbell with your palms turned inward towards your body. Lift the dumbbell up and out until it is directly in front of your body. For shoulder dislocations go no higher; for other types of shoulder injuries proceed to lift the weight on over your head until it is in a vertical position. Lower it slowly, resisting the weight on the way down. Stop momentarily and repeat the movement. Do not allow your body to swing backward. This brings in muscles other than those which we are interested in at this point. The purpose of this exercise is to isolate the frontal deltoid, so do each repetition very deliberately.

Side Raises with Dumbbell

The lateral deltoid head is worked directly with the side raises. Stand erect and hold the dumbbells in your hands so that your knuckles are pointed out to the sides. Raise your arms directly to the side, keeping the knuckles out throughout the entire movement. If you are treating a shoulder dislocation, stop when the weight reaches shoulder height. Otherwise, take the resistance up to the completely vertical position. Lower the weight slowly and repeat. Some people find these dumbbell exercises easier to perform if they do both arms simultaneously rather than just doing one side at a time. Go right ahead and exercise both arms as it does seem to make this movement easier. Remember to keep the palms facing downward throughout the lifting motion so that when your hands come together above your head, the backs of your hands will be facing each other.

Rear Raises with Dumbbell

The final portion of the deltoid is stimulated with the rear raise. Stand erect and hold the loaded dumbbell at your side with your palms facing inward towards the side of your body. Now lift it directly back and upward. You may bend your elbow slightly as this action also involves muscles that affect the shoulder. Try not to swing the weight, but rather lift it up and back so that the deltoid is performing the bulk of the work.

Incline Presses

Incline presses also work the deltoids, but from a slightly different angle than the overhead presses. They also can be performed with either dumbbells or a barbell. The preference is purely individual. Lie on the incline and press the weight to an overhead position. Lower and repeat for the required number of repetitions.

Exercises modeled by Nick Frasca

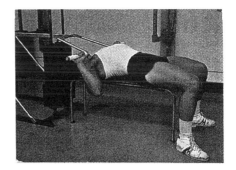

Bench Presses

Since the bench press is one of the best exercises to strengthen the shoulders, it is, therefore, an excellent rehabilitative movement. It is especially useful for rebuilding shoulder dislocations as the arm is not extended above shoulder level. Care must be taken, however, when the patient removes and replaces the weight on the bench press stands. He should not be allowed to reach back to take the weight so that his arm goes above shoulder level, especially in the early stages of recovery. A spotter should be near by to assist him. If a bench press machine is available, such as the Universal, then use it as it is safer.

While dumbbells can be used for the bench press, the barbell is preferred. The stronger side of your body can help to stabilize the weight and keep it from wandering to and fro. With dumbbells, there is the possibility that the weight will force the injured arm back or to the side and this action may cause further tissue damage.

Overhead Presses

This exercise can be performed with either dumbbells or a barbell and can be done behind the neck or in front. This movement is contraindicated for those with dislocations. Remember, **the injured shoulder should not be raised above shoulder level until the final stages of rehabilitation**. Wait until the medical expert gives the go-ahead before including any overhead work in the rebuilding program.

Stand erect or sit upright on a bench with the barbell or dumbbell on your chest or behind your neck on your shoulders. Push the barbell or dumbbells directly overhead. Lower them slowly and repeat. This movement is most useful for reconstructing the deltoids.

Shrugs

It may appear that the shoulder shrug is out of place in a section dealing with shoulder rehabilitation, but the shrug works the trapezius and the trapezius helps to stabilize the shoulder joint.

This movement may be done with a dumbbell initially, but a barbell is preferred so that sufficient weight can be utilized. Straps may be used for the patient for either the dumbbell or barbell phase of rehabilitation as the grip usually gives out on the high repetitions.

Grasp the weight in your hand and lift your trapezius up towards your ears. Hold the top-most position momentarily to insure a complete contraction and lower the weight slowly. Don't allow the weight to drop as this may irritate the damaged area.

A great deal more weight can be handled in this exercise than in any of the others mentioned so do not be apprehensive about loading two or three hundred pounds on the bar for the necessary twenty-five repetitions.

EXERCISES FOR THE ELBOW

The most common injury to the elbow is a sprain. It takes a great amount of force to dislocate the elbow as this is one of the more stable joints in the body. Even a slight sprain, however, restricts the use of the elbow joint and makes it impossible to perform normal athletic functions.

Even though dislocations of the elbow joints are unusual, they do occur; quite typically from being struck from behind while the arm is in a hyperextended position. The simple act of falling on an outstretched hyperextended arm can result in a sprain to the muscles, tendons, and ligaments that support the elbow joint.

Another injury which occurs frequently to the elbow is that of bone chips which float as loose bodies within the joint area. Falling or being struck on the elbow often produces these chips and they can be a cause of much discomfort.

All injuries to this joint should be diagnosed by a physician before physical rehabilitation is started. In the case of a dislocation or fracture be certain that you have the "go-ahead" before commencing the therapy program. Do not treat any elbow problem prior to medical consultation. A player complaining of a sore elbow may be experiencing merely a bit of tenderness from a blow to that joint, or his pain may be due to bone chips or a partial dislocation. Exercise treatment for the former is in order; for the latter however, it could prove to be quite harmful.

Any movement which extends or flexes the lower arm involves the elbow so there are numerous exercises the player could perform to rebuild damaged tissues. Since all of these exercises are explained fully elsewhere in the book, they will simply be listed for your convenience at this point. Two very good ones are illustrated.

Rehabilitating Exercises for the Elbows

Straight-arm Pullovers

The straight-arm pullover is a most useful rehabilitative exercise for the elbow in that when it is performed correctly, it does not put undue stress on the damaged area.

Lie on a bench in a supine position with your head hanging over the bench. Grasp the barbell just a bit closer than shoulder width (approximately 12 inches). Hold the bar straight overhead as you would lock out a bench press. While keeping the arms straight, reach back over your head as far as you can without unnecessary discomfort. It is a wise idea to have a spotter behind you. The spotter should keep his hands just under the bar as it is lowered. In case of pain, he should immediately take the bar to avoid further injury.

You want to keep your elbows straight for as long as you can, but they will bend as the bar lowers past the horizontal position. Go ahead and let them bend at this point, so that there is a certain amount of flexion.

After you reach the bottom-most position, pull the bar up and over your head back to the starting position. Reset and do another repetition.

This movement is preferred over the bent-arm pullover or any triceps extension exercises which require a full flexion of the upper arm. The full-flexion movements are more useful for healthy elbows as the risk is greater in re-damaging this joint. The one exception to this rule is the triceps push-downs on the lat machine.

Triceps Push-downs on the Lat Machine

Triceps push-downs on the lat machine are a relatively safe way to rehabilitate an injured elbow. Care should be taken so that you do not put stress on the injured area.

Keep the elbows tucked to your sides and push the bar down until it touches your thighs or until the bar is completely extended. Bring it back to the starting position slowly. In fact, do this movement very slowly throughout.

The machine is most valuable in the initial stage of rebuilding the elbow as it adds a bit of support while you are performing the exercise.

When the player is just starting on a rebuilding program for the elbow it would be better to do an exercise which is performed slowly, rather than one which is very dynamic. For example, dumbbell or barbell curls would be selected over power cleans since it is almost impossible to do power cleans in a slow fashion. This rule applies to rebuilding all body parts and not just to those of the elbow.

In many cases, the player does not have to perform any specific movements just for his elbow — he only has to change the sets and reps of his regular routine. Most players already include a sufficient number of exercises that involve the elbow, so they merely have to cut back on the sets and increase the reps as directed.

EXERCISES FOR THE WRIST

The wrist, like the elbow, is most often injured when the player falls on this joint and it is hyper-extended. This trauma can result in various degrees of sprains or even a fracture. When pain lingers in a sprain, it is recommended to have the injury rediagnosed. Very frequently, a fracture cannot be detected on early X-rays and a later reading is required for a more accurate diagnosis.

The wrist contains very little muscle tissue and its size is primarily determined by heredity. The area can be strengthened, however, as tendons and ligaments do respond to progressive resistive exercise just as muscle tissue does.

There are a number of exercises that can be performed to help strengthen the wrist after an injury or surgery. In cases of severe damage the player should start very slowly and not attempt to handle a too heavy resistance too early in his recovery program or he will redamage the area. Squeezing a rubber ball or a hand gripping device are excellent methods for getting some circulation into the weakened area. This type of exercise can be done almost constantly. Carry the ball or gripping device everywhere and work on it until the wrist becomes fatigued.

A player, when rebuildling the wrist, is basically attacking the extensions of the muscles of the forearm and in all likelihood, these muscles will fatigue before the tendons in the wrist. When the injury permits, move on to the more strenuous exercises. Two of the best are wrist curls and wrist rollers.

Rehabilitating Exercises for the Wrist

wrist curls (palms up)   wrist curls (palms down)

Wrist Curls

While in a seated position grasp a barbell and rest your forearms on your legs so that only your wrists are extended out over your legs. All the resistance should be on the hands and wrist. Flex the wrist to its full contraction and lower the weight slowly. You will set up a sort of rocking motion with the weight and you should feel a thorough "pump" in the wrist area. This movement should be performed with the palms up for full flexion and also with the palms down for total extension. Use as much weight as possible for the required number of repetitions.

Wrist Rollers

Some of the machines, such as the Universal, have a wrist roller incorporated on it which are useful but, these devices are very simple to construct should you not have one available. If your weight room does not have one, make one. Cut a foot length of broomstick; drill a hole in it; insert a piece of clothesline through the hole; tie a knot in one end of the rope and a barbell plate to the other end. The rope should be about four feet in length.

Hold the stick at arms' length directly in front of your eyes. Begin rolling the rope up the stick until the barbell plate reaches the top. Slowly, let the rope roll out again, resisting the force of the weight all the way. Repeat for the required number of repetitions or until the wrist is absolutely fatigued.

A PROGRAM FOR REHABILITATING THE BACK

Undoubtedly, the most difficult area for the Strength Coach to rebuild is the back. Not so much because the muscles of the back are hard to stimulate. On the contrary, these muscles respond remarkably well to exercise therapy. It is, rather, because back injuries are so difficult to pinpoint. An injury to the cervical region may be causing problems way down in the lumbar area. When treating back injuries, the Strength Coach has to be aware that the entire back is involved. Lumbar injuries also affect the cervical and thoracic regions. Merely treating the damaged area seldom results in complete recovery. Only when the entire back is considered — with special emphasis on the damaged area — is the patient able to regain full use of his back.

The Back — A Critical Area

It should be needless to point out the importance of a healthy back to anyone, but the athlete is especially aware of this area of his body. Even slight back pains can severely limit performance. A lower back injury can affect the use of the player's legs. More severe injuries can result in paralysis and quickly end careers.

Sprains, strains, and fractures can occur in any portion of the back. There are a wide assortment of injuries that can occur to the various portion of the vertebrae itself or to the supportive structures which surround the spine. When the bodies of the vertebrae are forced together violently, a herniation of the posterior longitudinal ligament results in a "slipped disc." Compression injuries result from improper lifting techniques or from a traumatic blow and cause damage to the intervertebral discs. Sometimes, portions of the vertebrae will be fractured.

A common back injury occurs when the player suddenly turns, twists, or falls and places some portion of his back in an awkward position. The vertebrae moves slightly out of its correct alignment. The spinal erectors, those long strap-like supportive muscles which run from the base of the skull to the sacrum, go into spasm to prevent the bones from slipping out of alignment even further. They become almost rock-hard and will remain that way until the spine is correctly realigned. Pain is often radiated down the legs, in the case of lumbar injuries, and through the shoulders, in the case of cervical spasms.

Consider the Entire Back

When rehabilitating an injury that involves any portion of the back, the entire back should be considered. In other words, the cervical and thoracic regions of the back must be exercised as well as the lumbar regions even though the injury may be only to the lumbars. Keeping this fact in mind, you can set up a series of exercises for the entire back, but you can give added attention to the injured area. That is, have two or three specific movements for the injured portion of the back, but also include at least one exercise for the middle (thoracic) and upper (cervical) back. Or, you may include one exercise that works both of these areas, the power clean being one such movement.

This section on back injuries will also encompass neck injuries as the latter always involves the cervical vertebrae.

EXERCISES OF THE UPPER BACK (NECK)

Power Cleans

Power cleans are a very basic exercise for all of the muscles of the back. Review the proper procedure of doing this overall exercise found on page 44. They are especially useful when rebuilding the upper portion of the back.

Shrugs

Shrugs are a specific movement for the trapezius and when done correctly, they stimulate muscle growth right up the base of the skull. They are most useful when rehabilitating injuries to the neck and cervical region of the back. This movement is described in detail on page 76.

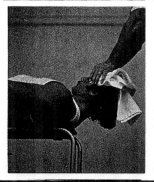 

Dynamic neck movements are very excellent for rehabilitating injuries to any portion of the neck. Work the front, back, and both sides for 8-10 repetitions each, resisting just enough to force the subject to totally work the various muscles.

Rehabilitating Exercises for the Neck

Wrestler's Bridge

The wrestler's bridge, either performed on the front or on the back, is one of the more advanced neck exercises so it should only be performed after the athlete has sufficiently recovered from his injury and has had the opportunity to do a period of remedial neck work.

Lie on your back and slowly arch upward, keeping the weight on your heels and back of your head. You may want to use your hands for balance and as a measure of safety at first by placing them by your head. They will take some of the pressure off your neck until it becomes strong enough to do the movement without the added support. Rock gently back so that your nose touches the floor and then straighten your body out again.

The front bridge is performed in a similar fashion except the pressure is on your forehead and toes. Your hands will be against your thighs for balance and support. Again, you will attempt to touch your nose to the floor.

Both versions of this exercise are toughies and should not be done without some warming up of the neck muscles.

Up-Right Row

The up-right row will involve the trapezius and can be done as a lead-in exercise for the shrugs. Shrugs are preferred, however, as much more weight can be handled and they force the deeper spinal erectors to work as well as the surface muscles — the trapezius.

Grasp the barbell with a grip which is just a bit more narrow than shoulder-width. Keep the back straight and pull the weight up to the point where the clavicle meets the sternum. Hold momentarily and lower slowly. Make sure that the elbows stay ahead of the bar, that is higher than the barbell. Do not let the weight drop down but rather resist it on its decent.

Rehabilitating Exercises for the Middle Back

Once again, the power clean should be used as "the" basic exercise for all back work, unless the rapid movement involved irritates the injured area. If this is the case, then more localized and less dynamic exercises are in order.

Bent-Over Rows

The bent-over row works those muscles which protect the middle or thoracic region of the back. It must be done properly, however, or other muscles will be involved.

Grasp the barbell with a grip approximately six inches wider than your shoulders. In other words, a relatively wide grip. Bend over so that your back is parallel to the floor. Keep an arch in your back and pull the bar up to your chest. Make sure that it comes all the way up. Lower it slowly and repeat.

As the muscles become fatigued, you will have a tendency to lift your back higher and higher and jerk the weight up. Avoid this as it will throw more stress on the middle portion.

Lat Pull-Downs

The wide grip pull-downs, often called "lat-pulls," are very useful when rehabilitating the middle back. The pull-downs will serve as an excellent lead-in movement for the wide-grip chins, as the latter exercise is much more difficult.

Kneel or sit directly under the lat bar, allowing your arms to completely extend. Pull the bar straight down until it touches the back of your neck. Resist momentarily and slowly allow the bar to return to the starting position.

Be certain that you get a complete range of movement with this exercise. Let the arms extend fully so as to thoroughly work the latissimus dorsi and be sure to pull the bar all the way down to the back of your neck.

Wide-Grip Chins

The wide-grip chin works the latissimus dorsi and it is important to keep these muscles strong so that they will aid in supporting the deeper spinal erectors. Since the lats are seldom called into play for the football player, they often are quite weak. Any exercise that strengthens them also involves the spinal erectors that cover the thoracic region of the spine.

Any injury to this middle back area will benefit from some work on the lats and the wide-grip chin is the best — but also the most advanced. They can be performed either by touching the chinning bar to your chest or to the back of your neck. Be sure to let your body extend fully before commencing another repetition so as to get a full stretch and thorough contraction of the latissimus dorsi.

Obviously, few will be able to perform anywhere near the recommended twenty-five repetitions on wide-grip chins, unless the athlete has a strong background in gymnastics. So just do as many as possible for five sets and add to the total number of repetitions each workout. Be sure to do at least twenty-five in total per workout session.

Rehabilitating Exercises for the Lower Back

The majority of the injuries to the back occur in this relatively precarious lumbar region of the back. The reasons for this are manifold, but really are quite obvious. The lumbar vertebrae are totally dependent on the strength of the spinal erectors for support. Unlike the thoracic and cervical regions there are no overlapping muscles for extra protection. The abdominal muscles lend a little extra support but not very much. Add to this the fact that all downward pressure on the back is terminated in the in the lumbar region and it's a wonder that this area holds together as well as it does. Any improper lifting technique will reveal itself quickly via lower back problems.

These lumbar muscles can become fantastically strong, but when they are fatigued, they give away like any other muscle. When this happens, the lumbar vertebrae is left without any protection and problems result.

When rebuildling weakened lower back muscles or overcoming a lower back injury of any sort, start off very, very slowly and increase only when the back is ready to handle more resistance. It cannot be emphasized too emphatically the necessity of not rushing the recovery of a lower back injury. All injuries should be handled gently, but the lower back requires a velvet touch. Get in a hurry and the injury is sure to recur. To rehabilitate a recurrent injury takes three or four times as long as it does to rebuild it the first time. Be cautious and fully appreciate just how delicate the lower back really is.

Good Mornings

An excellent exercise for the lower back is called the "good morning" as it resembles the greeting of the oriental folks. Do this without any resistance until the lower back becomes strong enough for you to perform 100 repetitions without any added weight. As I mentioned earlier, it is imperative to move very slowly when rehabilitating the lower back.

Stand erect and place your hands behind your head. Your feet should be about shoulder-width and pointed straight ahead. Bend your knees slightly and lean over so that your head lowers below your knees. Do not attempt to keep an arch in your lower back. The opposite is desired, a rounding of the lower back so that all the action is placed on those lumbar muscles. Keep your weight well forward so that you are almost tipping forward at the bottom of the exercise.

Come back erect slowly and repeat. Keep the same bend in your knees throughout the exercise. Do not allow your body to squat down, but rather force it to bend over. Do these slowly and deliberately and when you can perform 100 repetitions without any weight, then you may add a 25-pound resistance. Do not be in a hurry, but increase slowly and the lower back will be strengthened considerably.

Back Hyperextensions

It should be emphasized from the very onset that some of these suggested exercises will actually irritate the injury. If this is the case, then merely select another which does not. Follow the guidelines set up in Chapter Sixteen when making this decision.

The back hyperextension is performed either on an apparatus especially designed for the exercise or on a table, leg extension machine, or some other broad, flat surface that sets approximately 36 inches off the floor. The Universal Machine has a back hyperextension station and Paramount has a special piece of equipment designed just for this exercise. If these aren't available then a training table will do, but this requires the assistance of a training mate.

Lie across the table, face down, so that only your thighs are in contact with the table. Have a partner hold your ankles. Place your hands behind your head and arch your lower back upward so that you are looking at the ceiling. Lower slowly and repeat. Resistance may be added in the form of barbell plates as the back becomes stronger.

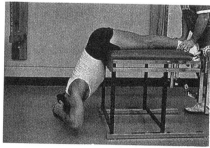

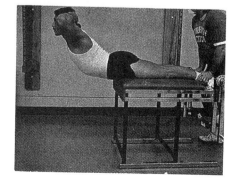

Rehabilitating Exercises for the Hip

EXERCISES FOR THE HIPS

Generally speaking, the hips are the least troublesome area of the body for the athlete. It is quite stable in comparison to the other joints of the body as it is designed by nature for supporting heavy loads. There are lots of muscles, tendons, ligaments, and strong joints supporting this entire region. Fractures do occur, but are not common in athletes. Occasionally, the hip will be dislocated, but this too is rather unusual in football.

The majority of the injuries to the hip consists of strains and "hip pointers." The term "hip pointer" is almost specific to football and refers to a severe bruise to the lateral portion of the hip. It is usually caused by a helmet or some other hard object striking the hip from the side. These injuries are quite dehabilitating for a short period of time, but rest and ice therapy generally allows them to recede without any undue problems.

Squat

The squat is one of the best exercises to perform in order to rebuild weak or injured hip muscles. Utilize this movement as soon as the injury allows. A complete explanation is found in the "Big Three" chapter.

Hip Extensors

This exercise is also called hip hyperextensions to differentiate it from the back hyperextension. It can be performed either in a leg extension machine or free moving over a table or high bench. Lie in the prone position with your hips and legs extended over the bench. If you are in a leg extension machine, fit the lower pad into the back of your knees. Lift up with your heels so that you are arching high; resist; lower; and repeat.

In lieu of having a machine, either have someone put a slight resistance against the back of your heels or attach iron boots to your feet. You will not need any resistance initially for the required twenty-five repetitions as this movement is most difficult for most people at first.

The Nautilus hip and back machine is specifically designed to work these hip extensors and is quite useful when you are rehabilitating or building this particular area of your body. It can be accomplished without the expensive machine, however.

Hip Adductors

If the hip adductors (muscles that pull the legs together) are injured — as often happens if the football player is forced into a wide split position — then the following exercise will help reconstruct that damage.

Pulleys are extremely useful for rebuilding the adductors and should they be available, utilize them in this exercise. Stand sideways to the pulley and attach it to the near ankle, which should be on the injured side. Pull your injured leg straight in to your opposite leg; let the resistance pull you back slowly and repeat. Stand far enough away from the pulley so that you are getting a full range of motion. Most machines have a pulley station and if the ankle pad is available, use it. A towel can be wrapped around the ankle in case the ankle pad is not provided.

Since not all weight rooms have machines or pulleys, here is a simple variation of the same exercise which is equally as effective and requires no additional equipment.

Lie on your side with the damaged leg nearest the floor. Position your other foot on a table or chair or have someone hold it approximately 2 or 2½ feet high. Now lift the bottom leg up to the one rested on the table. Lower slowly and repeat. As the adductors get stronger, add resistance to the injured leg in the form of iron boots or ankle weights.

Hip Abductors

The hip abductors (the muscles that pull the legs apart laterally) are also injured frequently on the football field. The pulleys, once again, can be used to reconstruct and strengthen this group of muscles. Stand erect with your feet together. Fasten the pulley to your injured leg at the ankle. That leg will be the furthest away from the pulleys. Move your leg out and away from the pulley, lifting it as high as possible. Lower slowly and repeat.

A similar movement can also be performed without extra equipment. Lie on your side with your feet together. Lift your injured leg straight up as high as you can. When possible, add resistance in the form of iron boots or ankle weights.

Pulley exercises which entail lifting the weight off the floor also involve the many muscles that make up the hip. Exercises such as the power clean, high pulls, and dead lift all utilize the muscles of the hip. One or more of these movements can be incorporated into the rehabilitation program when the athlete is ready.

Rehabilitating Exercises for the Knee

Whenever one thinks of football injuries, he first thinks of the knee. Unfortunately, football and knee injuries are unhappy bed partners. The reader would do well to review the section on the anatomy and kinesiology of the knee joint found on page 3 of chapter 1 .

The majority of the knee injuries in football result from a sharp blow to the outside of the knee, pushing it inward. This blow forces the medial collateral ligament to tear and there may also be accompanying damage to the medial meniscus. A blow which forces the knee to be driven outward will cause damage to the lateral collateral ligament. Since the lateral miniscus does not attach to the lateral collateral ligament, there are fewer cases of lateral meniscus injuries than there are medial meniscus ones.

Another frequently occurring injury to the knee joint is damage to one of the cruciate ligaments. The role of the anterior and posterior ligaments, you may recall, is to prevent hyperextension and hyperflexion of the knee joint. When the lower leg (tibia) is forced backward when the upper leg (femur) is in a fixed position, then the posterior cruciate will be damaged. When the lower leg is driven forward when the upper leg is fixed, then the anterior cruciate ligament will be injured.

The anterior cruciate is more often injured in football and the high injury rate is one reason why there are such severe penalties against clipping. A "clip" forces the lower leg forward violently and often results in damage to this anterior cruciate ligament.

Setting up a rehabilitation program for the knees should be done in close coordination with the team's medical expert. A full knowledge of the extent of the injury is necessary. In the event the athlete has had surgery, then a slow but progressive rebuilding program is in order. Be very cautions and move slowly.

Leg Hyperextensions

Leg hyperextensions can be performed either on a machine or with added resistance in the form of an iron boot or ankle weight. Initially, it may be necessary for the athlete to do the movement without any resistance.

Sit on a leg extension machine or with your lower leg extended out over a table or high bench. Lift the lower leg up so that it is fully extended. Hold momentarily, lower slowly and repeat.

Leg Biceps Curl

To rebuild the attachments which support the posterior portion of the knee joint, specifically the leg biceps tendons which attach below the back of the knee to the tibia, the leg biceps curl is most useful.

These are easily performed on the leg extension machine, but can be done without weight, with iron boots, ankle weights, or with a training mate applying resistance. Be sure to do the movement slowly and concentrate on a full flexion of the leg biceps muscles.

Squats

Since the knee is only as strong as its weakest supportive structure, a full-range exercise that brings all of the major muscles that surround the joint into play is most beneficial. The full squat is a most useful exercise to rehabilitate a damaged knee and should be incorporated into the rehabilitation program, just as soon as is permissible.

Once the cast is removed following knee surgery, the player should start doing full squats without any resistance immediately. He should do three sets of 25 repetitions per day, performing one set at a time with 4-5 hours of rest in between each set. The free squats are followed by one set of leg extensions and one set of leg biceps curls. For five or six days he will be doing just free squats, working the reps up to 100 per set. At this point he is able to add some resistance.

The next step in the progresson is to add some resistance in the form of weight to all four exercises: squat, leg hyperextensions, leg biceps curls, and toe raises. The weight should be very light, as the key to a successful recovery is constant work and a slow, but steady progression. Twenty-five pounds is sufficient for the squat and the repetitions will drop back to twenty-five. Just add 10 pounds to the leg extensions and leg biceps curls. Continue to do three sets, with the 4-5 hours of rest between sets for another week.

As the muscles develop, the weight will increase. When the weight becomes heavy enough in the squat (a good rule of thumb is to use the athlete's bodyweight as a gauge) then he should begin training only every other day and increase the sets to five per workout for all three movements. Also, when the squatting weight reaches the athlete's bodyweight, he should begin doing all of his sets at one time, rather than spacing them out at intervals during the day.

If there is a trick to getting the knee back together rapidly, it is in having the athlete start to exercise as soon as he gets out of the cast. The longer a muscle atrophies from disuse, the longer it takes to recover.

Follow the principles set forth in the preceding chapter concerning acute versus chronic pain and you can proceed quite safely and rather rapidly.

Rehabilitating Exercises for the Ankle

Ankle injuries generally mean ankle sprains. In football, the most frequently occurring type of sprain results from the ankle being turned outward in a violent fashion. This results in damage to the supportive ligaments, namely the 1) anterior tibiofibular, 2) anterior talofibular, and 3) caleaneofibular ligaments.

The ankle can also be sprained if it is forced to be turned in forcefully, but these are less common because of the great strength of the deltoid ligament. The ankle can also be sprained when force is applied from the rear, causing the ankle to hyperextend and the strong achilles tendon can also be stretched by just the opposite action.

Fracture and dislocations are not uncommon to this weight-bearing joint so it is well for the Strength Coach to be aware of some rebuilding exercises for the ankle.

The nature of the injury dictates the specific exercises to be used in successfully rehabilitating the ankle so, once again, be certain that you consult with the medical expert before starting any athlete on a rebuilding program with resistive equipment.

Special Ankle Rehabilitative Equipment

In order to successfully rehabilitate the ankle, a special piece of equipment is required. The special piece of equipment consists of a foot plate balanced on a lever so that action can be performed laterally as well as fore and aft. The apparatus is illustrated. It is just a simple matter of programming the athlete to do the required number of sets and reps by putting the resistance against the injured portion of the ankle.

Extreme caution should be displayed in the initial stages of rehabilitation so that there are no quick, snappy motions involved while using the ankle rehabilitation equipment. Do not allow the athlete to snap the injured ankle to the side, as this will create new problems.

Should it not be possible to purchase or build the ankle machine, then toe raises with resistance on the shoulder is the best substitute movement. Go slowly at first and then increase the resistance slowly as the ankle strength increases. These are most beneficial to the posterior stabilizers of the ankle.

CONSIDERING THE ELEMENT OF PAIN IN REHABILITATING INJURIES

The primary difference between a series of exercises designed for rehabilitation purposes and a program for general strength building is that the former involves the element of pain to a much greater extent than the latter.

The Strength Coach must be very cognizant of the fact that the athlete is fighting a terrific battle to get his body totally whole again. The Strength Coach must make it a point to be present when the athlete trains on the rebuilding program, especially in the early stages of recovery. The movements must be done exactly right and the athlete must be given all the moral support possible. It is a mind-bending time for many athletes. Some are faced — for the first time in their lives — with a problem that they cannot handle alone. Some injuries are so severe that the athlete has to learn to perform simple tasks, such as walking, all over again. The injured players often feel left out of their peer group, and anxiously want to become part of the team as rapidly as possible. An overzealous attitude has to be guarded against, just as much as an unmotivated one. The Strength Coach must control the pace of recovery. He must keep in constant communication with the athlete so that he can fully understand his physical and mental feelings.

Rebuilding the mental outlook of an injured player is just as important, and is sometimes far more difficult, as it is to rehabilitate the physical injury. Constant encouragement and reassurance goes a long way to enabling the injured athlete to recover 100%.

Close supervision and encouragement will assist the player to work through the early stages of pain which always accompany an injury. This is the genuine test of the Strength Coach's ability to gain the confidence of the athlete. The player must be sold on the methods and the person administering the methods in order for him to go through all the trouble of getting back into shape.

WORK THE UNINJURED AREAS THROUGHOUT

One way in which the Strength Coach can keep the athlete in the swing of things is to have him to continue training the uninjured portions of his body during that time in which he cannot exercise the injured area. Merely because a player has his leg in a cast should not keep him from doing upper body work. Likewise, a player with an upper body injury should continue to perform squats and other leg work.

Keeping the athlete engaged in the weight training program serves a number of purposes. It helps him to keep, or even to increase, his strength level in the uninjured areas. Most players start increasing in the exercises which they are doing as they can put more energy into less exercises. Then, too, by continuing to train, the player keeps the discipline of going to the weight room regularly. When this routine is broke, it seems that his entire training regimentation breaks down. He stops eating properly and doesn't watch his rest or other health habits as closely as before. Finally, the exercises he does for one part of his healthy part of his body has a beneficial effect on the injured area. Exercise increases circulation — not just in the muscles being worked directly but in every corner of the body. The injured knee is helped, ever so slightly of course, by upper body exercises.

Encourage the injured athlete to keep training, even if he can do but one exercise. That one exercise is better than none. If he keeps his habit pattern of training regularly, then he will be much more apt to start on the rehabilitation program sooner.

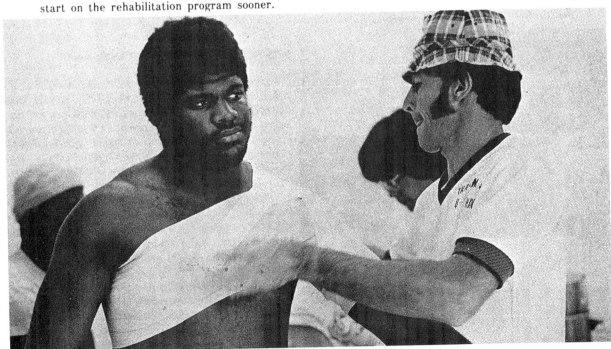

18

CHAPTER EIGHTEEN
THOSE EXTRAORDINARY EXERCISE MACHINES — AN EVALUATION

THE COACH HAS A DECISION TO MAKE

THE MACHINES VERSUS THE free weights. This battle has been going on ever since the first Universals hit the scene. Now, the Strength Coach and weight training athlete have to decide not only between the free weights and the Universal Machines, but they must also make a decision concerning Nautilus and Isokinetic Machines — the two newest concepts in machine training.

Just how effective are the various types of machines? Do they really build strength faster than free weights? Are they, in fact, safer than the free weights? How about the maintenance and up-keep factor? These are just a token of the many questions every Strength Coach has to answer for himself, his team, and his school when he goes about organizing his strength program.

Football coaches have been deluged with various kinds of information in the last couple of years concerning the effectiveness of machine training. The Nautilus machines have captured the imagination of many coaches across the country. These coaches like the concept of rapid training, rotary form resistance, automatically variable resistance and high intensity training. The Nautilus Machines are well-constructed, sturdy, and durable. Many professional and college teams have purchased the equipment and have installed the Nautilus program. The concepts set forth by Arthur Jones appear sound. But how totally sound is his program. Is Nautilus training superior to training with free weights?

Likewise, Isokinetics has emerged as the "newest concept" in strength training. Their "accommodating resistance" principle has drawn applause from such notables as Jim Counsilman, swimming coach at Indiana University, Hank Stram and George Woods of shot putting fame. Where does the Isokinetic machines fit into the strength program? Is it the best form of strength training? Does it have limitations which the manufacturers overlook?

The concerned Strength Coach is often left confused and bewildered by all the material which floods his desk. He wants the best for his players and really does want some straight answers on the subject of machine training.

BY BASIS OF EVALUATION

This chapter is an attempt to evaluate the machines to some logical degree. This evaluating is based on three factors: 1) a study of the literature put out by the manufacturers of the various machines, 2) actually applying the suggested programs on myself and others and, 3) talking with numerous other strength athletes and Strength Coaches concerning their views and experiences with the machines.

I have gone to great length to make this a fair appraisal. When I examine a newer form of strength training, I do so with an open mind as I, like so many other Strength Coaches and athletes, would dearly love to find a better and faster way of becoming or staying strong. Heavy squats, power cleans, shrugs, and so forth are just as difficult for me as they are for anyone else. I would like a short-cut to strength. The machines offer a "less painless" and "faster" way to achieve my goals. I read all the information put out by the originator of the Nautilus Machines, Arthur Jones. I also visited with Mr. Jones on several occasions and had an opportunity to learn of the Nautilus program first-hand. I assisted Strength Coach Tommy Suggs at the Houston Oiler's summer training camp in 1973. We used Nautilus equipment as prescribed by Mr. Jones.

I visited the Isokinetic plant in Independence, Missouri and was in on the designing stages of some of the newer equipment. While I was employed by the Jack LaLanne organization in California, one of my responsibilities was to write a sales promotion brochure and exercise program for the Isokinetic Machines. I tried both forms of exercise under expert-supervision. It was not a hit-and-miss situation. Then I spent the next four years talking to every bodybuilder, football player, and competitive weightlifter who used the Universal, Nautilus, or Isokinetic Machines. The appraisal is as fair as I can possibly make it. I have no axe to grind with any of the various companies. The owners of these companies: Chuck Coker of Universal, Glen Henson of Isokinetics, and Arthur Jones of Nautilus are much more intelligent and conscientious than the majority of those who manufacture and sell the Olympic sets. So when I conclude that the Olympic barbell is a superior tool in building strength it is certainly not because I am in cahoots with these barbell companies. On the contrary, I have a great deal more admiration for the machine people than I do the barbell folks. It's simply that I sincerely believe the free weights are better instruments by which the Strength Coach can develop strength in his players.

AN OVERVIEW OF THE MACHINES

Even though the various manufacturers like to point out the great differences between their particular products, there are more attributes which are similar than there are differences.

The machines, regardless of their training theories, are all basically substitutes for the free weights. The manufacturers and their representatives sold school officials and coaches, first of all, on their superiority over the free weights. Universal Machines made the initial inroads and did a fantastic job of merchandising. Rarely do I walk into a school or college and not find a Universal Machine. More recently, Universal has regeared its propoganda to compete with the Nautilus and Isokinetic companies, but they were the first to go "head-on" against the free weight system of resistive training.

The original arguments dealing with the superiority of machines over the free weights are still being used. The machine manufacturers contend that:

1) machines are much safer than the free weights.

2) more people can train faster on the machines than on the free weights.

3) machines are neat and compact. There is no clean-up problem as there is with the free weights.

4) there is no theft problem with the machines. There is with the free weights.

5) machines produce strength gains faster than the free weights.

These arguments will be put to the test. Just how true are the machine people's contentions? I will dissect each argument in turn.

MACHINES ARE SAFER THAN FREE WEIGHTS

I believe that this statement is relatively, but not absolutely, true. The statement would be more correct if it read: "free weights are potentially more dangerous than the machines, but they are not always more dangerous." Machines are, in most instances, safer than free weights but — and this is an important "but" to remember — many athletes have been injured while training on the machines. They injure themselves on the machines for much the same reasons that they injure themselves on the free weights. That is, the athletes fail to warm-up properly, or use faulty lifting technique, or put a muscle under undue stress while it is fatigued.

Performing an exercise on the Nautilus hip and back machine may be safer than performing squats with the free bar, but that does not mean the hip and back machine is fool-proof. Ken Patera for example, injured his lower back on the Nautilus machine and had never sustained an injury from squatting. My feeling is that if the squat is done correctly, then the machine is not safer by any significant degree. It's not a black and white situation of one being totally risky and the other being totally safe, but merely a matter of relative degree and very few degrees at that. I have never had anyone injure themselves doing full squats

"The key to safety in any strength program is proper supervision and not the type of apparatus used in that program."

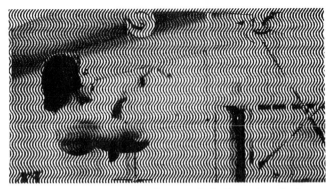

under my supervision, and I sincerely believe that the key to safety in any strength program is proper supervision and not the type of apparatus used in that program.

So which is safer, the free weights or the machines? All things being equal, the machines are safer, but this is not an all-conclusive statement. I personally believe that safety is directly proportionate to the level of supervision. An athlete can get injured on an Isokinetic, Universal, or Nautilus Machine. That is a fact. It is also possible to train over a long period of time on free weights and never get injured. This, too, is a fact. But neither statement is 100% accurate. Both methods can be safe and both can be dangerous. The difference is not so much in the equipment used in the strength program, but in the manner of supervision of that particular program.

MORE PEOPLE CAN TRAIN FASTER ON MACHINES THAN THEY CAN ON THE FREE WEIGHTS

False. The machine folks like to compare nuts to bolts. While it is true that more players can train on one Universal Machine than can train on one weight station, it is not true that as many athletes can train on a machine as can train on free weights of equal money value. The Universal Machines, for example, list around $3500-4000 depending on the number of stations involved. Eight people can train at one time — if they happen to be performing those exercises that fit the various stations of the machine. This is an optimistic statement on the part of the machine people because very seldom are all the stations being used at once. In fact, some are never used. For the same money, a school, or college could set up fifteen stations utilizing Olympic barbells in nine of those stations. Instead of the eight station Universal, the money could purchase: nine Olympic sets, three power benches, three squat racks, three sit-up boards, and three leg extension machines, for a total of fifteen stations.

The Nautilus equipment in its entirety for ten stations runs close to $25,000 and the Isokinetic Machines would be anywhere from $4000 to $6000 depending on which 15 stations were selected.

The machines are actually more confining than the free weights. The free weights are flexible, they can fit into tiny nooks and cranies. Olympic bars, squat racks, benches, sit-up boards, leg extension machines can be spread out to fit into various types of rooms. The machines are not nearly as adaptive to space limitations and are difficult to move about. Free weights can be utilized in corners and one 10'x10' area can be used for **all** the exercises.

LACK OF VARIATION ON THE MACHINES

Another point often overlooked by the school officials when they are considering machines as against the free weights is that while it is true that the Universal has eight, ten, or twelve stations, those stations are set. There is little variety available from them. If your player does not happen to be doing lat work, then that station is wasted. Not so with free weights. They can be used to exercise any portion of the body from the arms, chest, shoulders, back, or legs — all in the same floor space with the same barbell.

The factor of speed is often over-emphasized when considering the purchase of exercise equipment for the school program. Or perhaps I should say it is minconstrued. There is no question that speed is an important factor to consider when setting up a program, but it should not be put out of proportion to the overall goals of the athletic program. It certainly is important to be able to train the entire team in a relatively short period of time, but the time spent in the weight room can serve many purposes other than just the building of strength.

A team should be able to move just as rapidly on free weights as they do on machines. Again, it's a matter of direction and supervision and not a matter of which instrument is being used. A player can go from one station to another using free weights just as easily as he can get up from one station at a machine and move to another.

With one station each for bench presses, power cleans, squats, leg extensions, and set-ups, the organized weight coach can put twenty-five players through the program in less than an hour. This is figured on five sets of five on the "Big Three" and four total sets on the leg machine, plus one to three sets on the sit-up boards. An hour is not excessive and most coaches agree that the time the team spends together while weight training helps to build team unity.

WEIGHT ROOM SERVES AS A MEETING PLACE

The weight room is the social club for the team, especially during off-season. This is especially true for college and professional teams. These players seldom see each other, except in practice and then they only get to see and talk to men in similar positions. During weight training, linemen lift with running back, quarterbacks visit the linebackers. Between sets they discuss more than football or weights — usually legs or wheels. They learn about each other; become more conscious of each other as individuals; and as a result develop closer feelings or as Lombardi said "a love for each other." So the time spent in the weight room should not be written off as merely strength training time.

Personally, I am not in favor of ultra-rapid workouts. I do believe in high intensity training and short exercise periods, but I think that it's useful for the players to spend some time visiting while doing their extra arm work, or their mid-section training and not be hurried out of the training room. As the players spot for, load for, and encourage each other they are cementing the team bond much more than many coaches realize.

Time is definitely a factor, but it should not be put out of context of the goals of the program. If time is short, break up your team into an A and B section and have them come in on separate days. If you have but two hours allotted per day; have group A come in the first hour and group B, the second. Or, have four smaller groups train on alternate days for one hour apiece.

"Time, alone, should not be the guiding factor to consider when installing a strength program. The prime consideration should be results."

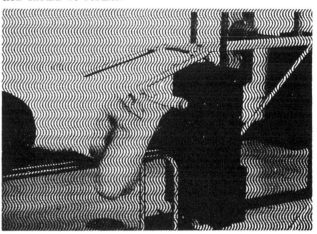

The time aspect can be dealt with by using just a bit of imagination. Time, alone, should not be the guiding factor to consider when installing a strength program. The prime consideration should be results. That specific subject will be handled in depth later in this chapter.

THE MACHINES ARE NEAT AND COMPACT. THERE IS NO CLEAN-UP PROBLEM AS WITH THE FREE WEIGHTS.

True. The machines are easy to clean-up after a training session as everything is housed in one compact unit. It does take some time to replace the loose weights to the plate holders, but, not really that much total time. It should not take over five minutes to straighten up a weight room after everyone is finished. This responsibility can be delegated to a student, but even if it falls on the Strength Coach's shoulders, it's a small chore.

A fact that needs to be pointed out is that while the free weights are more messy and do require some cleaning up, they are less prone to being damaged than the machines. The machines are constantly having small, but bothersome mechanical problems, regardless of what the manufacturer's contend. Fail to oil the Universal or Nautilus or Isokinetic Machines and they will rub and wear. So the time spent fussing with the various types of exercise equipment may just balance out in the end. As in the factor of speed, do not let tidiness completely dictate which program to install. Five minutes a day is not really that much extra to spend on a program that guarantees reults. I would rather clean up plates than repair a piece of equipment.

THERE IS NO THEFT PROBLEM WITH THE MACHINES. THERE IS WITH THE FREE WEIGHTS.

Only partially true. It is a fact that **standard** sized free weights do get stolen. The athletes take them home to add to their dumbells or barbells. They are easy to slip into a gym bag without a lot of notice. But — and this is the important exception to the fact — **Olympic** type plates rarely get ripped off. The reason behind this rather strange phenomenon centers around two facts: 1) the Olympic plates only fit Olympic barbells and few players have Olympic barbells at home and, 2) there is something about quality equipment that the athlete respects and the Oympic sets are the Cadillacs of the sport. They are respected for the quality.

In my twenty plus years of directing weight programs for YMCAs, Boys' Clubs, prisons, detention homes, high school, college, and professional teams, I have only had a single Olympic set stolen from the weight room. Not perfect, but it was perfect for 19 years.

The standard weights will disappear unless they are permanently fastened to barbells or dumbells, but the Olympic plates will not be bothered. This is a minor point in favor of the machines.

THE MACHINES PRODUCE FASTER STRENGTH GAINS THAN THE FREE WEIGHTS

False. This is the primary criteria to consider when installing a strength program and the one most overlooked by uninformed school administrators and coaches. The majority of the machines in this country have been sold to people who are not at all knowledgeable on the subject of strength training. The people who plop down the dough for the various machines are usually those who control the purse strings in a school or organization, not the people who run the programs.

The manufacturers of the various machines are extremely wise businessmen. They are also super salesmen. They can corner a school principal and sell him on the safety, the theft, the cleanliness factor of the machine in a jiffy. They can portray free weights as instruments of the devil and liken them to pool rooms and narcotics before they are finished. They bombard the superintendents, athletic directors, with terms like "matching resistance," "accommodating exercise," "automatically-variable exericse," "negative accentuated training," "ballistic action," "neuromuscular pattern carry-over," and the school official is left reeling. He usually doesn't know the difference between a bench press and a fire hydrant so the golden-tongued salesman has him on the ropes from the onset.

THE FREE WEIGHTS ARE BETTER INSTRUMENTS FOR GAINING STRENGTH

The machines are bright and shiney. They are well-constructed and look substantial. They cost lots of money and anything that is expensive in the American way of thinking has got to be superior to that which costs less. By comparison the Olympic weights seem archaic. The weights appear cold, unless there happens to be a chrome Olympic set on display, but they do work better.

This last statement is based on a number of facts, but the most important is that the athletes who are most interested in the element of strength — the competitive powerlifters and Olympic-style weightlifters — do not use machines to increase their power. They use the free weights in order to become stronger. I have made it my business to talk to as many strength athletes as I possibly could on the subject of machine versus free weight training. The consensus opinion is that there is nothing, as yet, in way of machines to replace the free weights for improving strength. A great many of my lifting friends utilized the Nautilus program in hopes of becoming more proficient in their chosen sport. Their lifts progressively dropped and the venture was abandoned. Ken Patera, who certainly was the strongest athlete in the world at the conclusion of his lifting career, related his experience with the Nautilus to me.

"I went to the Nautilus system in hopes of finding a faster way of retaining or perhaps even improving my strength. Since I travel so much in professional wrestling, I have little time for long workouts. The first few times I went through the Nautilus program I was exhausted, but within two weeks I was going through the required exercises not only twice, but three times and I was not even breathing heavy at the end. When I started the Nautilus program I was benching 435 for a single. After just three weeks it had dropped below 400, but I felt that if I perservered it would start climbing back. After a month I was down to 385. At that point I had had enough and started training with the free weights again. I felt that I gave it a fair test and it failed."

I have met at least fifty athletes who have had a similar experience. The two top physique men in the world, Arnold Schwarzenegger and Franco Columbu, both related that their strength dropped after going on the Nautilus program. Two of our university's top linemen went on the Nautilus system the year before I arrived. Each dropped over 50 pounds in their bench press and lost strength in their backs and legs. They spent the entire next season getting back to where they were before the Nautilus experiment.

It is not at all my purpose to pan the various machines or to debate the merits of Nautilus or Universal or Isokinetic training, but since it is of concern to all coaches who direct strength programs, perhaps a brief rationale of why free weight training is a superior method of obtaining strength is in order.

The Russian Superman, Alexeev, uses free weights — not machines — to lift more weight overhead than anyone in history.

WHY FREE WEIGHTS PRODUCE STRENGTH FASTER THAN MACHINES

The key in my argument concerning the superiority of free weights lies in the joints of the body. The joints are the supportive structures. For the athletes, they are most critical. These are the areas most susceptible to being damaged in any sport — but this fact is doubly true in a contact sport such as football. When I speak of strength for an athlete, I am speaking primarily of joint strength.

Free weights develop joint strength to a much greater extent than any form of machine training. The reasoning is really quite obvious. Since machines are, out of necessity, set in a constant pattern of movement, the trainee does not have to balance the resistance. This is a built-in convenience of the machines, but the convenience also brought with it a short-coming.

The free weights have to be balanced by the trainee in any movement. Only the body supports the weights — not a chain, lever, or piece of metal. This balancing action builds joint strength. As the football player takes a loaded barbell off the bench press stand, he must steady the bar before lowering it to his chest. The controlling action builds tendon and ligament strength in the wrist, elbow, and shoulder joints.

Machine training misses this facet of strength development and, ironically enough, this is the most critical aspect of strength training for the athlete. Without joint strength, very little else matters as the "weakest link" factor takes over and the body breaks.

STRENGTH CONVERTIBILITY

This fact can be tested quite simply. I call it "strength convertibility." Take an individual who has been training the bench press on any machine and have him perform a bench press with free weights. What always happens? The trainee is barely able to remain on the bench while trying to support the free weight. It's as if he's holding an electrified barbell. His motions are jerky and uncoordinated. Typically, he handles 50-75 pounds less with the free weights than he did on the machine in the same exercise. In short, his strength is not convertible.

The opposite is true for the free weights trainee. He can go from free weights to machines and perform as well or better so his strength is very convertible. This is true because he has built joint strength along with the muscle strength.

The point for the Strength Coach is very plain and simple. If an athlete's strength is not convertible from machines to free weights, then how is it possible to assume that his strength will be convertible from machines to any form of athletics?

Free weights training is very convertible, or will be if the program is developed properly. An athlete who is strength trained with the free weights can convert and utilize his strength for any activity as he has a solid structural strength base.

The free weights enable the trainee to utilize athletic attributes such as: timing, speed, coordination in his workout. While it is true that these factors are displayed to some degree with the machines, it is to a much smaller degree. There is very little comparison between the quality of athletic ability necessary to perform a power clean, for example, as against any involved movement on any machine.

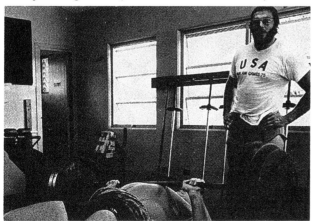

Terry Albritton, World Record Holder in the shot put, spots for powerlifting champion, Randy Frish in the University of Hawaii gym. Both of these athletes utilize free weights to increase their strength.

BODY CONTROL

An athlete learns much more control of his body when performing any exercise with free weights than he does doing the same movement with a machine. He learns a feel of the weight. He must balance the bar properly, align it in a definite groove, and apply force at a specific angle. These things are all done for him by the machines. Body control is definitely an attribute desired by every athlete.

The free weights can actually enhance athletic attributes. The machines do very little in the way of developing any carryover benefits for the athlete on the playing field. Free weights are definitely better for the athlete. They may lack some of the class of the machines and they may not have quite as many "principles of training" floating around them, but they work best and that should be the prime consideration of the Strength Coach when he goes about developing his program.

THE PSYCHOLOGY OF FREE WEIGHTS

Another factor which I have observed is that athletes stay motivated to lift more and more weight on a barbell, but do not keep this incentive on the machines. The pounds lifted become badges in an athletic community. Players develop a great deal of pride in a 300-pound bench press or a 400-pound squat. The enthusiasm is not there for a 500 leg press or a 300 bench press on the machines because there is no exact transfer to pounds. Adding another stack of weights does not have this same uplifting effect as does adding ten pounds to each end of the barbell.

The machines become very boring. They are closed with build-in limitations. The barbell has very few limitations. Should you become satisfied at any point in your progress, then more weight can be added or an entirely new exercise can be put in your program. There is no limit as to where you stop. You can load lots of weight on an Olympic barbell.

I cannot fully explain this psychological phenomenon but I do know that it exists. Athletes are challenged by the barbell, especially an Olympic bar. They grow tiresome of the machines. Coaches tell me this, as do the players themselves. Perhaps it is explained, in part, by the fact that athletes, competitive by definition, once they start becoming stronger want to be tested, either against themselves or against each other.

I have walked into hundreds of institutions and found the machines pushed against the wall while dozens of players are pushing and pulling on a bent standard bar. The free weights are more intuned with the nature of a competitive person and when the program is for football players, then it is dealing with extremely competitive people.

THE VALUE OF THE MACHINES

The free weights are a superior means of obtaining strength, but this does not mean that the machines cannot be a part of the total strength program in a school or college. The machines can be most useful to the Strength Coach who knows how to best use them for his program. The free weights are best, but they are not the best in every single case, 100% of the time every time. There are exceptions and I would like to point out a few ways in which machines can be very useful to the Strength Coach in his overall program.

"Free weights develop joint strength to a much greater extent than any form of machine training."

INCORPORATING THE MACHINES INTO THE "BIG THREE" PROGRAM

The Strength Coach is often faced with the problem of how to utilize the machines, usually the Universal, which are already a part of the school's athletic equipment. Since three to four grand has been invested in the Universal it cannot simply be tucked away out of sight and forgotten, regardless of the coach's views on the subject of machine training. Universals, because of their sheer bulk, cannot be tucked away at all and they are difficult to sell so they might as well be put to use.

While the Universal will not be the central focus of the strength program, it can become an integral part of the total program. There are many stations which are most useful to the Strength Coach as he sets up his schedule centered around the "Big Three."

The sit-up board makes an excellent warm-up station as does the hyperextension station. The chinning bar is very useful as both a warm-up and can be used as an advanced exercise station for the lats. Leg presses are useful for those who cannot as yet perform full squats.

Some coaches who are very short on Olympic equipment use the Universal as the first set of the "Big Three," having the players do a set of benches, partial pulls, and leg presses in place of the initial set of benches, power cleans, and squats.

In cases where a player is extremely weak or is recovering from an injury, the Strength Coach may find it advisable to have him work exclusively on the Universal until his strength level improves to the point where he is on a par with the bottom level of the rest of the group. This procedure saves breaking the Olympic bar below a base weight of 135, 115, or whatever the base weight is for that particular group.

MACHINES AND REHABILITATION

The machines can also be very valuable to the Strength Coach as he goes about setting up rehabilitation programs for his athletes. The weak point of machine training, that is their inability to affect the joint strength to as great a degree as the free weights, is by the same token their strong point in rehabilitation work.

In 90% of the rehabilitation cases in athletics, the Strength Coach is faced with strengthening injured joint areas, such as knees, shoulders, elbows, or backs. The rehabilitation program has to be started very conservatively. It is imperative to protect the injured joint and not to take any risk in a recurrence of the injury. The free weights increase this risk factor since they do affect the joints. The machines are safer as the majority of the stress is on the muscles and not on the tendons and ligaments that surround the joints.

In the early stages of rebuilding any injured area, it is preferred to have the athlete use a machine rather than the free weights. In the case of a dislocated shoulder, for example, the free weights are much more risky than the machines. In taking the free weight off the bench stand, the arm may travel back past the head and a recurrence of injury is much more likely than in the case of using the machines.

As soon as the injury progresses to a point where the joint can take some stress, then the athlete should be switched to the free weights so that the tendons and ligaments will be strengthened. But, in the initial stages of recovery, the machines are best.

MACHINES AND THE YOUNG TRAINEE

The machines are also a fine way to initiate a youngster into resistive training. When I speak of a youngster, I am referring to someone under fourteen years of age. I do not advocate weight training for anyone under this age, unless they are unusually physically mature. The reasoning behind this statement was explained in chapter 7, but it basically revolves around the fact that the youngster is still growing and performing heavy lifts can damage the long bones, which in turn affects overall growth and development.

The machines are useful to start anxious youngsters because once again, they do not affect the joints as much as the free weights. While any strength program does not want to come head-on at the joints of mature athletes, it is not advisable to do so for the youngsters.

A youngster can obtain a great degree of muscle tone and strength on the machines without running the risk of injuring his joints. As he grows and becomes physically more mature, this lead-in activity will serve as a useful preparation for more serious strength training later in his life.

MACHINES AND GENERAL FITNESS

The machines are excellent pieces of fitness equipment. Youngsters, older men, and females of all ages can develop a higher level of fitness by utilizing the machines. These folks are not as interested in the factor of joint strength as an athlete must be. The athlete's performance, health, and longevity in the sport he selects depends very directly on how well his joints hold together under stress.

The machines are ideal fitness tools, but the athlete can only build superior structural strength with the free weights. It's a fact, denied only by those who manufacture and sell the machines. Athletes who depend on their bodies as a means of making a living, know that the optimum tool for strength development is the old, but reliable, free weights.

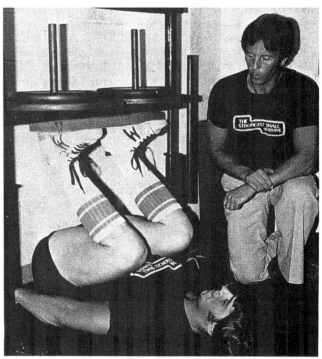

"In the early stages of rebuilding any injured area, it is preferred to have the athlete use a machine rather than the free weights."

MACHINES AND THE FUTURE

The people who are behind the two more progressive forms of machine training, Isokinetics and Nautilus, will, I believe, add a most influential chapter to the science of strength training before they are finished. They are interested in methods as well as merchandise and are making a valiant attempt to learn all they can about improving their equipment for the best possible results. And while I believe that the free weights are the most superior form of resistive training at present, it does not necessarily follow that they cannot be replaced by some other form of training. I just do not think that it has come about as yet.

NEGATIVE TRAINING

The most useful aspect of the Nautilus program from the standpoint of strength training, is not the pre-exhaustion system, but rather the negative training which they have incorporated into their machines. Negative training is not a new concept with Nautilus by any means. Many members of the York Barbell Club Weightlifting Team were using this method of strength training during the mid-sixties under the direction of Dr. John Zeigler.

It is a very involved and quite complicated form of strength training in that the fatigue factor of each trainee must be recognized by the Strength Coach very quickly or overtraining results. There are many shortcomings to the present program, with overtraining being the number one villain, but the program has distinct possibilities. As the number of athletes who utilize this form of training increases, then so will the practical data. Some competitive weightlifters are into this method of training already and they will be able to supply many of the answers. It has possibilities, but the methods are still experimental at present, regardless of what the proponents of the system report.

THE ISOKINETIC POWER RACK

The other instrument which may change many concepts of strength training in the next decade is the Isokinetic Power Rack. This piece of equipment will allow the athlete to perform isometric and isotonic contractions in a manner never possible previously, or at least not possible on a large scale since it is a new kind of power rack.

The Isokinetic Power Rack is scientifically engineered and has tremendous possibilities for the advanced strength trainee and for rehabilitation work.

I trained on one of the first experimental models of the Isokinetic Power Rack in Independence, Missouri, in 1973 and was very impressed with its potential. I truly believe that isometric-type training will return to the strength scene in the next few years. Isometrics was the center of attention of the strength world during the early sixties and then abruptly dropped from favor almost overnight. My feeling is that the principles were and still are sound but the methods were never properly formulated by anyone who thoroughly understood strength training for athletics. The only exception to this statement is Dr. John Zeigler, whom I consider the "Main Man" of Strength Training. He produced two world record holders, Bill March and Louis Riecke, in competitive weightlifting with his application of scientific training principles to isometric rack training.

Dr. Zeigler built a prototype of the Isokinetic Power Rack in 1960 where it still remains in his home gym. Dr. Zeigler knows how to build strength on the rack, but unfortunately, Dr. Zeigler is not of the nature to document his methods and findings so that information is virtually lost except for those who talk directly to the doctor. Those who did perpetuate the isometric cause did so only for the economic gain and not for the benefit of the strength sport.

The Isokinetic Power Rack is currently being used by a few competitive weightlifters and some football teams and, hopefully, these people will, in the next few years, come up with some findings that will be of value to everyone connected with the field of strength training for athletics.

SUMMARY

In summarizing my view on the machines, I believe that the free weights work better than the machines in building total body strength and this is what really matters to the athlete. Free weights work best because they strengthen the joints better than the machines. I believe that the machines can be of genuine value in rehabilitation work, in training youngsters, and in fitness development. I do recognize the fact that anyone can become stronger on the machines, but must add that he can become stronger faster and be able to use the new-found strength better if he uses the free weights. Strength obtained via free weights is more convertible than that which is derived from the machines. For the athlete, convertible strength is crucial.   ★

19

CHAPTER NINETEEN
DRUGS AND STRENGTH TRAINING

ATHLETES ARE ALWAYS LOOKING for ways to improve performance. The modern athlete is faced with such a high level of competition that he is constantly seeking that extra "edge." The athlete of today is bigger, stronger, faster, and more intelligent than his predecessors. And the level of competition continues to go up and up. Ten years ago a four-hundred-pound bench press was as rare as a four-minute mile. Now there are as many as half a dozen college football players performing this feat on just one team. The linemen are becoming as quick as the backs, but now the linemen are 6'6" and weigh 275, rather than 6'3" and 245. The physical specimens being created are awesome. The equipment manufactured to protect the athletes from each other on the football field is no longer adequate. The players now crush face guards, crack helmets, and shatter shoulder pads.

As the level of competition climbs, so do the rewards for those who make it to the top. Professional football players who establish themselves become financially well-set for life. They also receive the additional rewards of recognition and prestige within their community. They are often nationally-known and accepted on a par with statesman, scientists, and performers from the arts.

With this glittering pot of gold waiting for the accomplished football player, it's no surprise to find him trying any method to reach the end of the gridiron rainbow.

AMERICA IS DRUG-ORIENTED

Anyone, athlete or non-athlete, living in modern America is in the midst of a highly-developed drug culture. Youngsters entering high school and college are often more aware of the effects of various types of drugs than are the medical men who prescribe them. I know athletes who keep a Physicians Desk Reference (a book published for physicians describing the effects of all drugs currently on the market) next to their bedside and read from it each day. They become extremely knowledgeable on the subject of drugs.

Athletes also learn about the use of drugs from one another. Seldom does the coach ever know that one of his players is using steroids or amphetamines. The trainer and team physician are also bypassed as they are a part of the organization. Members of the organization, i.e. coaches, trainers, physicians and so forth, may speak out against the practice and the athlete's future may be jeopardized so why risk telling them?

Unfortunately, too many coaches (and this certainly includes those in the position of Strength Coach) are totally unaware of the undercurrent of drug use among the athletes. The coaches are also flagrantly uninformed on the effects of various drugs on their athletes. This ignorance is certainly not in the best interest of the team.

THE COACH MUST BECOME DRUG EDUCATED

I must pause briefly in this dissertation to point out emphatically that I am not encouraging the use of any drugs for athletes. What I do believe, however, is that the effective coach must be very aware of what is going on all about him. A knowledge of the use and the effects of various drugs can enable him to detect their use and, most importantly, allow him to be in a position to counsel and help the user.

One truism that I have found prevails among athletes. If they sincerely feel that a certain drug or combination of drugs will enhance performance, then they will obtain the drugs and they will use the drugs — whether the NCAA, coaches, parents, or best friend object.

We have, in effect, created a monster in this competitive sports society. The competition is high, yet the rewards are so great that the athlete is now willing to risk life, limb, and future health to obtain his goal.

HOW CAN THE COACH HELP THE ATHLETE?

So what can the Strength Coach do to prevent the athlete from harming himself with drugs? First of all, it should be made very clear that he cannot stop the athlete from taking drugs. Even though many of the drugs are obtained only by way of prescription, they are always available via black-market. I know athletes who pay five times the regular price for anabolics, and secure them by mail from friends who live three thousand miles away. No amount of trouble is too much if the player really believes that the drugs will enable him to perform better in his sport.

Policing the players is also quite impossible. Few, if any, will admit that they are taking any form of drug as they realize that they may be penalized. Since a great majority of the drugs are obtained through underground channels there is little chance to trace the origin of the source. Blood tests are expensive and really rather ineffective. If the athlete knows that a blood test is to be done he just stops using the drug prior to the test or switches to a form of drug which cannot be detected by the test being conducted.

THE SWITCH AT THE WORLD CHAMPIONSHIPS

To illustrate just how well informed the modern athlete is on the subject of drugs, I cite an example from the 1971 World Weightlifting Championships held in Columbus, Ohio, where I served as assistant coach for the United States team. The Organization Committee of the Championships was so concerned about the rampant use of amphetamines in the competition that they decided to test the top three finishers in each weight division immediately after the competition. Urine samples were taken the first three days and eight out of the nine place winners were found guilty of using amphetamines and they were disqualified.

Testing for any foreign substance in the body is really quite involved and the tests are rather specific. In other words, a test has to be set up specifically for amphetamines or specifically for barbituates or specifically for steroids. One test does not identify all of these foreign substances. The testing at Columbus was for amphetamines.

Knowing this, the athletes started some hurried research. The European teams put their doctors on the task while the United States lifters dug into their own research sources. By the fourth day of competition there were no other lifters using drugs — or so the tests reported. "Success," said the officials. "We stopped the weightlifters from using drugs." While the officials were patting each other on the back the athletes continued to perform on stage under the influence of "pep pills." The officials underestimated the athletes. They usually do.

The testing only forced the athletes to switch brands of uppers. They did not stop using them. Now they were using types that could not be detected by the tests being administered. The officials were never aware of this fact and most of them still aren't. If they would have caught on and changed the tests, the athletes would have changed too. The trouble with all those who govern and direct athletics is that they fail to understand just how deep the motivation is of those who play the game.

Regulations, testing, policing, penalizing will not stop the athletes from securing and taking anything which he believes, rightly or wrongly, will enhance his performance. This is an absolute fact and must be recognized by all those who deal with highly-motivated athletes.

Head Coach Jerry Claiborne of the University of Maryland is one of the nation's leading exponents of the value of strength training for football. His Terrapins have gone to five consecutive Bowl Games.

THE COACH MUST BE AN ADVISOR

The aware and conscientious coach must become, out of absolute necessity, an advisor rather than a policeman. He must learn as much as he possibly can about the various chemical agents and their effect of the body. Then, and only then, will he be in a position to be of genuine value to his players. Merely sermonizing to the players that alcohol or amphetamines or steroids will hurt them is just not enough. The useful coach must be in a position to tell the players exactly how alcohol or tobacco'or amphetamines or steroids act on the body.

The information related must be honest and total because chances are the athlete has already read some of the research and talked to other athletes who have used the drug. Any form of "snowjobbing" will only alienate the coach from the player and cut off all lines of communication on the subject. When this happens, the coach is of no further use to the players on the question of drug usage.

HONESTY HELPS IN COMMUNICATION

My basic philosophy is to be completely honest with the athlete. Lay the facts, all of the facts, before the athlete. Should he choose to risk his health by using a drug which may have dangerous side effects for the sake of increasing his performance then there is really not a whole lot that the coach can do to actually stop him from doing so. At least the coach, if he is honest with the players, will remain in a position where he can counsel him should he run into problems. The athletes will, however, risk their longeviety and total health for the sake of playing a better football game, but the coach must be armed with facts if he is to persuade the player against using drugs. He cannot merely exert his authority (as is usually the case) because the free-thinking athlete of the seventies will simply ignore the "authority" and go his own way.

This chapter is an attempt to present some of the facts on some of the drugs used by athletes in various sports.

None of the testimonies are documented as any athlete realizes the consequences of confessing to drug usage publicly. This personal information was given to me in confidence and if some scientific value is lost because of this lack of validation, then so be it. It is based on fact, however, and fact is what I am seeking.

DRUGS ARE DELICATE SUBJECT MATTER

Since I am dealing with a most touchy subject, that drugs and athletics, I must again reiterate that I am not advocating the use of any of these substances for any athlete. This is not my role. Legally, I cannot do so and ethically I do not care to do so. Yet I do not deny the facts that lie before me. Some of the drugs that I will mention do enhance performance. Some do make athletes stronger. It has become rather conventional to deny facts that do not fit the current pattern of thought in our country. To deny these facts is to present a lie and this is not my purpose. If you do not like the facts then that is your prerogative, but that does not mean that the truth goes away. It's time the coaches and administrators of all sports lifted their collective heads out of the sand and started looking at a few facts, and then perhaps they would be in a better position to help the athletes they direct and govern.

My purpose is not to encourage the use of any drugs by the athletes, but to inform the coaches and athletes of the effects of many of the drugs currently making the rounds in team dressing rooms. Like it or not they are there — in abundance.

THE RISK IS INDISCRIMINATE USAGE

The greatest problem in the use of drugs in athletics is not so much that they are being used, but the manner in which they are being used. Each athlete who uses any form of drug should be doing so under medical supervision. It's the user who obtains his steroids from a teammate who is really risking his health. Concerned people must funnel these athletes back to the medical experts and the athletes must be directed to the experts without fear of reprisals.

The danger of drug use is not so much in the drugs themselves, as they are manufactured by reputable drug firms and have been tested for many years before being put on the market, but rather how they are being used, and that is indiscriminately and without supervision. In a sense, the officials have driven the athletes underground. At this level they are impossible to advise, counsel, or examine. A new philosophy has to emerge if we as coaches of athletes are to be of genuine use to the modern-day athlete. One fact is certain — athletes are now using all forms of drugs and there are health risks involved in their use. The Strength Coach is the obvious advisor on this subject, so he carries a great deal of responsibility for the total health of the team.

Jack King of Winston-Salem, North Carolina is one of the finest Strength Coaches in the nation. The former Olympic Weightlifting Champion instructs his athletes in all aspects of strength conditioning: proper nutrition, flexibility, and cardiovascular, respiratory fitness. He is highly respected by his athletes because of his knowledge and honest approach. Here he works with North Carolina middleweight champion Jimmy Cook.

The following are some, although not all, of the foreign chemical agents taken into the body by some athletes. Some, like amphetamines or anabolics, are taken specifically to enhance performance. Others, such as tobacco, alcohol, and marijuana, are used for entertainment. The Strength Coach needs to be aware of the effects of these substances on the athletes he is coaching.

TOBACCO

Coaches have traditionally been against the use of tobacco by their athletes as it is a practice that has been proven to be detrimental to overall health. The mortality rate of smokers is 30% higher than that of non-smokers. Men show a doubling of deaths from all forms of cancer and eight times as many cases of lung cancer. Besides the huge number of deaths attributable to smoking, there are also the increasing number of disabilities resulting from other respiratory ailments.

There have been many tests conducted on smokers and non-smokers to determine the effect of cigarettes on athletic performance. Some of these comparisons were conducted under exercise conditions while others checked the physiological changes during rest periods.

Dr. Thomas Cureton, in 1936, reported that non-smokers were superior to smokers in swimming. Arthur Steinhaus and Florence Grunderman in **Tobacco and Health** tested long distance runners and concluded that the non-smokers performed much better than the smokers.

The effect of tobacco smoking on strength and muscular endurance was tested by C.E. Willgoose and reported in volume 18 of the 1947 edition of **Research Quarterly**. He noted that smokers scored higher in strength and endurance tests on non-smoking days.

One of the more important research facts to athletes is that smokers have been found to have a decreased pulmonary diffusion capacity. Researchers R.B Chevalier, R.A. Krumhole and J.C. Ross in **Annals of Internal Medicine** found that smokers had a smaller total lung capacity, decreased respiratory capacities, decreased vital capacities, and greater oxygen debt accumulation during exercise.

Smoking does nothing remotely positive for your body and does do lots of things that are very definitely negative to athletic performance.

NICOTINE IS THE VILLAIN

The nicotine and carbon monoxide in the cigarettes causes the problems to the body. A person retains about 1 mg. of nicotine from each cigarette he smokes. The nicotine is absorbed, not only in the lungs as most people realize, but also in the mouth, throat, and bronchial pathways since nicotine is water soluble. The nicotine increases the heart rate as much as 15 to 20 beats per minute, but this effect is short-lived and the pulse rate returns to normal within a half an hour after stopping smoking.

Smoking also reduces the blood flow to the skin and increases the systemic blood pressure. These two factors cause an increase in the cardiac workload both during rest and exercise. The heart muscle is found to be irritated much easier during bouts of exertion in smokers than in non-smokers.

It has been found that as few as fifteen puffs on a cigarette restricts the conductance of the airways by 31%. Dr. Roy Shephard states in his book **Alive Man!**: "The 31% decrease of airway conductance is rarely appreciated by a resting subject, but in near-maximum effort, breathing is noticeably more difficult immediately following the smoking of one or more cigarettes. There is also a measurable increase in the oxygen cost of breathing; 10% rather than 5% of the available maximum oxygen intake is diverted to the chest muscles, and this is probably one of the main factors that reduce the endurance performance of the chronic smoker."

It should be rather obvious to all athletes that smoking does nothing remotely positive for your body and does do lots of things that are very definitely negative to athletic performance. The wisest choice is not to smoke at all, but I realize that some are going to smoke regardless of the consequences. If you fall into this latter category then at least temper the habit so that you do not smoke immediately prior to a strenuous workout or a game. At least in this manner you will not be affecting your performance quite so severely. Likewise, smoking in moderation does not have the physical repercussions as does heavy smoking, so if you must smoke, cut down, avoid smoking prior to workouts and games, and smoke less on training days.

ALCOHOL

Can an athlete drink alcohol and keep a high level of strength and cardiovascular fitness? Coaches have been faced with this question for many years. Athletics and alcohol have always gone hand-in-hand. A great many beer and liquor manufacturers tie the successful athlete in with their product. The team builds unity over a few (or more than a few) pitchers of draft beer at the local pub. Beer blasts are a historical means of initiating new players or celebrating victory. Just how much does drinking really affect total performance? What does the Strength Coach need to know about alcohol so that he can advise the athletes?

When alcohol is ingested it immediately affects the brain. It impairs judgement, slows reaction time, limits self control, and adversely affects vision. None of these are healthy for the athlete either in the weight room or on the playing field. The use of all voluntary muscles is impaired even with the addition of moderate amounts of alcohol to the system. Again, this is not a highly desirable state in which to perform. Large doses of alcohol actually causes degeneration of the individual muscle fibers.

NOT ALL FINDINGS ARE NEGATIVE

Yet small doses of alcohol do not seem to have detrimental effects on the body and do not adversely affect athletic performance. Melryln Williams reported in the December, 1960 edition of **Research Quarterly** that: "the effect of a small and moderate dose of alcohol on initial strength, maximal strength, and final strength was found to be insignificant, although there appeared to be a tendency towards increased performance in initial and maximal strength." Ikar and Steinhaus also concluded that there was a 5.6% increase in strength following the ingestion of 15-20 ml. of 95% ethyl alcohol.

It has also been found that the factor of endurance is not adversely affected by small and moderate doses of alcohol. Two Danish researchers, Graf and Strom, have demonstrated that ethyl alcohol does not affect the circulatory system negatively and thus does not decrease physical working capacity.

THE CASE AGAINST ALCOHOL FOR ATHLETES

The effect of alcohol on the factors of strength and endurance is not a negative one, but it does not follow that alcohol is beneficial to the athlete. The factors of speed, timing, and muscular coordination are adversely affected. This information might suggest to the athlete that he can weight train while using alcohol but that he should not participate on the gridiron. This is not the case, as all of the lifts, especially when performed with a heavy weight, do require a certain degree of coordination to achieve success. To attempt to power clean a maximum weight for five repetitions under the influence of alcohol would be a mistake. Not only would the trainee fail to achieve his goal but he would run a very high risk of injuring himself.

Joe Gano serves as Strength Consultant to many athletes in the Metropolitan Washington area. One of his most promising trainees, Charlie, has only been under Joe's tutelage for the past year, but shows enormous development for a two-year old.

ALCOHOL AND NUTRITION

It should also be remembered that the use of alcohol affects the overall nutritional program of every athlete. Alcohol calories take priority over glycogen stores in your body. The carbohydrates ingested are therefore not utilized as energy and they are stored as body fat. Fat may not be the number one enemy of all athletes but it definitely is up near the top of the list. Alcohol also destroys many of the valuable vitamins and minerals in your system and a heavy drinking bout will leave you with a nutritional deficiency.

Heavy drinking bouts are generally followed by headaches, states of depression and feelings which could not be considered healthy. Very few athletes feel motivated to go to the weight room or playing field the night after boozing it up. Some don't really feel like living any longer, yet alone doing heavy squats, power cleans, or bear crawls.

Football players are going to drink. It's as much a part of their sub-culture as reading **Playboy**. It's part and parcel with the "hairy-chest" image. Any effort to curtail the activity is usually met with ingenious methods to circumvent the rules. Every athlete also knows that he is not at his best after drinking so a step towards moderation is usually accepted.

A VOTE FOR MODERATION

A simple but effective rule is don't drink the night before a heavy training session or a hard practice and, naturally, a game. This may necessitate abstaining all week and having only Saturday night to party it up but it's a compromise that works fairly well. Others, who seem to enjoy the suds more than others, find that drinking immediately after practice or workouts allows them to enjoy their booze and not let it affect their performance adversely.

Moderation is really the key. Too much will certainly have detrimental effects on performance, this is for sure. If you must drink, limit yourself to small amounts and avoid drinking before strenuous practice or workout sessions.

MARIJUANA

Scientific data on the effects of marijuana on athletic performance are very scanty because of the law making possession a criminal offense. The various surveys have to be taken slightly under the point of absolute credibility because few people are prepared to jeopardize their lives merely to add to the body of knowledge on the subject.

I have talked to a great number of athletes who confessed that they had used marijuana both in training and in competition. Since a small amount of the active ingredient, tetrahydracannabinals, has been shown to increase self-confidence, relax the individual, remove symptoms of fatigue and give a mental lift, it serves as a form of tranquilizer for many athletes. Many that I have talked to used it prior to competition to settle jittery nerves.

Larger amounts of the drug do impair performance. The specific amount which could be considered excessive for each individual varies tremendously. Every batch of marijuana has completely different potencies from the other. For example, a joint (marijuana rolled in the form of a cigarette) from plants grown in Mexico or California has less potency than those grown in South America or Southeast Asia — or at least that is the general rule. So it becomes rather impossible to state that smoking two joints of marijuana is excessive unless the type of growing conditions is adequately spelled out. Likewise, individuals differ tremendously as to their tolerance to the drug. So when I refer to large amounts of marijuana I mean large amounts as it relates to that individual.

MARIJUANA AFFECTS MUSCULAR COORDINATION

When someone smokes, or ingests, large amounts of marijuana his muscular coordination will be impaired. The classical study showing that motorists who smoked marijuana displayed quicker reaction time than those who drank alcohol and those who neither drank or smoked used only a mild dose of marijuana. Excessive amounts have also been shown to slow reaction time and increase the pulse rate. Yet larger doses also result in perceptual disorders and even lead to hallucinations. The latter may be a desired end should the user be watching a sunset, but not quite so desirable if he is reponsible for watching the wide receiver on a pass pattern.

The effects of smoking the drug are short-lived and generally last only a few hours. The more potent the vintage, the longer the effect of the drug. Following smoking and "getting high" there is always a period of "coming down" off the drug in which the user experiences feelings of drowsiness and sometimes depression. This is not a desirable state for an athlete by any means.

MARIJUANA AS A TRANQUILIZER

Some athletes I quizzed found marijuana an excellent tranquilizer to be used in the days prior to games or competition. It helped them to keep from being overly nervous and allowed them to think of their assignments in the game without the usual flow of adrenalin that typically accompanies such pre-game thinking. I have talked to many competitive weightlifters who used marijuana as an aid in gaining bodyweight. Since marijuana acts as an appetite stimulate on most people, the athletes smoked before eating so that he could eat lots more. Strange but true.

The problem the Strength Coach is faced with concerning the use of marijuana is similar to that concerning any drug, whether legal or illegal. That is, discovering who is using it and advising them as to how to use it so that it does the **least harm** to their performance and overall health.

This is not to imply that the Strength Coach should recommend the use of marijuana, but to deny the fact that some players are using it is merely avoiding responsibility to the player and the team. From all available research and from talking to scores of athletes who use the drug, I must state that marijuana does not appear to deter from progress in the weight room or adversely affect athletic performance when used in moderation.

It is the excessive amounts of marijuana that do limit performance both in the training room and on the gridiron. I discourage use of the drug the night prior to a heavy workout as the lethargic feelings inherent in the drug often carry over to the following day, and the athlete is apt to skip a training session, or not to put as much energy into the workout. Also, counsel against heavy use at any time so that the athlete does not become dependent on marijuana as a relaxant.

■■■

The long-range effects of marijuana are not yet known.

■■■

LONG-RANGE EFFECTS ARE UNKNOWN

The long-range effects of marijuana are not yet known so it would be wise for all users to consider the possibility that it will prove to be detrimental to their overall health. Users should be wise enough to keep their dosage to a minimum and avoid using the drug immediately prior to any athletic endeavor. Give your body at least 24 hours to partially clear your system of most of the drug (it actually takes 48 hours to completely do so) before taking part in any form of competition, training sessions, or practice.

Marijuana, like so many other drugs, is part and parcel of most athlete's fun times. It must be kept in perspective or the athlete will soon find his performance is being severely limited. Moderation, once again, seems to be the key to handling the problem.

HASHISH

Hashish or "hash" has basically the same properties as marijuana. It is a much more concentrated form of the drug tetrahydracannabinals, as it is a condensed form of the resin from the tops of the marijuana plants. It is smoked or put into foods much like marijuana but is about five times as potent. The same rules apply to hash as they do to marijuana.

AMPHETAMINES

Amphetamines come in many different names as each drug company has its own line. Dexedrine and benzedrine are just two of the more common. More often, the street names are used rather than the generic ones so: "black beauties," "blue babies," "policeman," "jolly beans," "minstrels," "bennies," "speed," or "uppers" are the names heard rather than the pharmaceutical ones. Specific geographic areas have their own pet names for certain kinds of amphetamines as do specific vocations. Truck drivers use "L.A. Turnarounds" and shift workers "all nighters."

CHARACTERISTICS OF AMPHETAMINES

The amphetamines have three outstanding characteristics: 1) they are mood elevators, 2) they prevent sleep, and 3) they depress the appetite. The great influx of amphetamines usage in this country has come about primarily because of the latter characteristic. They are used as diet pills and literally millions of men and women use a wide assortment of "speed" to help them keep their weight under control.

SIDE EFFECTS

Unfortunately, the drugs also have rather harmful side effects on the body. They raise the body temperature and the heart rate considerably. Extreme nervousness also results and periods of depression follows usage. Prolonged usage has been found to be physiologically addictive and withdrawal is as difficult as it is from heroin. Extended usage also results in irreversible brain damage. Ironically enough, it is the medical men who are dispensing these little goodies in massive amounts because it's much easier for a doctor to give a fat lady a few dozen pills than it is to counsel her on exercise and diet. Most medical men know so little about nutrition and exercise that they take the easy way out (for them) and place the patients health in jeopardy.

"UPPERS" AND ATHLETIC PERFORMANCE

What effect do amphetamines have on athletic performance? The American Medical Association sanctioned two studies on the subject of amphetamine usage in athletics in 1959. Gene Smith and Henry Beecher conducted one study at Harvard and reported their findings in the **Journal of the American Medical Association**, May, 1959. Their study concluded that 14 to 21 mgs. of amphetamine per 70 kgs. (154 pounds) of bodyweight ingested two or three hours before athletic performance resulted in an appreciable improvement in performance. Running, swimming, and weight throwing events were tested and 75% of the athletes tested improved their performance.

Dr. Peter Karpovich of Springfield College conducted the other study and his findings are displayed in that same volume of the **Journal of the American Medical Association.** His conclusions were different from those of Smith and Beecher, Karpovich showed that 50 out of the 54 subjects showed neither beneficial nor deleterious effects from the ingestion of 10-20 mgs. of amphetamine given either one-half or one hour before the tests.

Researchers Bill Lovingood, Carl Blyth, William Peacock, and Robert Lindsay of the University of North Carolina conducted one of the more extensive, and also one of the more recent, studies on the subject. Their report can be found in volume 38, number 1, 1967 of **Research Quarterly**. They concluded that: "15 mgs. of d-amphetamine sulfate significantly improved performance but caused a significant increase in heart rate."

"UPPERS" AND THE CENTRAL NERVOUS SYSTEM

The Strength Coach and the athlete both must be very aware of the dangers of amphetamines. They are closely related to adrenaline and effects are produced on both the sympathetic and the central nervous systems. It's really not wise to mess around with the central nervous system. Amphetamines cause a feeling of extreme well-being. Athletes ignore signs of fatigue. Injuries of joints and muscles typically result.

Large doses of amphetamines bring about blurring of vision, dizziness, excessive sweating, diarrhea, and a dryness of the mouth. None of these characteristics are especially conducive to outstanding performance. And there's more. Cardiac palpitations, cardiac arrhythmias and ventricular filrillations also result under amphetamine usage, especially when large dosages are used.

It is not a drug for athletes. There are just too many negative side effects associated with amphetamines for the conscientious player. The drugs carry a high risk to your health and also to your performance. Coming down off amphetamines is often very traumatic to the user. He becomes extremely depressed and experiences hallucinations which could not be termed delightful by any standard. Prolonged use results in a dependency. Withdrawal has to be carried out over a long period of time under medical supervision. Amphetamines, in short, are as risky to your health as heroin and should be avoided.

▪▪

It's really not wise to mess around with the central nervous system.

▪▪

CAFFEINE

Interestingly enough, the "upper of the populace," caffeine, can enhance athletic performance just as effectively as amphetamines and is nowhere as risky to your health. Caffeine is present in coffee, tea, and cola drinks. A cup of coffee contains approximately 150 mgs. of caffeine. Tea has about 100 mgs. and cola 50 mgs. When milk or cream is added to coffee or tea the caffeine potency is increased.

Caffeine stimulates the higher centers of the brain. It eliminates the feelings of fatigue and increases mental processes. Many students use coffee or caffeine tablets to study through the night. It has also been found that caffeine increases the capacity for work. Tests have shown that as much as 30% more work can be performed while using caffeine, hence the traditional coffee break serves a genuine purpose for management.

The military conducted a series of tests on the effects of caffeine on marching troops. It was discovered that caffeine allowed the soldiers to march much further and not experience fatigue. Not nearly as many soldiers dropped out when under the influence of caffeine.

It was felt for some time that the increase in ability to perform physical work was because of the stimulation to the higher brain centers, but it is now recognized that large doses of caffeine can cause an increase of both the cardiac stroke volume and aerobic power.

SIMILAR EFFECT ON PERFORMANCE AS AMPHETAMINES

From all that I can discover, caffeine has much the same effect on overall performance as do the amphetamines. Considering the fact that the side effects of caffeine are very mild in comparison to those of the amphetamines and it becomes clearly obvious that caffeine should be selected over the amphetamines if and when the athlete is determined to use some sort of stimulant.

SIDE EFFECTS

Caffeine does have side effects, especially large doses of caffeine, so a bit of moderation is in order should you be planning to use this form of stimulant. Coordination and recently acquired motor skills deteriorate when large doses of caffeine are used. Extremely large doses can cause tremors and convulsions in some people.

If the athlete restricts his intake of caffeine to three or four cups of coffee during a five to six-hour span, there seems little harm in the ingesting of caffeine. It is certainly much less harmful than the amphetamines and very readily available. Since there are no rules forbidding the use of caffeine in athletic competition, this does seem to be the more sensible route to take.

Many athletes find a cup of coffee some 20-30 minutes prior to a workout helps them get started much easier. The warm liquid helps to elevate the body temperature and the caffeine increases the activity level. Like many of the other drugs, caffeine when used in moderation can be a valuable aid to your training. If overdone it can be detrimental.

ANABOLIC STEROIDS

The anabolic steroids, or androgenic hormones, are perhaps the most topical subject in the drug world of athletics today. The use of anabolics is now world-wide.

Unfortunately, so is the ignorance about the effects of the drugs. Some of the information I will present on this subject is not documented. I have personally talked to over 500 individual athletes who confessed to using some form of anabolic steroid. They passed on the information in confidence, did not record any information on paper, and signed nothing. If one overtly admits that he is using steroids he could, and probably would, be excluded from further sports activities. What I present here is an accurate picture of steroid usage, perhaps the most authentic ever presented, because I was not hampered by the athlete's fear of reprisal.

PROPERTIES OF STEROIDS

The naturally-occurring testosterone is secreted by the interstitial cells of the testes from the time of puberty. It is the testosterone that brings on the various male characteristics such as facial and pubic hair, deeper voice, and adolescent growth spurt. The drugs being used by athletes are actually synthetic forms of hormones. The steroids have two basic properties: anabolic and androgenic. Anabolic refers to the nitrogen retention and protein-building characteristics and androgenic to the masculine-producing properties. Ideally, the drug should have high anabolic and low androgenic properties. In other words, the manufacturers of the synthetic steroids have attempted to eliminate the masculanizing effects of the drug, leaving only the growth-stimulating effect.

There are quite a few anabolic steroids being used by various athletes. Some of the more popular are: Dianabol, Winstrol, Anavar, and Durabolin. Dianabol, (methandrostenolone) made by the CIBA Company is the most popular while Winstrol, (stanozolol) by Winthrop Laboratories, is considered lower in androgenic properties. Anavar, C.D. Searle & Company, is low in adrogenic properties but also has the lowest anabolic effect so is seldom used by athletes. Durabolin, Organol Inc., is taken by injection, which makes it rather safe since it by-passes the liver, but few athletes want to take shots.

The drug is used medically to treat severely dehabilitated patients such as those who have been seriously burned, critically ill for long periods, or bed-ridden for an extended length of time. Steroids are also used on patients who are physically weakened for whatever reason. Those with mononeucleosis or strep throat are often treated with steroids as the drug not only helps build muscle tissue but has a slight euphoric effect and increases appetite. The patient on steroid therapy feels better, eats more, and recovers faster.

The drugs being used by athletes are actually synthetic forms of hormones.

Competitive weightlifters were the first group of athletes to use anabolic steroids on a large scale. Soon thereafter, other athletes took a page from the weightlifting manual and steroid usage became widespread.

ANABOLICS AND ATHLETICS

The question of using anabolic steriods on healthy specimens raises many ethical eyebrows. Some contend that there is no evidence to substantiate the fact that anabolics stimulates any muscle growth in healthy, well-conditioned athletes. William Fowler, Gerald Gardner, and Glen Egstrom reporting in the September, 1965 edition of the **Journal of Applied Physiology** on, "Effect of an Anabolic Steroid on Physical Performance of Young Men," concluded that the forty-seven young men taking androgen-anabolic hormones for 16 weeks showed no significant differences in strength or working capacity. Likewise, a study on anabolic steroids and exercise at Long Beach State College failed to demonstrate any significant differences in either weight gain or strength gain.

Dr. M.E. Trout, Medical Director of the Winthrop Laboratories made this statement in connection with the use of Winstrol by athletes. "Even though it has been published in the scientific literature, we do not recommend the use of Winstrol by high school and college age athletes in weight conditioning programs." In the same vein, Dr. Graziano of the CIBA Pharmaceutical Company states: "The use of Dianabol in healthy males between the ages of 15 and 18 years is not well-documented. There would seem to be no contraindication to short courses of therapy using recommended doses as long as epiphyses are closed, but we here at CIBA cannot sanction its use. From time to time we hear of its use by football teams and weightlifters without the side effects; but, again, these are not in controlled studies. In general, the use of drugs of any kind for the expected improvement of athletic endeavor seems to be frowned upon."

The American Medical Association has officially recommended that athletes not use oral anabolic agents, all of which are related to methyltestosterone, as an artificial aid in building muscles. "The best way to excel in athletics is to have proper nutrition and graded exercises in order to build athletic proficiency without any artificial stimulus."

So according to the research and the drug companies, steroids should not be used by healthy athletes. Supposedly, the muscle fibers have already reached their maximum diameter and the drug does little or no good. Many coaches and athletic administrators spend a great deal of time trying to convince their athletes that the steroids are quite harmful and are useless in building strength. So why do the athletes continue to use them? Simply because they do increase strength in almost everyone who takes them. I have made it a point to talk to as many athletes as I possibly could on this subject and I have never talked to anyone who did not get stronger after taking steroids.

WEIGHTLIFTERS USED STEROIDS FIRST

Competitive weightlifters have been using steroids since the late fifties so there were many more subjects in that field of athletics than in any other. It was primarily from this group that I obtained my information. There has been research done which concludes that steroids do help athletic performance. John O'Shea of Oregon State did two studies dealing with the use of steroids, one on weight trainers and the other with swimmers. Both tests showed a significant improvement in performance during steroid usage. Hettinger, in his book **Physiology of Strength** used androgenic-anabolic hormones on older men (65-70) and found a positive increase in strength and body weight as well as a proportionate increase in the muscle cross-section.

ANABOLIC SIDE EFFECTS

The basic reason that so many athletes are now using anabolics is because they do work, but this does not and should not mean that they be a part of the team's training table. On the contrary, it has also been found that a systematic nutritional program will influence strength gains as well **or better** than an anabolic program and the nutritional program has no side effects except better health. The steroids do have side effects, some of which are quite serious and anyone using them without medical guidance may be risking his health.

The steroids affect the liver and kidneys. The steroids also juggle the entire endocrine system and it is not conducive to overall health to fool with the endrocrine system without understanding the full consequences of the act. Side effects may include: headaches, excessive acne, extreme irritability, loss of the sex drive, insomnia, voice changes, hirsutism (growth of body hair), and excessive cramping. Not too neat.

The amount of steroids prescribed generally depends on bodyweight, but many athletes do not stick to the recommended amounts. The dosages that individuals take is most inconsistent. A range from 5 mgs. a day to 100 mgs. a day has been reported. Most athletes take the anabolics for 4-6 weeks and then lay-off for a minimum of two months before taking the drug again. Some athletes I interviewed believe that they receive greater benefit from the drug if they use it but twice a year so they only go on two "programs" each year. The top lifters typically use an anabolic program prior to the Nationals and then again before the World Championships.

Each individual seems to have his own tolerance and capacity for the drug. As I mentioned earlier, I have never met anyone who used anabolics who did not experience some strength gains, but not everyone responded with the same amount of gains. The typical gain is 10% in the first four to six weeks. Later gains are often much less. Some athletes increase the dosage when they become stuck in their progress but this system does not always work. In fact, it often only brings on the side effects with no appreciable strength gains. It's the old tale again, that just because a little is good does not mean that more is better. It seems that some steroids allow the individual to meet his full capacity but an excess cannot be utilized by the body. In other words, anabolics cannot take the athlete past his potential but it may elevate him to his full potential, strength-wise.

RISK IS AN UNSUPERVISED USAGE

The danger in anabolic usage is not so much that they are being used, but rather in how they are being used. Too many athletes are using them without the benefit of medical supervision and this could prove to be dangerous. Periodical check-ups, especially for the liver and prostate, are most important for overall health. The doctors will also be able to advise the athletes on the normal dosages, expected side effects, and other pertinent data. Without professional advice, the athletes often take far too much of the drug, stay on them for too long a period of time, and do not lay off quite long enough.

The Strength Coach must act as a counselor in the matter of anabolics. I do not believe that you can simply tell the athletes that they cannot or should not be taking steroids. It also does little good to insist that they do not work or that it is unethical to use them. If an athlete hears that a friend or fellow player has greatly improved his strength by taking anabolics, then he may decide that they will also make him stronger — regardless of what the coach may say.

ETHICS AND ANABOLICS

As for the question of ethics in taking anabolics it really becomes rather impossible for the Strength Coach to convince an athlete that he is doing a moral wrong by taking the drug when many of his friends or competitors are doing so. Ethics, in the final analysis, become very personal and are often altered to meet the current situation. What one does to his own body is perhaps the most personal decision an athlete makes. Ethics often become the scapegoat and carry very little weight when discussing steroids.

The Strength Coach should become as well informed on the subject of anabolic usage as possible so that he is in a position to answer any questions intelligently and honestly. Only when he is completely honest with the players will they feel secure in coming to him for advice.

ANABOLICS AND THE TEENAGER

Those coaches who deal with players still in their teens have a special responsibility to counsel them on the effects of anabolics. In the author's opinion, the risks are minimal to most adults who use steroids. Some do, of course, have problems as a result of taking the drug but these people are of an age where they should be responsible for their decisions. If an adult athlete decides to risk his health then it should be his right to do so.

But this rationale does not hold true for teenage athletes for a number of reasons. The first being that teenagers are rarely responsible enough to understand the full consequences of their choices. Secondly, anabolics carry a much higher risk to teenagers than they do for adults. Since anabolics influence the hormonal system, they can alter some of the secondary sexual characteristics of young males. If they are taken, for example, when the youngster is just coming into adolescence, it could greatly influence things as testical size, voice, amount of body hair, and overall body shape. Not things to be taken lightly at all. It has also been shown that anabolics cause a premature closing of bone epiphyses. What this means basically is that a youngster in his quest for superior strength at a young age will actually stop his long bone growth and end up being shorter in stature than he would have been normally. A steep price to pay for strength gains which could be obtained by other methods.

The dangers are much higher for teenagers.

It has been found that a systematic nutritional program will influence strength gains as well or better than an anabolic program.

The dangers, then, are much higher for teenagers. The anabolics may also have long-range effects to mature adults but these facts are not as yet available. The Strength Coach must, in order to effectively deal with his younger players, establish credibility. He must obtain facts and he must be willing to convey all the facts whether he agrees with some of them or not. The athletes have heard the success stories via the grapevine so it will serve no useful purpose to attempt to conceal any information on the subject. This pertains to all matters and not just to anabolic steroid usage, by the way.

In my opinion, the most important function of the Strength Coach is to get the players to work with the team doctor or a local physician when they become interested in anabolic steroids. If you can persuade your players of the necessity of keeping a close medical contact then you have gone a long way in alleviating any problems that may result from flagrant anabolic usage.

SUMMARY

The use of pharmaceutical preparations by athletes has opened an entirely new field for those who deal with athletes. It means that the successful Strength Coach must spend some time catching up on the current drugs being used in sports if he is to be most useful to his players. Merely forbidding their usage does not work any longer. The modern athlete is an inquisitive being. He wants to find out for himself. Add to this the fact that most college and high school players have been raised in a culture where drugs are easily obtained and frequently used. The experimentation of the current generation is definitely one of their dominate characteristics.

The Strength Coach is in a perfect position to advise and counsel on the subject of drug usage. The players will relate to him first concerning matters of health, fitness, and strength because he is the authority on those subjects. Be armed with facts and be prepared to answer all questions honestly. While the whole area of drug usage in athletics may be one of the most distasteful for coaches to understand or tolerate, it is also an area which is growing in acceptance among players more and more each year. To be an effective Strength Coach you must know your subject matter and learn to accept what is going on about you. This does not mean that you are to condone or promote drug usage. But you must be knowledgeable and you must be honest. Only then will you be in a position to be of genuine assistance to your athletes.   ★

20

CHAPTER TWENTY
SLEEP AND STRENGTH TRAINING

THE STRENGTH PYRAMID

Sleep, along with proper nutrition and systematic training, makes up the three sides of the strength pyramid. Without sufficient rest, an athlete does not perform up to his full potential. When an athlete performs with an insufficient amount of rest his reactions are slower, his timing is slightly off, his endurance lags, and his strength is adversely affected.

Surprisingly enough, there has been very little research conducted concerning the effects of sleep on athletic performance. Why more researchers in the fields of physical education, physiology, psychology, and other related sciences have not examined this important variable is indeed a mystery. One third of our lives is spent obtaining necessary rest. Certainly, no physiologist or psychologist would suggest that rest is not a most necessary part of an athlete's daily routine, yet a systematic study dealing with this topic has not been conducted.

No other factor affects athletic performance as quickly as the lack of proper rest. A highly-conditioned athlete can turn in a poor performance should he fail to obtain sufficient rest the night before competition. Unfortunately, extra rest does not help an athlete to perform beyond his physical capacity, but the lack of rest does have a limiting effect on his performance.

THAT MYSTERIOUS THIRD OF YOUR LIFE

Sleep is often referred to as "the mysterious third of your life." Sleep is indeed still clouded in mystery even to those who spend their lives studying the subject. The research in this particular field is still in its infancy and this partly explains why some direct studies have not been aimed at the athletes. It should also be mentioned that controlling the variable of sleep is quite difficult and merely testing to insure that the subject is genuinely asleep requires some expensive and rather sophisticated equipment. The researchers know how we do sleep, however.

WHAT HAPPENS WHEN WE SLEEP?

With the invention of the electroencephalograph, scientists were able to learn a great deal about what happens when we sleep. The electroencephalograph or EEG was instrumental in discovering just what goes on during those mysterious sleeping hours. The name of the machine explains its function. The prefix "electro" indicates that it measures electricity from the body, specifically from the brain in this instance. "Encephalo" comes from the Greek root for brain; and graph, also from the Greek, means to write. The EEG is a device that is attached to the sleeping individual which records his brain action on a graph. It is used in sleep laboratories and allows researchers to learn about what happens during those sleeping hours.

When you go to sleep, you actually go through a series of stages from light rest to deep sleep. Once you reach the deepest stage of sleep, you do not remain there but back-pedal out to the light stage, then re-enter the deep stage again in ninety minute cycles.

THRESHOLD OF SLEEP

The pattern typically follows this routine: When you first lie down to sleep you become very relaxed. You may drift off briefly, awaken, then dose off again. This light sleep is known as the "threshold of sleep." It is quite light and is not considered a true stage of sleep. Should you awaken during the threshold stage you probably would not feel that you had slept at all.

STAGE I

From the threshold, you move into Stage I, the first genuine sleep stage. Your body becomes completely relaxed, your body temperature begins to drop, and your heart rate slows considerably. Researchers believe the sleeper is thinking disconnected thoughts which are more akin to daydreams than true dreams.

STAGE II & III

Stages II and III are yet deeper levels of sleep. The body temperature continues to go down and the heart rate slows even more. After about an hour the sleeper enters the deepest stage of sleep, Stage IV. He is extremely hard to awaken during this stage of sleep. His brain may hear sounds, but only a very loud noise will affect his sleep. Even though the sleeper is in the deepest level of rest, he has not yet begun to dream.

STAGE IV — REM STAGE

It takes about ninety minutes for the sleeper to reach this deepest level of sleep — and then a rather unusual (or perhaps unexpected would be a better term) pattern begins. The sleeper reenters Stage III, then Stage II, then Stage I. The Stage I which the sleeper returns to is not really identical to the original Stage I, however. While it is not the restful world of Stage IV, it nevertheless takes the sleeper further from the waking world than he has been thus far. The sleeper tosses and turns almost as though he were awake. This is the dreaming time and is referred to as the Rapid Eye Movement or REM Stage of sleep. The eyes indicate this dreaming stage of sleep, hence the name. It is the only part of sleep during which it is definitely known that dreaming does occur.

The body of the sleeper is quite active during REM sleep. His eyes are in constant and rapid motion. His arms and legs move about, but there is more action internally than externally. His heart rate beats wildly and his blood pressure slips up and down much as if the sleeper were experiencing a terrifying situation. Strangely enough, the muscles of the neck remain completely relaxed through the REM sleep. The bodily actions do not necessarily mean that the sleeper is dreaming of a bad experience, however. These actions occur during pleasant dreams as well as during nightmares.

The first REM period lasts only about ten minutes, then the sleeper goes through the four stages of sleep once again. At the end of the ninety minute cycle, he is back to REM sleep, dreaming once again.

Individuals vary as to the actual length of each sleep cycle, but ninety minutes is most typical. On the basis of eight hours of sleep, the average person goes through the various stages four or five times each night.

At the end of the sleeping period, which is usually seven or eight hours, the sleeper's body prepares itself slowly for wakefulness. His body temperature and heart rate begin to rise and if he was not disturbed during the night, he will feel rested and ready for the day ahead.

"The REM stage is the only part of sleep during which it is definitely known that dreaming does occur."

Mike Tice trained with the author at the University of Maryland in 1979. He went on to an outstanding pro career and is now the Head Coach of the Minnesota Vikings.

SLEEP AND ATHLETIC PERFORMANCE

Just how important is the factor of sleep to the performance of a well-conditioned athlete? The answer is not absolute, but is variable to the individual. Each person has different requirements when it comes to sleep and it is most important that these requirements be met for optimum performance.

There are many recorded instances of individuals getting by on ridiculously small amounts of sleep. Reportedly, there is one gentleman in Baltimore who obtains but one hour of sleep but functions just fine. Some athletes have stayed up all night just prior to high level competition and performed most admirably. But I would rather not deal with the exceptions in regards to sleep, but rather with the rule and I have to believe that the rule is that an athlete performs much better if he has obtained sufficient rest.

One interesting aspect of weight training is that the trainee gets an immediate feed-back concerning his day-to-day living habits. Should a trainee shortchange his nutrition, it will often show up during his workout that same day. If he is overtrained or fatigued for whatever reason, he will be able to tell as soon as he approaches the heavier poundages. Likewise, a lack of rest will show up immediately.

The athletes training at the University of Hawaii are subject to certain periods during the school year which dictate a breaking of their rest schedules. Mid-terms and finals always take their toll in the weight room. When the athletes begin missing sleep to study or to finish term papers, their proficiency in the weight room drops off considerably. It is quite easy to pick out the player who has not had sufficient rest. He lacks speed in his movement and his strength level drops off as much as 20%.

During this period of time it is best for the Strength Coach to adjust the player's program so as not to further fatigue him and run the risk of injury.

WEIGHT TRAINING INCREASES THE NEED FOR REST

This is another observation which I have made in watching athletes throughout the years. Athletes relate that their requirement for rest goes up in direct proportion to the amount of work they perform in the weight room and on the playing field. Players in summer football camp who are taking part in strenuous two-a-days rest during every spare moment. As the athlete increases his weight training load from three days a week to four or sometimes five, his need for rest also increases. Players tell me that whereas they could manage on six or seven hours of sleep before they began weight training, they soon discovered that they needed a minimum of nine to ten hours per night in order to feel rested after beginning a program.

Most trainees also mention that they sleep much sounder after they begin a program of weight training. They go to bed physically weary and go to sleep much faster than before. Many experts in this field believe physical activity to be an important factor in the degree of sleep obtained. Much of the nation's insomnia problem could be remedied by a systematic exercise program, rather than via drugs. The athlete who is in serious training seldom has difficulty sleeping. His problem is often getting enough rest.

INDIVIDUAL VARIANCES

The factor of individual variance was mentioned briefly, but I would like to emphasize it even more as I think it is a most important fact to remember when dealing with sleep requirements. While it should be obvious to any aware person that not everyone has identical sleep requirements, it is rather surprising to find many people who do not take this fact into consideration.

Some people just need more sleep than others. A basic truism, often neglected by individuals or coaches. Our culture seems to still be unduly influenced by the Puritanical Code and the Ben Franklin philosophy when it comes to relaxing or sleeping. Sleep is considered by many as "wasted time." Anyone who sleeps excessively is often regarded as lazy. Many individuals feel this social pressure and get up at a certain hour, even when they do not want or need to. Or in some instances, the parents of individuals feel that they should be up and around doing something more constructive than just sleeping. Some folks arise at a pre-set hour and go about their routine groggy and semi-alert all day. In many cases they could have rested for another hour and been much more productive as a result of the additional rest.

It is quite important for the athlete to learn as much about his own rest requirements as possible. Should you find that you need more than the typical eight hours of sleep to operate at the optimum performance level in the weight room and on the playing field, then you must set priorities in order to obtain sufficient rest. It may mean skipping a party or cutting short your reading by an hour. It may mean leaving a group of friends early or not attending a movie that night. One thing is certain. Should you neglect getting adequate rest then your training will suffer. Most athletes find that they can get away with short-changing their rest requirements for one night without adversely influencing their training, but two nights in a row spell trouble.

The lack of rest seems to affect the endurance factor more than peak strength. Quite a few athletes can perform well on the first exercise of a series, but begin to "give out" as the exercises progress. They seldom get a full workout in and do

"Much of the nation's insomnia problem could be remedied by a systematic exercise program."

not meet all their sets and rep requirements, especially on a heavy training day.

It is extremely important for the weight trained athlete to obtain sufficient rest the night before a heavy training session. Very rarely is an athlete able to perform at the 100% level without sufficient sleep the night prior to training. There are exceptions to the rule of course, but anyone who pushes his luck over an extended period of time is asking not just for limited performance in the weight room, but is inviting injury. When the body is fatigued from lack of rest and the brain not completely alert, the chances for injury are multiplied greatly.

LET'S HEAR IT FOR NAPS

Since the athlete has somewhat different sleep requirements from the non-active citizen, he also may have different sleeping habits. Most athletes need much more sleep while engaged in hard physical training. This extra work may be in the form of weight training or in two-a-day summer practices. As the activity level increases, so does the need for additional rest.

Most athletes find it advisable to take periodical naps sometime during the day. Some like to rest immediately after the noon meal, before they train. Others prefer to rest after they train. Personal needs and schedules dictate as to when it's the best time to take these short rest periods.

By breaking up the day with a one or two-hour rest period, many athletes find that they stay mentally and physically alert throughout the day. When the stress of exams, term papers, or extra-heavy training begins to lay heavy on the player, then a brief rest break is definitely good tonic.

HOW TO REST BETTER

There are a number of things each person can do to help himself to rest better. It is quite important to rest as thoroughly as possible during the allotted sleep time. If you toss and turn and have difficulty in making connections with the sandman, then eight hours in bed does not always add up to eight hours of sleep.

Here are some suggestions set forth by sleep experts to assist you in obtaining a fulfilling rest.

1) **Keeping Your Bedroom Dark and Quiet**. This is not always easy to do if you live in a dormitory setting or at home where there is limited living space. One player at the University of Hawaii turns on a fan and the humming sound blocks out all outside noise. Another keeps his stereo on low enough so that no one else can hear it, but yet loud enough to combat the outside noise. Quiet is conducive to sound sleep.

2) **Keep Your Room Cool**. Folks in colder climates often overcompensate to the point where they heat their bedrooms excessively. The higher room temperature dries out the mucus membranes in the respiratory tract and not only makes breathing more difficult, but it also invites respiratory ailments. Your bedroom should be cool, but you should have proper bedding so that your body temperature is warm and comfortable.

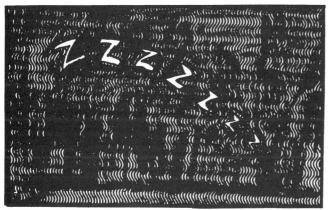

3) **Have A Medium Hard Resilient Bed.** If you are burdened with a soft, spongy mattress or a saggy bed, pull the mattress off the frame and place it flat on the floor. Many institutions provide a minimum in bedding. Be aware enough of the inherent problems to your rest and also to your lower back to avoid using a poor grade of bedding.

4) **Keep Your Bedding Clean**. Cleanliness is a most important factor in obtaining wholesome rest. Ever notice how much better you sleep on clean sheets? Everyone does, so make it a point to launder your bed clothes often. Every little bit helps so keep the odds on your side.

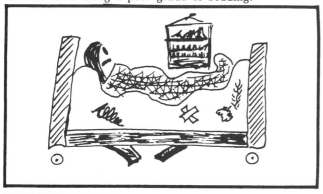

5) **Soft Shades Enhance Rest**. For those living in dormitories the color of the walls may be permanent. But in most cases, you can paint or decorate your room if you care to go to some extra effort. The reason that hospitals and rest homes abound with soft shades of blues and greens is that the officials want a peaceful and restful environment. For proper sleep, you too need soothing colors around you. Work out a scheme to make your living space soothing, color-wise.

These are but some of the physical things that you can do to enable you to obtain a better night's sleep, but the primary villain to satisfying sleep is not hard beds, or harsh colors, or noise, but worry. Worry is much more difficult to counteract than all the physical problems and, unfortunately, there is no capsuled solution to wipe out the problem.

YOU CAN LEARN TO RELAX

The ability to learn to relax, even when under physical or mental stress, is a learned trait and takes considerable practice to master. It is also beyond the range of this book to go into these methods in any depth. It would behoove every athlete to learn as much as possible concerning total relaxation. A few hints on the subject may be useful.

When you are mentally or physically tense, you must be certain that as many things are working in your favor when you lie down to rest as possible. Have your room dark, cool, and quiet. Lie in a comfortable position and center your concentration directly in your body. Think of totally relaxing the muscles of your feet, then your ankles, calves, thighs, lower back, and so on right up to the top of your head. Do it slowly and feel the muscles become supple and limp. When you reach the crown of your head you should be like a blob on the sheets. If not, go through the procedure again — and again if necessary. Think of nothing else but each muscle group. Do not let business, school, or personal matters slip into your brain. Keep the gray matter occupied with thoughts of muscles becoming supple.

As was mentioned, total relaxation is a learned skill and it does take some practice to master. There are also breathing methods which facilitate relaxation and if you are troubled with any degree of insomnia you would do well to take some time to learn of these various disciplines. One such method is presented in the Mental Rehearsal chapter.

NUTRITIONAL AIDS TO RELAXATION

Just in case you skipped over the section of the book dealing with the minerals, perhaps a brief review is in order concerning "nature's own tranquilizer," magnesium. Magnesium, along with calcium, is very involved in the action of the nervous system. A lack of this important nutrient causes severe nervousness, depression, and irritability. All of which make it extremely difficult to rest properly. Conversely, an adequate intake of magnesium, in the proper balance with calcium (two parts calcium to one part magnesium) soothes the nerves and allows you to relax much better.

Magnesium-calcium tablets are available and they are safe and inexpensive. Be certain the ratio is correct and choose one derived from calcium gluconate or calcium lactate over calcium phosphate or calcium chloride as the first two absorb much more readily.

Two to four tablets of magnesium-calcium with a warm cup of milk will greatly assist you in your quest for rest. This method is much safer than the one selected by millions of Americans every night — the highly dangerous sleeping pills.

THE DANGER OF DOWNERS

The highly-motivated athlete in his pursuit for superior performances often touches on dangerous ground. As was noted in the chapter on drugs, he experiments with anything and everything that he feels may help his performance. Some of his inquiries have been more fruitful; others harmless; and some most dangerous. The use of barbituates or sleeping pills by athletes constitutes one of the greatest health risks in sports. While a great many officials are fretting and testing for amphetamines and anabolics, they seem to ignore the barbituate usage and the "downers" are being used much more indiscriminately and are a greater health risk than any of the other drugs making the rounds in athletic circles today.

"The use of barbituates by athletes constitutes one of the greatest health risks in sports."

Emile Fischer, a German chemist, developed sleeping pills in 1903 and named them barbituates. Every pharmaceutical company manufactures and sells some form of barbituates to the tune of fifty million dollars a year. A conservative estimate suggests that doctors prescribe barbituates to twenty million patients each year. The pills are easy to obtain, if not through legitimate sources, then by way of friends or your friendly pusher.

BARBITUATES ARE ADDICTING

Barbituates are physically and psychologically addicting. Even worse, they trap the user slowly. The casual user slowly but surely begins relying on the sleeping pills more and more frequently. Soon, he must have them in order to sleep. The trap closes and the exit is pure agony. Withdrawal from barbituates is a long and difficult procedure. It seems that the longer it takes to become addicted to any drug, the longer it takes to completely withdraw. Withdrawal is virtually impossible without medical supervision and then it's a tough row to hoe.

Current statistics show that there are over one million known barbituate addicts in this country and unfortunately some of these come from the athletic ranks. Athletes began using barbituates to help them rest the night before a game or a heavy workout. Then they used them to rest after the game. The pills are handy and soon the player finds himself relying on them to rest during the day.

I have seen two or three of our top weightlifters succumb to the barbituate come-on. Since the body adapts to the drug, more and more is needed to produce the desired effect. The lifters begin skipping training altogether as they were too hung over from a high barbituate dosage. Soon, they resorted to taking amphetamines or "uppers" to counteract the "downers" so that they could train, then they found they needed even more barbituates to rest the following night. The vicious cycle became impossible to break and the lifters faded from the top levels of competition. As of this writing, they are still deeply entwined in the addiction.

Another class of drugs, tranquilizers, were discovered in the early 1950s and they, too, have become a part of some athlete's training table. Tranquilizers are also easy to obtain and have many of the characteristics of barbituates. Both drugs reduce the amount of REM sleep that a person receives. This is the dreaming segment of sleep and a lack of it brings with it many psychological problems. Tranquilizers are also habit forming and they can be addicting.

Tranquilizers and barbituates reduce the amount of REM sleep that a person receives.

■■■

There is no question but that any sleep-inducing drug on the market today poses a severe health problem to the athlete. They are most dangerous to toy with in any dosage.

Learn to relax either by some form of breathing ritual, self hypnosis, or by using nature's resources. Skip the pharmaceutical preparations. They will become your masters and dictate your life. Those who spend a great portion of their working hours building a stronger and healthier body should not be even remotely tempted with the likes of pills which can virtually destroy everything they value.

IN SUMMARY

While the research on the effects of rest on the performance of athletes is practically nonexistent, it is, nevertheless, hypothesized from observation that it is a most critical variable.

The three sides of the pyramid of strength are made up of: 1) proper nutrition, 2) systematic resistive training, and 3) sufficient rest. To neglect any one of these three factors will adversely affect your strength level.

Each athlete must be very aware of his special individual needs in regard to sleep. If your performance in the weight room begins to drop off, then check and see if you are obtaining sufficient rest. If not, be sure to supply your body with enough rest for future workouts.

Remember that individuals differ greatly on their sleep requirements. Also be aware that the same individual has different needs at various times. When you are in heavy training, then your sleep needs increase considerably. Do not be unduly influenced by what works for your roommate, training partner, or other members of your family. If you find that you perform best with ten hours of sleep, then be certain that you receive this amount. Be guided by your individual needs and no one else's.

Set priorities so that you do obtain your necessary rest. It may mean passing up a good time, but if excellence on the playing field or in the weight room is your goal, then you must pass it up. The adage of "you have to give some to get some" rightfully applies to all aspects of physical training, but especially to the factor of sleep.   ★

B.J. Moser gave up a promising career in football to concentrate on Olympic weightlifting. He became one of the strongest lifters in the country, winning the American Championship in 1986.

21

CHAPTER TWENTY-ONE
MENTAL REHEARSAL AND
STRENGTH TRAINING

EVERYONE WHO HAS BEEN involved in any aspect of athletics for any length of time realizes the full importance of being mentally prepared for competition. The top competitors in all sports emphasize the mental preparation before a game or contest as much as they do the physical preparation. The manner in which an athlete controls his mind determines, to a great extent, just how well he will perform on any given day.

Those of us who have been engaged in competitive weightlifting have long understood the importance of mental preparation and how it relates to total performance. Some of our more notable champions, such as: Tommy Kono, Norbert Schemansky, Bill March, and Louis Riecke could summon physical reserves which few others could match when the battle became critically tight.

STRENGTH IS LARGELY MENTAL

Strength is only partly derived from physical training. The remainder comes directly from your mind. Every reader has come across a story of a ninety-year-old grandmother who lifted a Volkswagen off her injured Shetland Pony and saved its life. She tripped some mechanism in her brain that allowed her to use her full strength potential. Physiologists recognize that the human animal has not even come close to realizing his strength capacity. It was concluded by a group of scientists that the human body could be developed to the point where it could lift 1500 pounds from the floor to overhead. The world record is just under 550 pounds at present so it is obvious that the record will climb much, much higher in the future.

The human machine is a fantastic piece of equipment and it is the brain that triggers all the action. Hence, the mind must be dealt with in a positive manner in order to elevate performance levels.

It doesn't take too long for the beginning trainee to realize the importance of mental preparation in the weight room. Since the original program outlined in this book only calls for a heavy work load once a week, he really only has to be "up" one day out of three. Those who begin preparing themselves mentally for those "heavy days" two or three days prior to the workout, immediately fare much better than those who just walk in the gym to train. Even on the basic beginning routine, mentally preparing for the heavier lifts is an absolute necessity for overall progress.

MENTAL REHEARSAL INCREASES YOUR SKILL LEVEL

Mental preparation is in actuality mental rehearsal. By mentally going over the various details involved in any sports activity the athlete is assuring himself of learning the skills inherent to that activity much more thoroughly and also much more rapidly.

Strength training for athletes does not take the same degree of physical skill as does competitive weightlifting, but many of the same principles still apply. Take the power clean as an example. It is a relatively involved movement which most trainees do not master for months. Those who spend time thinking of the form involved in the correct execution of the lift outside of the weight room develop the technique much more quickly than those who do not.

The same is basically true with respect to all the other movements, but to a lesser and lesser degree depending on the complexity of the exercise. It is easier to master the technique of a simple movement such as the bench press or squat than it is a power clean or shrug. All movements, however, do require some degree of learning and each one can be more quickly mastered through mental rehearsal.

MENTAL REHEARSAL HELPS TO BREAK BARRIERS

When an athlete is first introduced to strength training, he immediately discovers the problem of mental barriers. These mental barriers are not exclusive to weightlifting by any means, but are also inherent in any sport which is graded on an absolute scale such as time, height, or distance. Pole vaulters, runners, long jumpers, swimmers, and shot putters are all acquainted with the barriers within their own sports. Team sports seldom have such absolute barriers and football players, when they first enter the new individual activity of weight training, generally find this new factor both intriguing and perplexing.

The strength training athlete is always one-on-one with the barbell. Success or failure falls quickly on the participant's shoulders and on no one else's. It is an individual activity in the purest form and the numbers soon begin to loom larger and larger in the participant's mind.

John Saxe was a three-sport, scholar-athlete at Johns Hopkins. He was the captain of the tennis team, an academic All-American and defensive standout in football, and competed in two National Collegiate Weightlifting Championships.

DEFINING MENTAL REHEARSAL

What exactly is mental rehearsal? Mental rehearsal in the context of sports refers to mentally going over each physical movement involved in that particular skill. In weight training, it specifically means thinking of the various aspects of the lift, going into as much detail as possible. Take the power clean as an example. Here's how you would mentally rehearse for a heavy attempt on this lift.

You actually visualize the barbell being loaded with the various plates. You picture yourself gripping the bar and like a slow motion camera, you see the bar come to your chest in the correct fashion.

The idea is to drill the brain so completely with correct positioning and proper form in the movement that once you step up to the barbell in the gym, the technique is automatic. The proper way to perform the lift is so ingrained in your brain that you can fully concentrate all of your mental energies on pulling, rather than using some of that energy thinking of technical aspects of the lift.

THE PROCESS STARTS PRIOR TO THE EVENT

The process of mentally preparing yourself for a personal record lift, or lifts, should begin a day or two prior to the actual workout. The first step is to write out your proposed workout, listing all of the warm-up attempts and selecting a top weight for that particular day. I might add that the top weight should be a realistic one based on prior training. The sooner this limit poundage becomes a part of your planning, the better. For purpose of an example, our subject will be attempting to power clean 225 for 5, bench press 300 for 5, and squat with 365 for 5 on his heavy day, which is Monday, two days away.

He will list all of his warm-up attempts up to these new personal records and he should not deviate from the proposed pattern one iota on that heavy day. On Saturday night, the subject will find a quiet place and go through the work-out lift-by-lift, mentally. Some lifters go so far as to visualize that they are changing into their workout gear in the locker room and continue to think through each step in great detail.

Our subject sees himself load each attempt and in textbook form successfully complete each lift for the required number of repetitions. He pays special attention to any technical points with which he has been having difficulty. Perhaps it's a matter of bending the elbows too soon in the power clean or not keeping his head up while coming out of the squat. During the mental rehearsal he corrects these and other faults and all of his power cleans are done with speed and precision.

The entire process may take 15-20 minutes. Some prefer to go through the same lift two or three times before going on to the next. Others mentally rehearse the entire workout, then go back to the beginning and run through it again.

Sunday night, the night before the actual workout, we will find our subject following the same procedure, but this time he may put more emphasis on the top weights. Each time he handles the personal record weight he does it smoothly and is always in command of the barbell. Success becomes associated with the poundage itself, so that when the 250 pounds is loaded on the bar on Monday, the subject is familiar with this weight and is poised and confident. He is self-assured because he has already successfully completed this weight mentally perhaps a dozen times in the last two days.

CORRECTING FORM ERRORS

One of the more useful aspects of mental rehearsal for the more technical lifts such as the power clean is that it allows the athlete to work out his form mistakes outside the weight room. It is quite often difficult to work on technical aspects of any lift in the weight room because of the lack of time and/or equipment. Or, as is often the case, the athlete gets involved in the social atmosphere of the weight room and finds it difficult to concentrate on his form. By mentally practicing each lift two or three dozen times, the lifter soon gets a complete picture of himself doing things correctly. This mental image is converted to actual performance and his technique improves considerably.

■■■

The mental image is converted to actual performance.

■■■

THOSE NUMERICAL BARRIERS

There are certain natural numerical barriers with which every weight trainer comes face to face as he proceeds up the ladder of improvement. The even numbers seem to cause the greatest mental constellation. Two hundred pounds is a formidable figure for every trainee, regardless of the lift. Three hundred looms like a brick wall and four hundred takes on dimensions of a Caterpillar tractor.

Each individual also has his very own personal barriers. There are certain weights which seem to give him an unproportionate amount of trouble. And strangely enough, some of these numerical barriers are actually less than the lifter's best effort. Every competitive weightlifter whom I have visited, confesses to these irrational, yet existing, barriers. Bill March, the great American 198-pound National Champion and World Record Holder, when he was pressing 390 and clean and jerking 425 still could not handle 340 pounds on either of these lifts with any degree of confidence. Bill would have to start under or over that poundage or he would surely lose an attempt. He could not even take 340 as a warm up or he would break form and miss.

Some lifters get beaten by certain poundages so many times that they finally just skip over that particular weight and go on to higher poundages. My personal bugaboo was 300 pounds in the clean and jerk. I missed it so many times that I finally just went on to 305 instead. Success breeds success, and likewise, failure plays with the brain to instill more failure. In time, a certain weight, like 200 or 300, registers failure in the brain and it's hell getting it to change over to success. Sometimes, it's much easier simply to go around it.

If I see a trainee missing at the same poundage, week after week, I simply move him up five or ten pounds anyway. If he has not built up a long series of failures at the original weight, he can usually go back to the poundage after a week or two and master it quite easily. But, if he fails often enough at a certain weight, then that poundage will be permanently ingrained with failure and he may never gain full control of it.

By mentally rehearsing for a heavy training session or a limit lift, the athlete diminishes the apprehension associated with a particular poundage. Familiarity brings about both a respect and contempt for a weight. As the athlete rehearses for power cleaning 250 for five repetitions over and over in his mind, he builds a success quotient which carries over in the weight room.

"Success breeds success and, likewise, failure plays with the brain to instill more failure."

Should he, on the other hand, walk into the weight room without any prior thinking of the workout for the day and be faced with 250 for five, he is, in all likelihood, going to be unduly impressed with the poundage on the barbell. The procedure to follow in mentally preparing for the heavy days will be outlined later in this chapter.

MENTAL REHEARSAL ALLOWS YOU TO CONCENTRATE PURELY ON THE STRENGTH FACTOR

What I mean by this statement is that through the process of mental rehearsal the athlete augments such attributes as: poise, confidence, and concentration. I mentioned earlier in this chapter that an athlete's physical skills are enhanced by mental rehearsal. Skills such as timing, speed, and coordination. With these skills sharpened, the athlete is able to concentrate all of his physical and mental energies into pushing and pulling on the barbell.

This fact becomes obvious as the trainee perfects the various movements. No longer does he have to expend mental energy on thinking of the position of the hips and back at the start of the power clean or of thinking of turning the elbows up and out, rather than back at the top of the pull. When the technique becomes automatic, the trainee can pull with all of his might and when this happens, strength increases much more rapidly.

The author set a National Record with this 666 dead lift at the 1968 Senior National Powerlifting Championships in Los Angeles, while competing in the 198-pound division.

Mental rehearsal helps the trainee to become advanced much faster because it basically helps him to learn the skill involved in lifting faster. As the athlete's technical skill level goes up, so does his overall strength level. This is why it is so useful to begin practicing mental rehearsal from the very onset of strength training. It produces faster results.

USING THE KEYS

When you are mentally rehearsing any technical movement it is most useful to go over the various "keys" to be remembered and group them all under one key which will trigger all of the rest. Key points become very individualistic and different lifters utilize a wide assortment of triggering words or phrases to help them to get their form in proper order.

Let's look at the power clean once again. There are a number of key technical points to be remembered as the bar travels from the floor to your chest, but there is not sufficient time to think of each and every one of these as the bar travels upward in a split second.

Your back must be flat, shoulders taut, deltoids slightly over the bar, and your head up as the bar clears the floor. Now you must quickly concentrate on keeping the bar close to your body and think on hyperextending your elbows so that your arms do not bend too early. As the bar passes your knees you must violently snap your hips forward, shrug your trapezius, and pull with your arms all in one continuous, dynamic motion. At the very top of the pull, you should be fully extended on your toes and with your elbows lifted up and to the sides. As you feel the bar reach the tip-top part of the pull, you drive your elbows under the bar and rack it solidly on your chest. A lot to remember in a short period of time.

In order to let all of your energy be concentrated into merely pulling the barbell, you must break these many technical points down into but one or two points. Keying on the point of keeping your shoulders tight at the starting position is often enough to assure the bar of traveling in a correct line to your knees so that could be your initial key. As the bar passes your knees, you could keep on driving your elbows out and upward and this will be sufficient to take care of the rest of the points. Your brain has time to relay a couple of quick messages in this short second, but no more. If you attempt to send four, five, or six notes to the brain, it merely gets caught in a communication mixup and the form breaks down miserably.

Every athlete has experienced this fact as he attempts to learn a new physical skill. The same rule applies in learning a new blocking or tackling technique. Until the movement becomes second-nature, the athlete appears uncoordinated and clumsy. This is because he is over-thinking the skill and has not yet simplified the key points. The various technical aspects have to become so ingrained in the athlete's mind that the movement becomes as natural as running or jumping.

The mind can only concentrate on one thing at a time.

A skill can be mastered much more easily and much more rapidly through mental rehearsal. The keys go from many to few. The movement from complex to simple. Individuals do, of course, learn complex physical skills without utilizing mental rehearsal, but it take much longer to do so. It should also be noted that some individuals learn any physical skill much more readily than do others. These people are blessed with high levels of coordination and are quite easy to teach. But, even the more gifted athlete can benefit from mental rehearsal as he, too, can learn faster.

For the majority of athletes, however, mental rehearsal is not a luxury, but rather a necessity. Skills have to be drilled over and over before they become natural. The learning process is enhanced considerably by practicing the skill mentally. The athlete must learn how to employ mental rehearsal as this, too, is a learned skill so I will elaborate on the "how to" a bit further.

RELAXATION AND MENTAL REHEARSAL

It is most important to be completely relaxed when you practice mental rehearsal and for many athletes, this is easier said than done. When they begin thinking of handling a limit poundage, their heart starts pounding, the adrenalin surges, and they become extremely excited. Since a great many athletes practice their mental rehearsal while lying in bed just prior to sleeping, this poses an additional problem. If they become too excited then they cannot rest and the process of mental rehearsal becomes self-defeating.

So the athlete must learn how to relax as he begins the process of mentally picturing each movement. If he starts getting excited then he must learn how to calm himself so that his body does not physically prepare itself for a workout.

This is best accomplished through systematic breathing exercises. The martial arts have always stressed the importance of breathing in their sport, so competitive weightlifters merely took a page from their book. One of the truisms that every athlete should learn early is that the mind can only concentrate on one thing at a time. Your thoughts may flash from subject to subject, but I am speaking of pure concentration. You cannot be concentrating on making a tackle and thinking of your little lady friend simultaneously.

Likewise, when you are thinking of proper breathing you cannot be getting hyped over a maximum lift. Herein lies the secret of keeping calm when rehearsing for the up-coming workout. As you go through the process of mentally rehearsing each lifting movement and suddenly realize that you are becoming excited, you stop thinking of the workout and begin the breathing exercises.

WHILE SEATED

Deep breathing exercises are doubly therapeutic in that they switch the mind off the subject which is exciting your body and at the same time allows more oxygen to get to the cells, which has a relaxing effect physiologically on your body.

The type of breathing exercise which I teach is quite simple and is simply an adaptation of those used in judo, karate, and aikido. There are many more involved methods but seldom does a Strength Coach have the time to teach these; nor does a player have the deep interest to learn them. This breathing technique is simple to learn and can be used anywhere, even when you are driving your car, which is where I used to do a great deal of mental rehearsing as I was on the road so often. It's best to learn in a kneeling or seated position and then adapt it to other postures.

SYSTEMATIC BREATHING — SIMPLIFIED

Find a quiet place where you can be alone to learn this skill. After you master it you can perform it in noisy and crowded situations, but it's much easier to learn it when you are isolated completely. Sit on a soft surface, such as on your bed or a large pillow on the floor. It's best to sit either with your feet tucked under your seat or in a position with the bottom of your feet together and your knees turned outward. This position may be slightly uncomfortable initially but you should soon be able to relax quite well seated in this manner after just a bit of practice.

Sit erect with your lower back slightly arched, your shoulders back, and your head high. Place your palms on the inside of your knees. This is quite similar to the lotus position of yoga, a most comfortable posture to assume.

Let your mind go blank and begin thinking only of the action of the air as it passes in and out of your lungs. Think the process out in great detail, even to the point of visualizing the oxygen being exchanged in the individual cells.

Hold your head slightly upward and slowly begin inhaling only through your nose. Slowly filly your lungs with air. Let your chest expand fully and take in as much air as possible. When you are at 100% capacity— or believe yourself to be — take one more sniff and hold it. Count to 15, then very, very slowly and deliberately begin blowing the air out through your mouth so that it makes a tiny whistling noise. More of a "whooshing" sound. Empty your lungs all the way. When they are 100% empty — or when you believe they are 100% empty — blow a bit more air out. There's always some left. Now, hold once again. Don't breath in for another 10-15 seconds. In all likelihood, you will only be able to hold for 5-10 seconds at first, but in time you will be able to refrain from inhaling for 15-20 seconds and some are able to hold even longer.

At the end of the oxygen starvation period, start inhaling very slowly once again through your nostrils. The tendency is to gulp the air, but fight this urge and breathe in slowly. The inhalation phase should be about 30-40 seconds eventually, the pause just after inhalation 10-15 seconds, the exhalation 20-30 seconds, and the pause after exhalation 5-10 seconds. It should be noted that these times will not be accomplished initially, but will come after a short period of practice.

THE "KI"

Some exponents of systematic breathing like to think of bringing in the energy of the universe as they inhale and releasing energy or "ki" back to the universe or exhalation. It is a very simple procedure, but it also takes a bit of time to master. The first few times that you attempt to do this exercise you will find yourself becoming light headed and you will stop the procedure to suck up as much oxygen as you can. There is a definite rhythm to this breathing routine and once you pick up the rhythm, the air flows in and out quite easily and naturally with no stress or discomfort.

Initially, you may only be able to successfully complete two or three cycles of this exercise. Don't become perplexed if this is the case. Merely regroup and do two or three more cycles, trying to relax and to allow the natural rhythm to take over. Do not force it. You will quickly discover after only two or three breathing sessions that you are able to inhale and exhale for a much longer time and also be able to "hold" the in-between segments much longer.

After a period of time you will be able to follow this rhythmic breathing routine for 15 to 20 minutes. Upon completion of the breathing exercise your entire body will feel thoroughly relaxed as if you had just had a sauna and massage. At this point, you may begin your mental rehearsal for your heavy workout. If, at any point during the mental rehearsal you discover yourself becoming tense and excited, stop the mental rehearsal and begin breathing exercises once again.

"The breathing exercise has tremendous carry-over value for football."

WHILE IN A LYING POSITION

You can also perform your breathing exercises while lying on your back just prior to going to sleep. Lie perfectly flat with your hands resting at your sides. Look slightly upward so that your chin is not down and your airway is not blocked. Begin the rhythmic breathing in the exact same fashion as you did while kneeling. Start off rather conservatively so that you are not holding the pause after inhalation and exhalation for too long. Otherwise, you will just become dizzy and stop the exercise. Hold for just 5 to 10 seconds initially and as your cycles become more natural, then you can add to the time pause.

After some practice you will find that you can employ your breathing exercise anywhere and at any time. It is most useful when you are actually engaged in competition. I utilized it between lifts during contests to help me relax to a degree and also to enable me to concentrate more fully. It can be used while traveling in a plane or car and is most useful for dull parties.

Augie Maurelli was a four-year starter for Johns Hopkins in football. In a two-hour session, he set the school total record for The Big Three with a 605 squat, 375 bench, and 330 clean in the spring of 1996 at a bodyweight of 225. After football, he began competing in Olympic lifting and is currently the Strength Coach for the Georgetown football team.

The breathing exercise has tremendous carry-over value for football. I can envision coaches teaching this method to entire teams to be utilized before the game and at halftime. It facilitates relaxation and the athlete must learn how to bring his body down from a high tempo to a slower one if he expects to retain his drive and motivation over a long span of time. It is quite difficult for a football player to be fired up for the entire two hours it takes to play a game — without the use of amphetamines. It is not so difficult for him to give 100% effort while he is actively participating in the game and then relax while he is off the field. It's a matter of conservation of energy. No athlete, regardless of his physical condition, can go as hard for two hours as he can for one.

RHYTHMIC BREATHING DURING THE GAME

The players, when their unit is not on the field, can still be mentally alert learning from the action in front of them while at the same time allowing their physical energies to be resting and regrouping. By employing rhythmic breathing just after you come off the playing field, you enable your body to calm down much more quickly than if you continued to stand or jump around the sidelines. This bit of energy conservation could pay off in a bonus play later on in the game.

The same thinking applies to half times. It would be much better if the players lowered their mental and physical excitement levels for a half hour break. They could still listen and learn from the coaches and allow their batteries to recharge.

It is really a perfect way to assist the coaches in teaching a new skill quickly or in reinforcing an old skill during the game. There is no time to have each player go through actual drills on revised blocking assignments or pass coverage but it is possible to diagram a play or responsibility and then have the players practice mental drills. They can best relax their bodies and clear their minds via rhythmic breathing and be much more susceptible to learning. In short, it's a terrific way to teach a skill in a short period of time.

MENTAL REHEARSAL IN THE WEIGHT ROOM

Rhythmic breathing can be most useful in your strength training and can be utilized right in the weight room during workouts. On your heavy days you will want to get your mind centered on the task at hand completely. As you find yourself mentally meandering you can use a short session of rhythmic breathing to help you regain your concentration. You may be puzzled as to how you can accomplish this task in a crowded, noisy weight room, surrounded by pesty friends. Here's a method that always works. Sit in a relatively quiet place — quiet in the sense that there is not a lot of traffic — and place a towel over you head. Sort of block out the world. Few people will be discourteous enough to lift the towel off your head to see what's going on under it. Shut your eyes and begin rhythmic breathing. In a few short

minutes your mind is isolated from the clank and clatter of the weights and you can practice your mental drills for the up-coming lift.

The same methods can be applied to almost any situation. If you find yourself going mentally flat during a written test, stop, put your pencil down, sit erect with your palms on your knees, and practice two or three minutes of the rhythmic breathing. The answers will come easier after this period of relaxation.

Rhythmic breathing is an ideal way to assist you in your quest for rest also. If you are anxious and troubled and find yourself tossing and turning in bed, just assume the correct posture for breathing and go through 5-10 minutes of breathing. Your chances of obtaining sound sleep is greatly enhanced if your body is relaxed and your mind clear.

TREMENDOUS CARRY-OVER VALUE

The skill of learning to relax through rhythmic breathing may just have more carry-over value to you after you cease playing football than any other skill you learn during your playing days. It is a tool that is most useful in any situation which requires mental alertness and there are many such situations which do pop up periodically throughout a lifetime. Rhythmic breathing is definitely a fine skill to know and master.

The entire concept of mental preparation is just now really being seriously examined by the scientists. Coaches and athletes have always know that it's very important to be "mentally ready" for any athletic activity. Strength athletes have taken great pains to understand all they can about mental readiness as most of the better lifters agree that competitive Olympic-style weightlifting is 75% mental and just 25% physical.

The ability to elevate higher and higher poundages becomes a mental, rather than a physical, challenge after a time. Overcoming weights that equal twice your own bodyweight has to be accomplished with the mind before it can be done with the body.

Mental exercises are essential to continued progress in strength training. The aware Strength Coach will assist his trainees as soon as he can in learning the skills required to breaking barriers in weightlifting. Mental rehearsal should become as much a part of the athlete's training program as his flexibility exercises. By instructing the player in how to relax through breathing, the Strength Coach will enable the player to be able to fully utilize his full physical potential.

SUMMARY

Both rhythmic breathing and mental rehearsal can be taught very simply and easily. They both will be very valuable tools to be utilized throughout the player's entire lifetime. There can be no underestimating the fact that the better the athlete is mentally prepared, the more positive the reaction. Bruce Ogilive, the renounced sports psychologist says, "Mental rehearsal makes game-day response as automatic as slipping into a jock strap." By preparing mentally, the athlete is free to execute with his optimum effort. A better performance is guaranteed.   ★

22

CHAPTER TWENTY-TWO
THE ROLE OF THE STRENGTH COACH

IN ORDER FOR ANY strength program to be successful, the individual responsible for directing the program must believe in the value of strength training and he must have confidence in the particular program which he is directing. To phrase it in another way, let me state that the strength program will only be as successful as the man behind it.

The better Strength Coaches have the following characteristics: 1) they have a deep interest in the individual players on the team; 2) they believe in the total success of the team; 3) they have a sound, working knowledge of the subject matter which they are teaching; 4) they are enthusiastic about strength training; 5) they utilize the program themselves; and, finally, 6) they have the capabilities to motivate players.

THE ATTRIBUTE OF INTEREST

The Strength Coach is generally an assistant football coach who has been delegated the responsibility of setting up and administering a strength program. Some Strength Coaches are placed in this position because they have expressed an interest in weight training at some point, but others have no background or interest in the activity. Often, the Strength Coach is appointed because he is at the bottom of the pecking order. For some in this latter category, the assignment is a chore and a burden as their primary and secondary interests are in teaching and coaching the skills of football. If they do not quickly understand the relevance of weight training to the game, they generally put together a mediocre program and do an adequate or less than adequate job as Strength Coach.

This, however, is certainly not always the case. Some coaches take on the task with enthusiasm and become extremely valuable to the overall football program. Some of the better strength programs which I have observed have been administered by coaches who, up to the time that they were appointed to the position of Strength Coach, knew or cared absolutely nothing about the field of weight training.

A bit of prior exposure to strength training is, of course, an advantage, but it is certainly not a prerequisite for doing a commendable job.

What is necessary, however, is a deep-seated and sincere concern in the overall success of the team. When this trait is present, then all the other variables that go into making a successful Strength Coach seem to fall into place quite naturally.

A BELIEF IN THE IMPORTANCE OF STRENGTH

The Strength Coach must understand the value of strength in the sport of football. Then he must realize that this program is the fastest and easiest way for his players to develop that prime athletic ingredient. If the Strength Coach thoroughly believes in strength training, he will be most anxious to learn all that he can on the subject. He will be willing to spend the hours necessary teaching the proper movements to his players. He can easily justify to himself, to the other coaches, and to the players the great asset strength training is to the overall success of the team. Once he decides and knows for sure that a stronger football team brings more victories, then he will be in a position to convince all those he comes into contact with on the critical value of strength training to the overall program.

KNOWLEDGE OF THE SUBJECT

Once the Strength Coach accepts the responsibility of his new position, he must begin preparing himself for the task ahead. On the surface, it may appear to be a simple assignment, but the science of strength training is akin to a giant iceberg. What surfaces in the daily workouts is merely the peak of the iceberg. What lies beneath a successful strength program is a vast storehouse of knowledge on a wide variety of subjects.

The Strength Coach must have a working understanding of many sciences in order to be of genuine use to his trainees. He must know how the body functions. A basic background in anatomy, physiology, and kinesiology is not a luxury, but rather an absolute necessity. When a player asks how a specific exercise affects his body, the Strength Coach must be prepared to answer in very specific terms and not in generalities.

The Strength Coach works in conjunction with the team's medical expert and must be able to converse with him in a common language. When the team physician calls and explains that a player recently had his lateral meniscus operated on, and asks for the Strength Coach's recommendations for a rehabilitation program, it certainly helps to establish some degree of credibility in the program if the Strength Coach knows exactly where this part of the anatomy is located.

It is very difficult to set up an individual program of exercises if you do not really understand exactly how those

A basic background in anatomy, physiology, and kinesiology is not a luxury, but rather an absolute necessity.

exercises affect the various muscles and joints of the body. A basic understanding is absolutely necessary. A stronger knowledge is even more useful.

Obtaining the necessary knowledge may require a bit of new learning for some and a review for others. Most coaches have a background in anatomy, physiology, and kinesiology, so it generally means that he has to take some time to review what he has already learned some years before. It is most useful to review this subject matter periodically, regardless of how strong a history you possess, as our minds only retain so much for so long.

Then there is the science of nutrition. A new and growing field and one in which very few coaches are familiar, but one in which they should be knowledgeable. The nutritional section in this book will serve as a firm information foundation on the subject of nutrition and the suggested readings will provide the Strength Coach with more knowledge on specific segments of this science.

The Strength Coach must also take some time from his schedule to learn of the many related areas of concern in regard to strength such as: the current drug usage in athletics, the importance of rest to performance, and the role of mental preparation. He must also be in a position to understand some of the laws of learning and psychology of human nature so that he can teach and motivate each player individually. A working knowledge of these subjects will enable the Strength Coach to help each player reach his full strength potential.

The Strength Coach must become an expert in his field, i.e. strength training. He should be as informed on current training theories as is possible. He needs to read all the available literature, with particular attention to the latest in research. The ambitious Strength Coach will make it a point to seek out all local expertise on the subject which he is teaching. The competitive weightlifters and the health club directors are often good resources to tap for this information.

ENTHUSIASM

Enthusiasm is very contagious. Find a Strength Coach who is hyped on getting his players super strong and you'll find a successful strength program, regardless of facilities or time allotted or whatever. A program is rarely motivated from the bottom upward. The enthusiasm engendered by the Strength Coach radiates downward to all the participants. When the Strength Coach gets excited about gains in the weight room, the players begin to find themselves getting more and more encouraged to work harder so as to make more progress.

Should the Strength Coach merely be fulfilling an assignment and just supervising the weight program, then only a token amount of success can be expected. Conversely, if the Strength Coach believes that his segment of conditioning is "the most important" in the whole framework of the operation, then the weights will fly and every trainee will get caught up in the tempo of high enthusiasm for strength.

BEING A PART OF THE PROGRAM

It is my firm belief, and one which has been confirmed throughout the years, that the successful Strength Coach must take part in the program himself. This does not mean that he has to be a competitive weightlifter or even lift more than his players. The fact is, however, that the Strength Coach who is actively engaged in the same program which he is teaching, is better able to understand the many small problems encountered by the trainees.

For example, the position of the bar as it rests on the trainee's back while he performs heavy squats is very critical to his progress. His feet must also be placed exactly right or he will not make strength gains as quickly as he would if he did everything perfectly. Yet, these and other small points are very easily overlooked (or forgotten) if the Strength Coach is merely an observer. On the other hand, if the Strength Coach is actively doing squats he will be very aware of these subtle, but important points. If he does an exercise he will be in a much better position to make these small adjustments because he **feels** the differences they make himself.

The adage that "those who can't, teach" does not apply to strength training. The Strength Coach does not have to be a powerhouse, but he should believe in the benefits of his program enough to take an active part in it.

It is very difficult to teach an involved movement such as the power clean if you have never done it. It is foreign to any other athletic endeavor. Watching another person perform the lift does help, but until you actually do the exercise yourself, it is nearly impossible to know when to drive the hips forward, when to shrug the trapezius, and so on.

EASIER TO LEAD THAN PUSH

The players are much more easily led than pushed when it comes to weight training. If they see their leader (the Strength Coach) performing the lifts he advocates then the players immediately recognize the validity of the program. There is also a binding force when the coach and athlete train together. When both are gutting out that last rep on a heavy set of squats, a closeness develops that opens the door to further communication.

It should also be noted that the Strength Coach is the authority on the subject which he teaches. To advocate strength training while being fifty pounds overweight and in pitiful physical condition is certainly a contradiction of the highest order. Strength training, at best, is pure, hard work. Why follow a leader who is the visible opposite of what he preaches? The successful Strength Coach does not have to be a rippling mass of muscles, although this would not be a handicap by any means, but he must be physically fit. He must be able to perform the exercises he teaches and he must have passable form in the various movements. He must be willing to invest part of his week in systematic training himself in order to stay fit.

No player is going to put his trust and effort behind a Strength Coach who looks like a Boy Scout reject. The Strength Coach is in a unique position, coaching-wise. Swimming coaches need not swim. Football coaches need not block or tackle, but Strength Coaches need to lift weights. It's part and parcel with the position.

THE STRENGTH COACH AS A MOTIVATOR

The task of the Strength Coach is to constantly motivate his trainees to higher and higher levels of strength success. He, initially, has to motivate them to begin weight training. Then, he has to encourage them over their sticking points — those dead periods when progress comes ridiculously slow or not at all. He has to reassure them that constant effort will pay off in further success. He must be able to analysis individual differences and to design specific programs for individual needs. He must find ways to keep his trainees going when they are bored, or physically tired, or depressed, or caught up in a new activity. How the Strength Coach plays this role of motivator, in the final analysis, will determine just how successful his overall, year-round program will be.

There are many motivational devices or gimmicks which will enable the Strength Coach to get his players started on a strength program. Some of these were mentioned earlier in Chapter 6 , but a reiteration at this point is in order.

PHOTOGRAPHS

One high school coach utilizes photographs to get his players interested in weight training. He takes Polaroid snapshots of early trainees and then shoots periodical shots every so often so that the trainees can visibly see their progress. Photos taken during workouts and posted on the weight room bulletin board also gives the players an added incentive to come to the weight room.

RECORD BOARDS

Record boards are fine motivational devices. The players will be encouraged to become the best in their respective weight class in at least one of the lifts recorded. Being the "best" at anything is often reward enough to continue on a program. It is also a good idea to list the current state records in those lifts which are performed competitively so that the players will have a gauge to judge themselves. They may not have a realistic chance of ever matching some of the lifts, but it will be visible and tangible proof that those lifts are possible for a person of his particular size.

MONTHLY PROGRESS REPORTS

Monthly progress reports, posted on the weight room bulletin board, serve as a constant reminder that the trainees are being tracked. The athletes are much more apt to keep at their program if they know the coaches receive a progress report periodically. If the athletes come into the weight room frequently enough, any Strength Coach worth his salt should see that they make progress.

INFORMAL CONTESTS

Informal contests bring about an up-grading of lifts in almost every instance. Since the Strength Coach is dealing with competitive people, this attribute can be utilized to spur them on to greater levels of proficiency. Set up these contests so that they fit into the team's yearly season. For example, have a contest (or a testing day) just prior to spring ball, and another just before summer camp. This will serve two purposes. It will encourage them to peak out at the right time, that is, just before going into a heavy football session and it will motivate them to be their strongest exactly when they need to be the strongest.

If there are local AAU-sponsored powerlifting contests in your area, encourage a few (or many) of your players to enter the meets. Even if they are not accomplished enough to place in the meet, they usually elevate their personal records and this, in the final analysis, is what you are seeking.

SPECIAL AWARDS

Special awards, such as T-shirts, letters, or trophies, can be given to those trainees who have met certain levels of proficiency. Many high schools have a 300-pound bench press club. Be sure to emphasize the squat and power clean as these lifts are even more essential to the aspiring athlete than the bench press.

SUCCESS IS THE GREATEST MOTIVATOR

All the devices and gimmicks may help get a young athlete started on a strength program, but unless he progresses quickly, he will lose interest. Once he starts making gains, your biggest job as a motivator is over. This is why the program outlined in this book has been adopted by so many coaches across the country. The program works. The trainees make gains immediately and they continue to make gains week after week. Even the most reluctant trainee will start getting enthusiastic about weight training if he begins making gains. Bubba Smith had to be coaxed, begged, and pleaded into the weight room the first few weeks, but once Bubba began making progress, which was immediately, he was as regular as clockwork.

Often, the Strength Coach's biggest job in the early going is to curtail some of the enthusiasm. The athlete becomes so excited about the gains that they mistakenly feel that "if some is good, then more is better." With this philosophy, the trainee can easily fall into the overtraining trap. The aware Strength Coach must educate his players that once they stimulate those major muscle groups, they need to leave the weight room. More work will not always result in more progress, it usually results in less.

The Strength Coach should be on hand for every workout, especially in the early stages of training. On the heavy days, he plays the role of a prodder. He pushes, coaxes, begs, and threatens the players to higher and higher levels. On the lighter days, he needs to be technician, teaching the finer points of form on the various lifts. These are the days when the grooves on the various lifts are established. The   limit days do not allow this type of instruction.

UNDERSTANDING INDIVIDUAL DIFFERENCES

The Strength Coach must be very aware of the fact that not all of his trainees are going to respond to the same type of motivational techniques. Some athletes need to be challenged. Others will withdraw and rebel when overly "pushed." These people have to be treated more tenderly. Coax them on with lots of rewards and attention. Some trainees only respond under heavy stimulation. Threats of hanging often work well with them. Others need lots of love and sympathy. Whatever it takes, the Strength Coach must be sensitive enough to adapt his methods to each individual. He cannot, if he is to be of genuine service to the team effort, have just one line and one motivational approach and expect all of his trainees to respond to that line.

The Strength Coach is faced with the difficult task of building a stronger football team. This means he must improve the strength level of all of his players, and not just concentrate on a select few. The team which will dominate a game will not be the one with just four or five super strong men, but the one which has twenty-two or twenty-three extra strong ones. The depth in strength is almost critical factor in the fourth quarter and also towards the end of the season.

THE STRENGTH COACH AS A RECRUITER

On the collegiate level, the Strength Coach can be a most valuable asset to the recruiting program. Any youngster coming out of high school is quite aware of the benefits of strength training. If he can be shown that the interested school has a superior strength program which will enable him to help reach his full athletic potential, then he is certainly more apt to select that school over one which does not offer him this advantage.

A great many colleges have identical recruiting approaches. They offer scholarships, nice facilities, travel and other advantages, but few have that extra something which the dedicated and ambitious athlete is seeking. He is often looking past college and to that pot of gold in professional football. A well-directed strength program can greatly enhance his chances of becoming a highly-paid professional football player. He need only check the ranks of the draft choices each year to see the high percentage of weight trained athletes. Whereas in the past, weight training was a luxury that just a few professionals indulged in, today it has become an absolute necessity.

As the sought-after high school and junior college athlete checks out the recruiting colleges, he is going to be influenced tremendously by the type of strength program which that school offers. The head coaches who are aware enough of this fact will definitely have a jump on those who do not.

STRENGTH COACHING — JOB OF THE FUTURE

In the next few years, the sport of football will be involved in a mild revolution as far as professional strength coaching is concerned. In the past, the head coach on the high school or college level, merely selected an assistant coach and assigned him the duties of directing (actually watching) the weight room. Some of these appointed coaches have done a remarkable job. They have read books, magazines, research journals, and talked to every expert or semi-expert they could find on the subject of strength.

The future holds great promise for those of us in the profession of making athletes stronger. We must, in the next few years, have some avenue whereby we can exchange training ideas and new training concepts. We, ideally, should come together periodically and discuss problems, methods, and successful formulas.

The Strength Coach, in the foreseeable future, will be just as much a part of the total sports organization in a school or college as the trainer or team doctor. His role is critical to the team's success and for those of us who enjoy working with athletes, watching them grow, seeing them gain confidence in themselves through their efforts with the barbell, strength training is a most rewarding profession.

It is my firm opinion that Strength Coaching will be one of the most sought-after professions in the athletic field in the very near future. ★

REFERENCE LIST
RELATED MATERIALS SECTION

Alderman, R.B. **Psychological Behavior in Sport.** Philadelphia: W.B. Saunders Company, 1974.

Ariel, G. "Residual effect of anabolic steroid upon muscular force." **Medical Science in Sports,** 5:59, 1973.

Battig, K. "The effect of training and amphetamine on the endurance and velocity of swimming performance of rats." **Psychopharmacologia,** 4: 15-27, 1963.

Begbie, G. "The effects of alcohol and of varying amounts of visual information on a balancing test." **Ergonomics,** 9: 325-333, 1966.

Bender, J.A. and Kaplan, H.M. "The effectiveness of isometric exercises in physical rehabilitation." **Journal Association Physical and Mental Rehabilitation.** 16: 174-175, 1962.

Bilik, S.R. **The Trainer's Bible, 8th Revised Edition.** New York: T.J. Reed Company, 1947.

Bobo, W. "Effects of alcohol upon maximum oxygen uptake, lung ventilation, and heart rate." **Research Quarterly,** 43: 1-6, 1972.

Bowers, R. and Reardon, J. "Effects of methadrostenolone (dianabol) on strength development and aerobic capacity." **Medical Science in Sports,** 4: 54, 1972.

Brown, B., and Pilch, A. "The effects of exercise and dianabol upon selected performances and physiological parameters in the male rat." **Medical Science in Sports,** 4: 159-165, 1972.

Brueckmann, R.F. "Postoperative quadriceps exercises." **Journal Association for Physical and Mental Rehabilitation.** 16:2: 52-61, 1967.

Cameron, J. and others. "Effects of amphetamines on moods, emotions, and motivations." **Journal Psychology,** 61: 93-121, 1965.

Cheney, R. "Reaction time behavior after caffeine and coffee consumption." **Journal of Experimental Psychology.** 19: 357-369, 1936.

Ciner, O.H. "The value of therapeutic exercises with special references to arthrotimes of the knee." **Journal Association for Physical and Mental Rehabilitation.** 9:4: 120, 1955.

Clement, M. "Restoration of the Quadriceps muscle by resistive exercises." **Journal of the Remedial Gymnast.** London, England, 68, 1956.

Coughlin, E. "Knee injury in athletics." **Journal National Trainer's Association.** June, 1959.

Crancer, A. and others. "Comparison of the effects of marijuana on simulated driving performance." **Science,** 164: 851-854, 1969.

Delza, Sophia. **Body and Mind In Harmony.** New York: David McKay Company, Inc. 1961.

Dement, William. **Some Must Watch While Some Must Sleep.** San Francisco: Charles Scribner's Sons, 1972.

Elkin, E. "Physiological basis for therapeutic exercise." **Archives of Physical Medicine.** 28: 555, 1947.

Eysenck, H., and others. "The effects of stimulant and depressant drugs on continuous work." **Journal Mental Science,** 103: 645-649, 1957.

Fahey, T., and Brown H. "Effects of anabolic steroids plus weight training on normal males — a double blind study." Paper presented at 19th Annual Meeting, American College of Sports Medicine, Philadelphia, May 1, 1972.

Ferguson, A.B. and Bender, J.A. **The ABC's of Athletic Injuries and Conditioning.** Baltimore: The Williams and Wilkins Company, 1964.

Golding, L., and Barnard, J. "The effect of d-amphetamine sulfate on physical performance." **Journal of Sports Medicine,** 3: 221-224, 1963.

Grimm, Z. "A study of combined exercise techniques used in the post-operative treatment of the knee." **Journal Association for Physical and Mental Rehabilitation,** 17: 2, 1963.

Grollman, A. "The action of alcohol, caffeine, and tobacco on the cardiac output of normal men." **Journal Pharmachology,** 39: 313, 1930.

Hartmann, E. (ed.). **Sleep and Dreaming.** International Psychiatry Clinic. Vol. VII. Boston: Little, Brown, and Company, 1970.

Kales, A. (ed.). **Sleep—Physiology and Pathology: A Symposium.** Philadelphia: J.B. Lippincott, 1969.

Kastner, Jonathan and Marianna. **Sleep, The Mysterious Third of Your Life.** New York: Harcourt, Brace and World, Inc., 1968.

Klafs, Carl and Arnheim, Daniel. **Modern Principles of Athletic Training.** St. Louis: The C.V. Mosby Company, 1963.

Klein, K.K. "Prevention Conditioning and Reduction of Knee Injury." **Athletic Journal,** 40: 7-28, 1960.

ibid. "Progressive resistive exercise and its utilization in the recovery period following knee injury." **Journal Association for Physical and Mental Rehabilitation.** 10: 94-98, 1956.

Kraus, H. **Therapeutic Exercise.** Springfield, Illinois: Charles Thomas Publishers, 1963.

Lannin, D.R. "Rehabilitation of meniscus injuries with associated malacia of the patella." **Journal of the American Medical Association,** 17: 1962-64, 1959.

Man-ching, Cheng and Smith, Robert. **Tai-Chi.** Rutland, Vermont: Charles E. Tuttle Company, 1967.

Moore, J.W. **The Psychology of Athletic Coaching.** Minneapolis: Burgess Publishing Company, 1970.

Murphy, O.D. and Payne, J.W. "Management of knee injuries." **Journal National Trainers Association,** August, 1962.

O'Donoghue, D.H. **Treatment of Injuries to Athletes.** Philadelphia: W.B. Saunders Company, 1962.

Patton, R. and Patterson, W. "The Pathology of Trauma: healing factors as they apply to injuries in sports." **Journal National Athletic Trainers Association,** Winter, 1961.

Rawlinson, K. "Rehabilitation knee exercises." **Journal National Trainers Association,** January, 1959.

Ryan, A.J. **Medical Care of the Athlete.** New York: McGraw-Hill Book Company, 1962.

Sarkison, S.A. **The Structure and Functions of the Brain.** Bloomington: Indiana University Press, 1966.

Smillie, I.S. **Injuries of the Knee Joint.** Edinburgh, Scotland: E.S. Livingston Ltd., 1951.

Smith, Robert (ed.). **Secrets of Shaolin Temple Boxing.** Tokyo: Charles E. Tuttle Company, 1964.

Stafford, G.T. **Exercise During Convalescence.** New York: A.S. Barnes and Company, 1947.

Starr, William A. "A personality study of weightlifters and bodybuilders." Unpublished master's dissertation, George Williams College, Downers Grove, Illinois, June, 1967.

Thorndike, A. **Athletic Injuries, Prevention, Diagnosis, and Treatment.** Philadelphia: Lea and Febiger, 1958.

Wolstenholme, G.E.W., and O'Connor, Maeve. **The Nature of Sleep.** Boston: Little Brown and Company, 1960.

INDEX

THE STRONGEST SHALL SURVIVE . . .
STRENGTH TRAINING FOR FOOTBALL

EPILOG

*This book is based on the premise that an instructional
text on the subject of strength training need not be dull.*

MAHALO

Bill Starr
Honolulu, Hawaii, 1976.
Bel Air, Maryland, 1978.

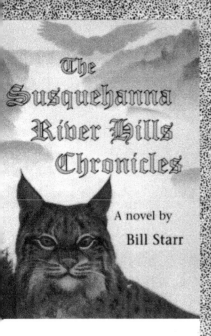

The Susquehanna River Hills Chronicles

A novel by
Bill Starr

Packed with excitement, it is a fictional account of the experiences of three 12-year-old boys in rural Maryland. The setting is the area along the western shore of the Susquehanna River known as the River Hills. It begins at the onset of the War of 1812 and culminates with the invasion of Havre de Grace in May 1813.

The novel revolves around the activities of Willie. He and his two friends, Leroy, a freed slave, and Owl-Boy, a remnant of the once mighty Susquehannock tribe, get into mischief, encounter villains, have perilous adventures, learn about life, and become attached to a very special bobcat. There are also tales of Willie's family and life on the farm.

✫ ✫ ✫ ✫ ✫

"This is a combination of Tom Sawyer, the Waltons, and Little House on the Prairie—a nice mixture of atmosphere, innocence, and adventure. Very enjoyable."
Mike Wilson, Reviewer

✫ ✫ ✫ ✫ ✫

725 pgs. $20 + $4 s/h

for another

Encyclopedia of strength Training

THE STRONGEST SHALL SURVIVE . . . STRENGTH TRAINING FOR FOOTBAL

The sturdy, hardbound edition
$25.00 plus $4.00 postage and handling

The practical, softbound edition
$20.00 plus $4.00 postage and handling

Defying Gravity: How To Win At Weightlifting
by Bill Starr

Hardbound edition
$20.00 plus $4.00 postage and handlin

Softbound edition
$15.00 plus $4.00 postage and handlin

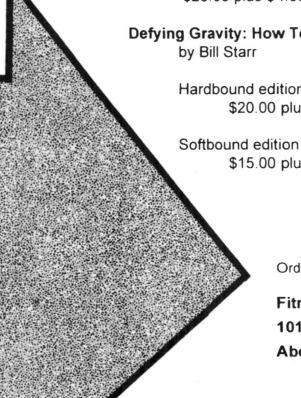

Order from:

Fitness Consultants and Sup
1011 Warwick Drive, 3-C
Aberdeen, Maryland 21001